MATHEMATICS I

FOR JUNIOR CERTIFICATE

ORDINARY LEVEL

FOURTH EDITION

GEORGE HUMPHREY

Gill & Macmillan

Gill & Macmillan Ltd
Hume Avenue
Park West
Dublin 12
with associated companies throughout the world
www.gillmacmillan.ie

978 07171 4129 6

The paper used in this book is made from the wood pulp of managed forests.
For every tree felled, at least one tree is planted, thereby renewing natural resources.

CONTENTS

Preface

This book was written to help you to revise for the Junior Certificate Ordinary Level Mathematics Examination. Chapters 1–15 deal with Paper 1 and Chapters 16–25 deal with Paper 2. Revision with this book will help you to achieve the best result you can in the examination. Unlike a textbook, this book has been organised to make your revision easier.

Throughout your course you can use the book to:

- remind you of what you have been taught
- help you with your homework
- do some extra practice at attempting the kind of questions you will meet in the examination
- sort out things you didn't quite follow in class
- focus on the essential points in each topic
- organise your revision and preparation for the actual examination.

To make the best use of this book, attempt to solve the problems yourself before looking at the solutions given. Redo any questions you answer incorrectly. Get into the habit of making your own notes as you work through the book and use these notes in later revision sessions.

I would like to thank Colman Humphrey and Eoin O'Reilly, students in St Andrew's College, Dublin, who read the entire manuscript and made many valuable suggestions which I have included in the final text and greatly reduced my errors!

I also wish to express my thanks to the staff at Gill & Macmillan for their advice, guidance and untiring assistance in the preparation and presentation of the text.

George Humphrey
St Andrew's College
Booterstown Avenue
Blackrock
Co. Dublin

Tips on Revision and the Examination in Mathematics

It is very important to realise that you are your own best teacher. Revision is when you begin to teach yourself. Thus, it is very important that you start your revision as soon as possible. Make notes while you are revising. If you are having difficulty with a particular question seek help from your teacher, a friend or a member of your family. As with all subjects, the best examination preparation is to work through past examination or sample papers so that you are familiar with the layout and style of questions.

There is no such thing as rough work in Maths – all work is relevant. Therefore any such work should be done beside the question, so that the examiner can see it. If the examiner doesn't know how you reached an answer, even a correct answer, then full marks will usually not be awarded. Thus, show all your work.

One-third of the marks will be awarded for any step in the right direction. Therefore make an attempt at each part of the question. Even if you do not get the correct answer, you can still pick up most of the marks on offer if you show how you worked it out. Also, draw a diagram where possible, because this can help in seeing the solution.

If you cannot finish part of a question, leave a space and come back to it later. Never scribble out any work or use Tipp-Ex. Put a single line through it so that the examiner can still read it. In many cases work that had a line through it received more marks. Avoid using pencil because the writing can be very faint and difficult to read.

There are two papers in the mathematics examination. Both papers have six questions and you have to answer all six; in other words, there is no choice on the examination paper. The time allowed is 2 hours (120 minutes) for each paper. Therefore do not spend more than 20 minutes answering any one question. Each question is worth 50 marks and the total number of marks per paper is 300, giving a total of 600 marks for both papers.

There is an attempt to divide each question into 3 parts: part A, part B and part C.

Part A – Straightforward, testing only one or two basic concepts and carrying a total of 10 marks.

Part B – More difficult, but still straightforward and carrying a total of 20 marks.

Part C – Much more challenging and may have several parts, carrying a total of 20 marks.

Therefore it is important to get the 'marks : time' ratio correct.

The 'marks : time' ratio in Ordinary Level mathematics is 5 : 2.

A part 'A', worth 10 marks, should be given 4 minutes.

A part 'B' or 'C', worth 20 marks, should be given 8 minutes.

Familiarise yourself with your calculator. Also, it is a good idea to show each stage of a calculation when using a calculator (in case you press a wrong key). Know all your formulas – your own formula dictionary can be useful – and don't forget to write down any formula that you use.

Glossary of the words used on the examination paper

Write down, State
You can write down your answer without showing any work. However, if you want you can show some working.

Calculate, Find, Show that, Determine, Prove
Obtain your answers by showing all relevant work. Marks are available for showing the steps leading to your final answer or conclusion.

Solve
Find the solution, or root, of an equation. The solution is the value of the variable that makes the left-hand side balance with the right-hand side.

Evaluate
Usually to work out, or find, a numerical value by putting in numbers for letters.

Plot
Indicate the position of points on a graph, usually on the x- and y-planes.

Construct
Draw an accurate diagram, usually labelled, using a pencil, ruler, set square, compass and protractor. Leave all constructions on your diagram.

Sketch
Make a rough diagram or graph, labelled if needed.

Hence
You **must** use the answer, or result, from the previous part of the question.

Hence or otherwise
It is recommended that you use the answer, or result, from the previous part of the question, but other methods are acceptable.

Chapter 1. PRIME NUMBERS, HIGHEST COMMON FACTOR, MULTIPLES AND LOWEST COMMON MULTIPLE

Prime Numbers

A '**prime number**' is a whole number greater than 1 that has only two factors, 1 and itself.

For example, 7 is a prime number, as it has only two factors (divisors), 1 and 7.
The first fifteen prime numbers are:

2, 3, 5, 7, 11, 13, 17, 19, 23, 29, 31, 37, 41, 43, 47

Notes: 1 is not considered a prime number, as it has only one factor, i.e. 1.
2 is the first prime number, and it is the only even prime number; all other prime numbers are odd.

Example 1

(i) Express 10 as the sum of two prime numbers.

(ii) Express 18 as the sum of three prime numbers.

Solution:

The word '**sum**' means '**add**'.

(i) $10 = 3 + 7$ or $10 = 5 + 5$

(ii) $18 = 2 + 5 + 11$

The factors (divisors) of any whole number are the whole numbers that divide exactly into the given number.

Prime factors of a whole number are prime numbers that divide exactly into the number.

Example 2

Find the prime factors of: **(i)** 6 **(ii)** 20.

Solution:

Write down all pairs of factors and then write down the prime factors.

(i) 6

1×6

$(2) \times (3)$

Therefore, the prime factors of 6 are 2 and 3.

(ii) 20

1×20

$(2) \times 10$

$4 \times (5)$

Therefore, the prime factors of 20 are 2 and 5.

Example 3

Express as the product of their prime factors: **(i)** 12 **(ii)** 90.

Solution:

The word '**product**' means '**multiply**'.

Start with the smallest prime number that divides exactly; repeat if necessary. Try the next prime number in the same way, and stop when you are left with 1. You can do the divisions with a calculator, but show your work step by step.

Solution:

$$\begin{array}{r|l} 2 & 12 \\ \hline 2 & 6 \\ \hline 3 & 3 \\ \hline & 1 \end{array}$$

$\therefore \quad 12 = 2 \times 2 \times 3$

$$\begin{array}{r|l} 2 & 90 \\ \hline 3 & 45 \\ \hline 3 & 15 \\ \hline 5 & 5 \\ \hline & 1 \end{array}$$

$\therefore \quad 90 = 2 \times 3 \times 3 \times 5$

Highest Common Factor (HCF)

The '**highest common factor**' of two or more numbers is the largest factor that is common to each of the given numbers.

In other words, the highest common factor of two or more numbers is the **largest** number that will divide exactly into each number.

To find the highest common factor of two or more numbers, do the following:

1. Write down all the pairs of factors of each number.
2. Write down the common factors of each number and select the largest.

Example

Find the highest common factor of 24 and 40.

Solution:

24	40
(1) × 24	(1) × 40
(2) × 12	(2) × 20
3 × (8)	(4) × 10
(4) × 6	5 × (8)

The common factors are 1, 2, 4 and 8.

Therefore, the highest common factor of 24 and 40 is 8.

Multiples and the Lowest Common Multiple (LCM)

The multiples of a number are found by multiplying the number by 1, 2, 3 … and so on.

The multiples of 3 are: 3, 6, 9, 12, 15, 18, 21 …

The multiples of 5 are: 5, 10, 15, 20, 25, 30, 35 …

The '**lowest common multiple**' of two or more numbers is the **smallest multiple** that is common to each of the numbers.

In other words, the lowest common multiple is the **smallest** number into which each of the numbers will divide exactly.

For example, the lowest common multiple of 2, 4 and 5 is 20, as 20 is the smallest number into which 2, 4 and 5 will all divide exactly.

The lowest common multiple of two or more numbers is found with the following steps:

1. Write down the multiples of each number.
2. The lowest common multiple is the smallest (first) multiple they have in common.

Example

M is the set of natural numbers from 1 to 20, inclusive.

(i) List the elements of M that are multiples of 3.

(ii) List the elements of M that are multiples of 5.

(iii) Write down the lowest common multiple of 3 and 5.

Solution:

$M = \{1, 2, 3, 4, 5, 6, 7, 8, 9, 10, 11, 12, 13, 14, 15, 16, 17, 18, 19, 20\}$

(i) Multiples of $3 = \{3, 6, 9, 12, 15, 18\}$

(ii) Multiples of $5 = \{5, 10, 15, 20\}$

(iii) Lowest common multiple is 15. (The smallest, and only, number both sets have in common.)

Chapter 2. SETS

Sets

Example 1

P is the set of prime numbers between 1 and 12.

(i) List the elements of the set P. **(ii)** Write down $\#(P)$.

Solution:

1, 2, 3, 4, 5, 6, 7, 8, 9, 10, 11, 12

(i) $P = \{2, 3, 5, 7, 11\}$ (prime numbers between 1 and 12)

(ii) P contains 5 elements $\therefore \quad \#(P) = 5$

Example 2

$T = \{2, 4, 6, 8, 10, 12\}$.

Write down the elements of T that are multiples of 4.

Solution:

The multiples of 4 are 4, 8, 12, 16, 20, …

The multiples of 4 that are elements of T are 4, 8 and 12.

Example 3

$A = \{p, q, r\}$

Write down a subset of A that has: **(i)** one element **(ii)** two elements.

Solution:

$A = \{p, q, r\}$

(i) Subsets of A that have one element are:

$\{p\}$ or $\{q\}$ or $\{r\}$ (any one will do).

(ii) Subsets of A that have two elements are:

$\{p, q\}$ or $\{p, r\}$ or $\{q, r\}$ (any one will do).

Terminology for Two Sets

The diagram below indicates the four regions when dealing with the sets U, A and B.

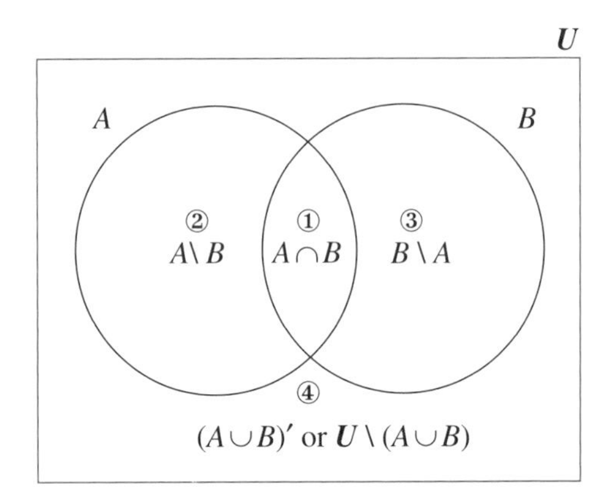

Set notation	Meaning
$\#(A)$	Number of elements in set A
$\cup$	or
$\cap$	and, both
$A \cup B$	In A or B
$A \cap B$	In A and B
$A \setminus B$	In A but not in B (A only)
$B \setminus A$	In B but not in A (B only)
U	Universal Set
A' or $\boldsymbol{U} \setminus A$	In U but not in A
$(A \cup B)'$ or $\boldsymbol{U} \setminus (A \cup B)$	In U but not in A or B
$(A \cap B)'$ or $\boldsymbol{U} \setminus (A \cap B)$	In U but not in A and B

When putting the values into a Venn diagram, always work from the centre outwards. Never repeat an element in a set.

Example 1

(i) Using the Venn diagram below, shade in the region that represents $P \cap Q$.

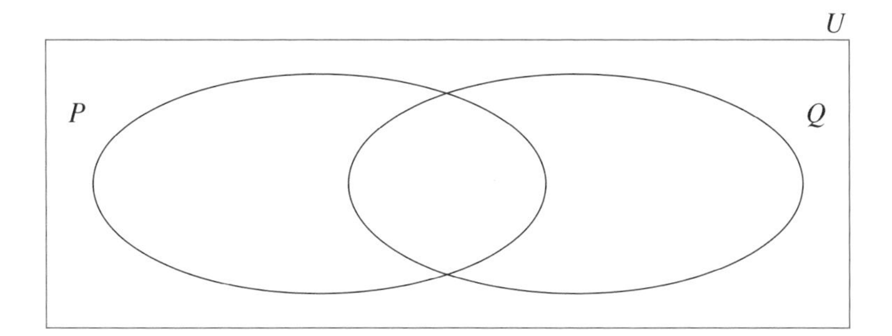

(ii) Using the Venn diagram below, shade in the region that represents $P \cup Q$.

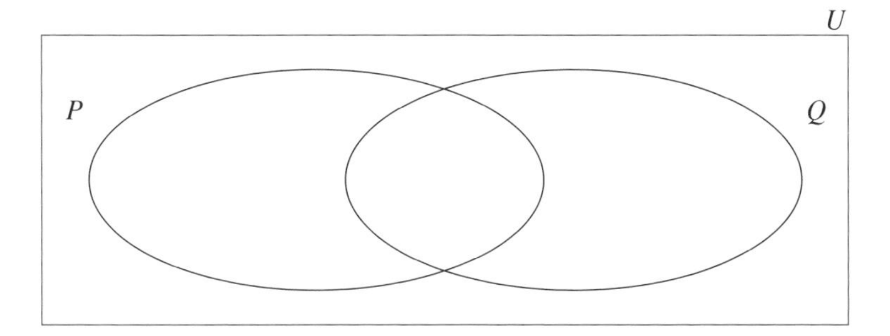

(iii) Using the Venn diagram below, shade in the region that represents $(P \cup Q)'$.

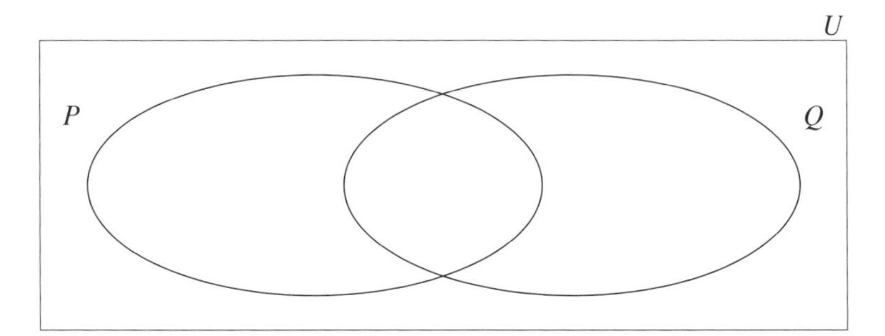

(iv) Using the Venn diagram below, shade in the region that represents P'.

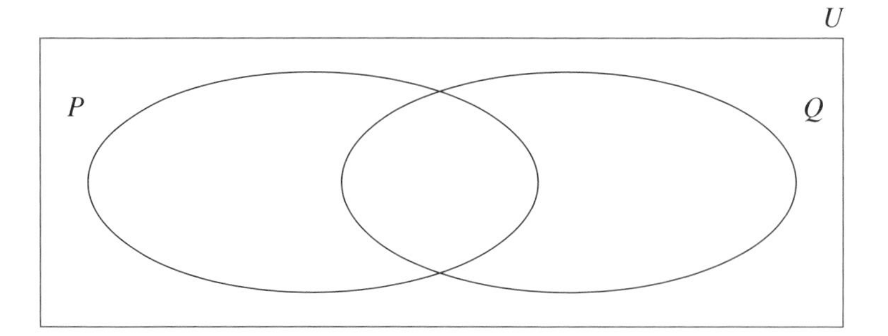

Solution:

(i)

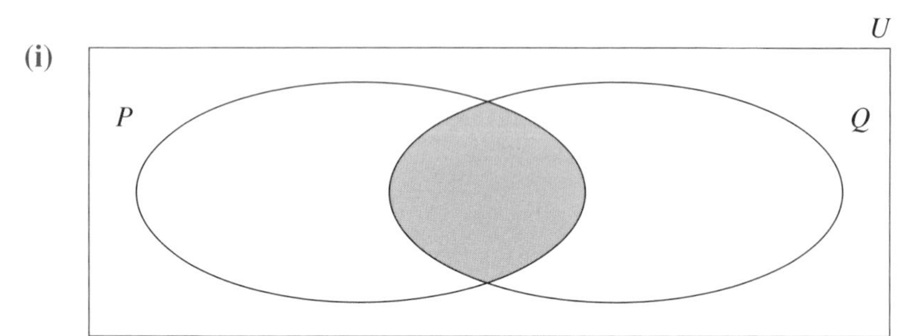

Shaded region

$= P \cap Q$

(in P and Q)

(ii)

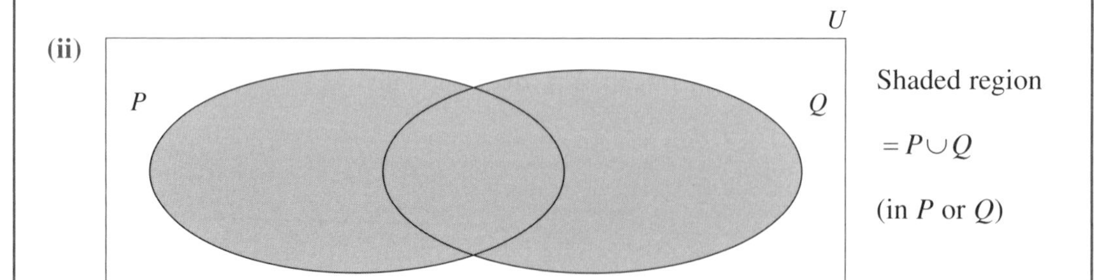

Shaded region

$= P \cup Q$

(in P or Q)

(iii)

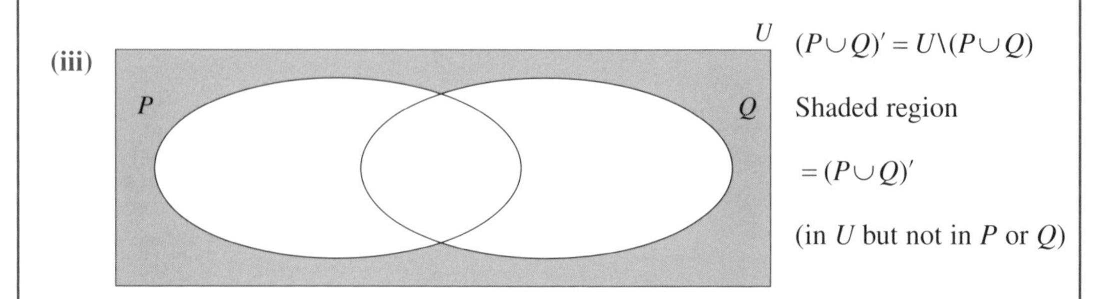

$(P \cup Q)' = U \backslash (P \cup Q)$

Shaded region

$= (P \cup Q)'$

(in U but not in P or Q)

(iv)

$P' = U \backslash P$

Shaded region

$= P'$

(in U but not in P)

Example 2

$U = \{a, b, c, d, e, f, g\}$, $P = \{a, d, f, g\}$ and $Q = \{a, b, g\}$.

Represent U, P and Q with a Venn diagram.
List the elements of:

(i) $P \cap Q$ **(ii)** $P \cup Q$ **(iii)** P' **(iv)** $(P \cup Q)'$

What is $\#[(P \cup Q)']$?

Solution:

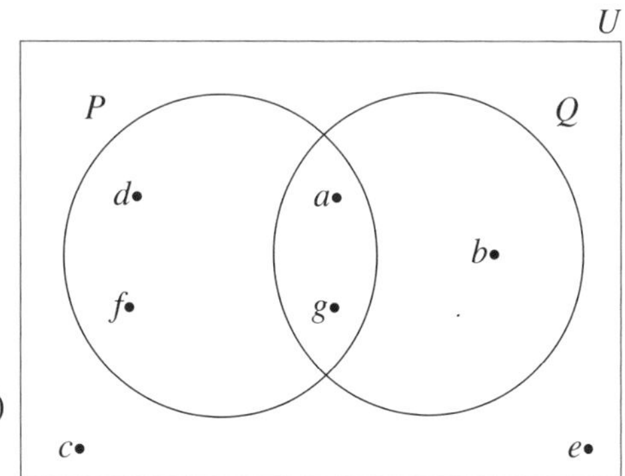

(i) $P \cap Q$

$= \{a, g\}$ (in P and Q)

(ii) $P \cup Q$

$= \{a, b, d, f, g\}$ (in P or Q)

(iii) P'

$= U \backslash P$ (in U but not in P)

$= \{a, b, c, d, e, f, g\} \backslash \{a, d, f, g\}$

$= \{b, c, e\}$

(iv) $(P \cup Q)'$

$= U \backslash (P \cup Q)$ (in U but not in P or Q)

$= \{a, b, c, d, e, f, g\} \backslash \{a, b, d, f, g\}$

$= \{c, e\}$

$(P \cup Q)' = \{c, e\}$

Therefore, $\#[(P \cup Q)'] = 2$ (the number of elements in $(P \cup Q)'$)

Example 3

There are 30 students in a class. 18 study French and 10 study German.
5 study neither of the two languages.

(i) Draw a Venn diagram to represent this information.

(ii) How many students study both languages?

(iii) How many study German but do not study French?

(iv) How many study only one of these languages?

(v) How many study at least one of these languages?

Solution:

(i) On the Venn diagram, let U represent the number of students in the class, F the number who study French, and G the number who study German.

The number of students who study French, German or neither language
$= 18 + 10 + 5 = 33$

The number of students in the class $= 30$
Therefore, the number of students counted twice $= 33 - 30 = 3$ (i.e. $\#(F \cap G) = 3$)

$\#(F \cap G) = 3$

$\#(F \backslash G) = 18 - 3 = 15$

$\#(G \backslash F) = 10 - 3 = 7$

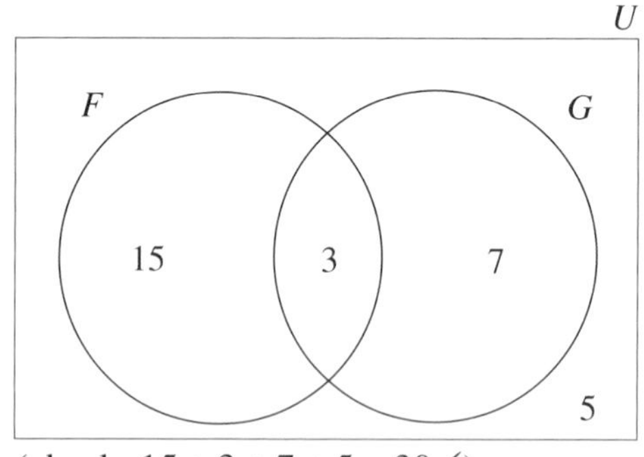

(check: $15 + 3 + 7 + 5 = 30$✓)

(ii) The number of students who study both languages $= 3$.

(iii) The number of students who study German but do not study French $= 7$.

(iv) The number of students who study only one of these languages $= 15 + 7 = 22$.

(v) The number of students who study at least one of these languages $= 15 + 3 + 7 = 25$.

Example 4

The Venn diagram shows the number of girls in a class of 32 who study maths (M), economics (E), or both. If each girl must study one of these subjects, how many girls in the class study **(i)** both subjects, **(ii)** maths only, and **(iii)** economics only?

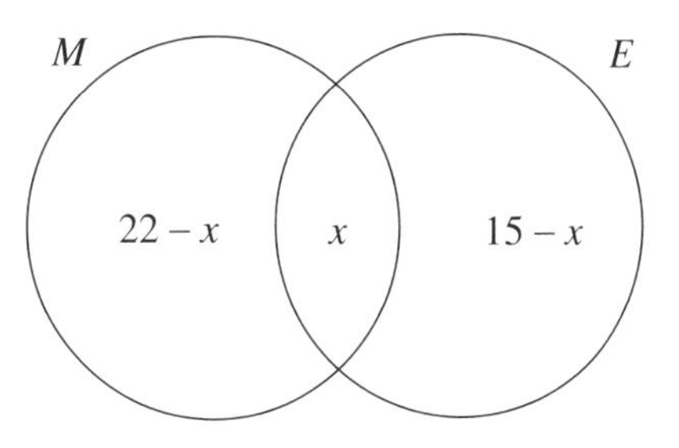

Solution:

Equation given in disguise:

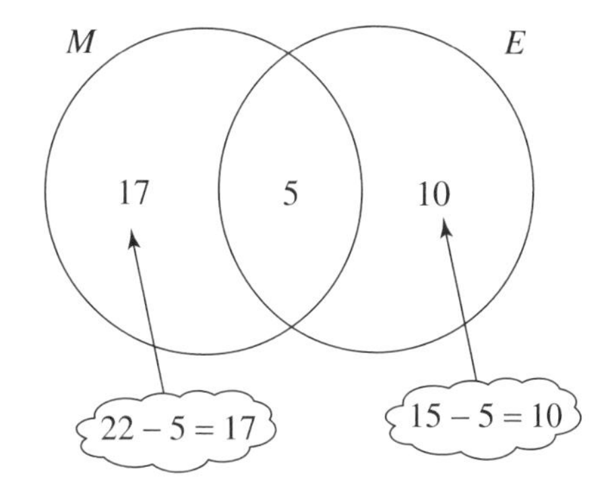

$$\text{The total number of pupils} = 32$$

$$\therefore \quad (22 - x) + x + (15 - x) = 32$$

$$22 - x + x + 15 - x = 32$$

$$37 - x = 32$$

$$-x = 32 - 37$$

$$-x = -5$$

$$x = 5$$

(i) The number of girls who study both maths and economics = 5.

(ii) The number of girls who study maths only = 17.

(iii) The number of girls who study economics only = 10.

Terminology for Three Sets

The diagram below indicates the eight regions when dealing with the sets U, A, B and C.

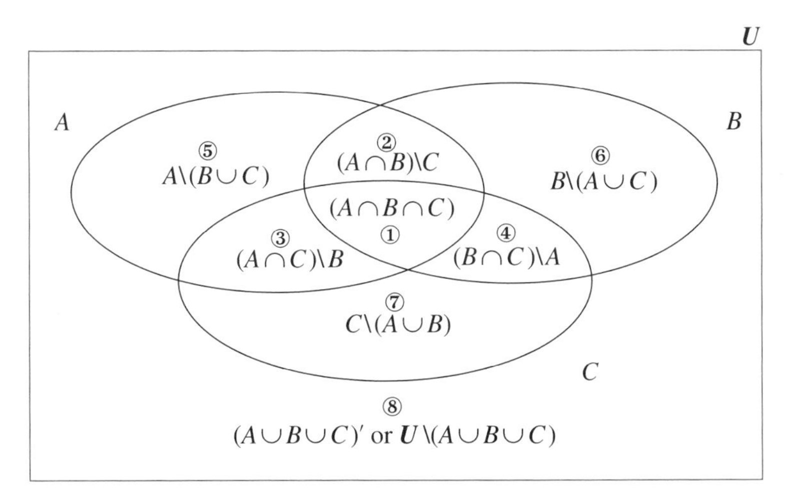

Set notation	Meaning
$A \cup B \cup C$	In A or B or C
$A \cap B \cap C$	In A and B and C
$(A \cup B) \backslash C$	In A or B but not in C
$(A \cap B) \backslash C$	In A and B but not in C
$A \backslash (B \cup C)$	In A but not in B or C (A only)
$(A \cup B \cup C)'$ or $\boldsymbol{U} \backslash (A \cup B \cup C)$	In $\boldsymbol{U}$ but not in A or B or C
$(A \cap B \cap C)'$ or $\boldsymbol{U} \backslash (A \cap B \cap C)$	In $\boldsymbol{U}$ but not in A and B and C

As before, when putting values into a Venn diagram always work from the centre outwards.

Example 1

The Venn diagram shows the sets U, P, Q and R.

List the elements of each of the following sets:

(i) Q **(ii)** $P \backslash Q$

(iii) $P \cap Q$ **(iv)** $(P \cup Q) \backslash R$

(v) $(P \cup Q \cup R)'$ **(vi)** $(P \cup Q) \cap R$

(vii) R' **(viii)** $R \backslash (P \cap Q)$

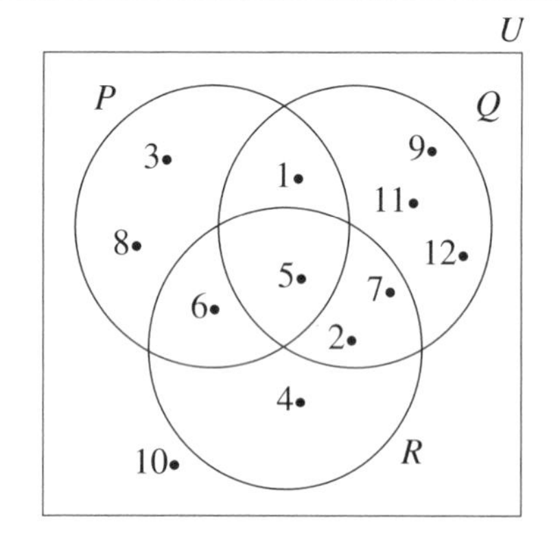

Solution:

(i) $Q = \{1, 2, 5, 7, 9, 11, 12\}$ (in Q)

(ii) $P \backslash Q = \{1, 3, 5, 6, 8\} \backslash \{1, 2, 5, 7, 9, 11, 12\}$ (in P but not in Q)

$P \backslash Q = \{3, 6, 8\}$

(iii) $P \cap Q = \{1, 3, 5, 6, 8\} \cap \{1, 2, 5, 7, 9, 11, 12\}$ (in P and in Q)

$P \cap Q = \{1, 5\}$

(iv) $(P \cup Q) \backslash R$

$P \cup Q = \{1, 3, 5, 6, 8\} \cup \{1, 2, 5, 7, 9, 11, 12\}$ (in P or Q)

$P \cup Q = \{1, 2, 3, 5, 6, 7, 8, 9, 11, 12\}$

$(P \cup Q) \backslash R = \{1, 2, 3, 5, 6, 7, 8, 9, 11, 12\} \backslash \{2, 4, 5, 6, 7\}$ (in P or Q but not R)

$(P \cup Q) \backslash R = \{1, 3, 8, 9, 11, 12\}$

(v) $(P \cup Q \cup R)' = U \backslash (P \cup Q \cup R)$ (in U but not in P or Q or R)

$= \{1, 2, 3, 4, 5, 6, 7, 8, 9, 10, 11, 12\} \backslash \{1, 2, 3, 4, 5, 6, 7, 8, 9, 11, 12\}$

$= \{10\}$

(vi) $(P \cup Q) \cap R = \{1, 2, 3, 5, 6, 7, 8, 9, 11, 12\} \cap \{2, 4, 5, 6, 7\}$ (in P or Q and also in R)

$= \{2, 5, 6, 7\}$

(vii) $R' = U \backslash R = \{1, 2, 3, 4, 5, 6, 7, 8, 9, 10, 11, 12\} \backslash \{2, 4, 5, 6, 7\}$ (in U but not in R)

$= \{1, 3, 8, 9, 10, 11, 12\}$

(viii) $R \backslash (P \cap Q) = \{2, 4, 5, 6, 7\} \backslash \{1, 5\}$ (in R but not in P and Q)

$= \{2, 4, 6, 7\}$

Example 2

In a survey, 37 people were asked which of 3 newspapers, A, B and C, they read.

2 people did not read any of these newspapers and 6 read all three.

3 read A only and nobody read B only. 10 read A and B, 13 read B and C.

23 read A and 28 read C. Represent the data with a Venn diagram.

Calculate how many people in the survey read:

(i) A and C only **(ii)** C only **(iii)** exactly one newspaper

(iv) exactly two newspapers **(v)** at least two newspapers.

Solution:

On the Venn diagram, let U represent the 37 people in the survey who were asked which paper they read, A the number of people who read paper A, B the number of people who read paper B, and C the number of people who read paper C.

Start from the centre and work outwards.

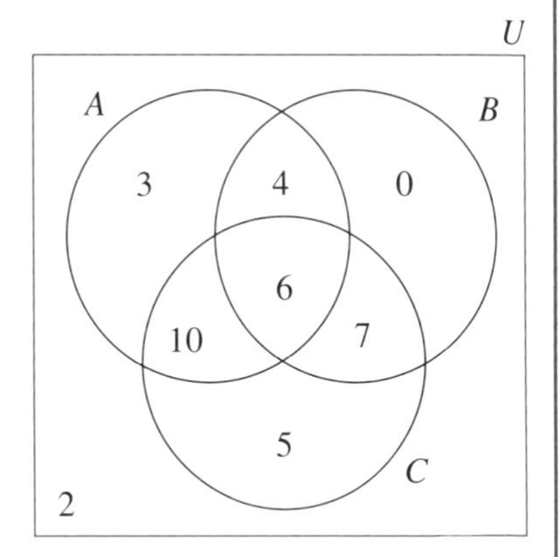

$\#[U \backslash (A \cup B \cup C)] = 2,$ $\#(A \cap B \cap C) = 6$

$\#[A \backslash (B \cup C)] = 3,$ $\#[B \backslash (A \cup C)] = 0$

$\therefore$ $\#[(A \cap B) \backslash C] = 10 - 6 = 4$

and $\#[(B \cap C) \backslash A] = 13 - 6 = 7$

Thus, $\#[(A \cap C) \backslash B] = 23 - (3 + 4 + 6) = 23 - 13 = 10$

and $\#[C \backslash (B \cup A)] = 28 - (10 + 6 + 7) = 28 - 23 = 5.$

Thus, the number of people in the survey who read:

(i) A and C only $= 10$

(ii) C only $= 5$

(iii) exactly one newspaper $= 3 + 0 + 5 = 8$

(iv) exactly two newspapers $= 4 + 7 + 10 = 21$

(v) at least two newspapers $= 4 + 7 + 10 + 6 = 27.$

Chapter 3. ESTIMATION AND THE CALCULATOR

Exact Values

Example

Using a calculator, or otherwise, find the exact value of:

(i) $(6.54)^2$ **(ii)** $\frac{1}{3.2}$ **(iii)** $\sqrt{94.09}$ **(iv)** $121^{\frac{1}{2}}$

Solution:

(i) $(6.54)^2 = 42.7716$ [(6.54) x^2 =]

(ii) $\frac{1}{3.2} = 0.3125$ [(1 ÷ 3.2) =]

(iii) $\sqrt{94.09} = 9.7$ [√ 94.09 =]

(iv) Note: $x^{\frac{1}{2}} = \sqrt{x}$

$121^{\frac{1}{2}} = 11$

[√ 121 = or

(121) y^x (1 ÷ 2) =]

Estimation and the Calculator

Being able to estimate the answer to a problem before using your calculator to make an exact calculation is an important skill. The estimate of the answer will show whether an error has been made, which could easily happen if you press a wrong key on your calculator.

Example 1

(i) By rounding each of these numbers to the nearest whole number,

estimate the value of $\dfrac{56.214}{2.31 + 5.79}$.

(ii) Using a calculator, or otherwise, find the exact value of $\dfrac{56.214}{2.31 + 5.79}$.

Solution:

$$\frac{56.214}{2.31 + 5.79}$$

(i) By rounding each number to the nearest whole number, the problem reduces to:

$$\frac{56}{2+6} = \frac{56}{8} = 7$$

Therefore, 7 is an approximate answer.

(ii) Using a calculator:

$$\frac{56.214}{2.31 + 5.79} = \frac{56.214}{8.1} = 6.94$$

Therefore, the exact answer is 6.94 (very close to our approximate answer of 7).

[( ] 56.214 [ )] [÷] [( ] 2.31 [+] 5.79 [ )] [=]

↑ ↑ ↑ ↑

Note: When using a calculator, it is essential to separate the top and bottom with brackets.

Example 2

(i) By rounding each of the numbers to its nearest whole number, calculate an approximate answer for:

$$\frac{\sqrt{25.1001} + 3.8 \times 2.1 + 0.69}{\sqrt{8.9401} + 4.21}$$

(ii) Using your calculator, or otherwise, find the exact answer.

Solution:

(i) By rounding each number to the nearest whole number, the problem reduces to:

$$\frac{\sqrt{25} + 4 \times 2 + 1}{\sqrt{9} + 4} = \frac{5 + 8 + 1}{3 + 4} = \frac{14}{7} = 2$$

Therefore, 2 is an approximate answer.

(ii) Using a calculator:

$$\frac{\sqrt{25.1001} + 3.8 \times 2.1 + 0.69}{\sqrt{8.9401} + 4.21} = \frac{5.01 + 7.98 + 0.69}{2.99 + 4.21} = \frac{13.68}{7.2} = 1.9$$

Therefore, the exact answer is 1.9 (very close to our approximate answer of 2).

[( ] [√] 25.1001 [+] 3.8 [×] 2.1 [+] 0.69 [ )] [÷] [( ] [√] 8.9401 [+] 4.21 [ )] [=]

Note: When using a calculator, it is essential to separate the top and bottom with brackets.

Example 3

(i) By rounding each number appropriately, show how to calculate an approximate value of:

$$\frac{(2.1)^3 - (3.8025)^{\frac{1}{2}}}{(7.99 - 5.01)^2 - 6.62}$$

(ii) By using your calculator, or otherwise, give your answer correct to two decimal places.

Solution:

Note: $(3.8025)^{\frac{1}{2}} = \sqrt{3.8025}$

An appropriate rounding is to write each number correct to the nearest whole number.

(i) By writing each number to the nearest whole number, the problem reduces to:

$$\frac{(2)^3 - \sqrt{4}}{(8-5)^2 - 7} = \frac{8-2}{(3)^2 - 7} = \frac{6}{9-7} = \frac{6}{2} = 3$$

Therefore, 3 is an approximate answer.

(ii) Using a calculator:

$$\frac{(2.1)^3 - \sqrt{3.8025}}{(7.99 - 5.01)^2 - 6.62} = \frac{9.261 - 1.95}{(2.98)^2 - 6.62} = \frac{7.311}{8.8804 - 6.62} = \frac{7.311}{2.2604} = 3.234383295$$

Therefore, the answer is 3.23, correct to two decimal places.

[( ] 2.1 [y^x] 3 [−] [√] 3.8025 [ )] [÷] [( ] [( ] 7.99 [−] 5.01 [ )] [x^2] [−] 6.62 [ )] [=]

Note: When using a calculator, it is essential to separate the top and bottom with brackets.

Example 4

Evaluate $(4.37)^2 \times \frac{1}{2.05} + \sqrt{50.9}$ and give your answer correct to two decimal places.

Solution:

$$(4.37)^2 \times \frac{1}{2.05} + \sqrt{50.9}$$

You are not asked to, but it is a good idea to work out an approximate answer.

An approximate answer is $(4)^2 \times \frac{1}{2} + \sqrt{49}$

$$= 16 \times \frac{1}{2} + 7$$

$$= 8 + 7 = 15$$

Using a calculator:

$$(4.37)^2 \times \frac{1}{2.05} + \sqrt{50.9} = 16.44998457 = 16.45 \text{ (correct to two decimal places)}$$

([( ] 4.37 [ )] [x^2] [×] [( ] 1 [÷] 2.05 [ )] [+] [√] 50.9 [=])

Chapter 4. ARITHMETIC

Basic Arithmetic

Example 1

The train fare from Cork to Dublin is €44.40 for an adult and €19.00 for a child.

How much does it cost one adult and two children to travel from Cork to Dublin?

Solution:

Total cost = one adult fare + two children's fares

= €44.40 + €19 × 2

= €44.40 + €38

= €82.40

Example 2

€2,400 is shared between John, Mary and Anne. John gets $\frac{1}{2}$ of the money.

Mary gets $\frac{1}{3}$ of the money. How much does Anne get?

Solution:

John's share = $\frac{1}{2}$ of €2,400 = €1,200

Mary's share = $\frac{1}{3}$ of €2,400 = €800

Therefore, Anne's share = €2,400 – €1,200 – €800

= €400

Alternative method:

John's + Mary's share = $\frac{1}{2} + \frac{1}{3} = \frac{5}{6}$ (1 [$a\frac{b}{c}$] 2 [+] 1 [$a\frac{b}{c}$] 3 [=])

Therefore, Anne's share = $1 - \frac{5}{6} = \frac{1}{6}$

$\frac{1}{6}$ of €2,400 = €400

Therefore, Anne's share = €400.

Ratio and Proportion

Ratios are used to compare quantities. We can be asked to divide quantities in a given ratio (proportional part) and solve problems on direct and inverse proportion.

Example 1

Divide **(i)** €480 in the ratio 5 : 3 **(ii)** 135 kg in the ratio 2 : 3 : 4

Solution:

(i) $5 + 3 = 8$ parts

$\therefore$ 1part $= \dfrac{€480}{8} = €60$

5 parts $= €60 \times 5 = €300$

3 parts $= €60 \times 3 = €180$

$\therefore$ €480 divided in the ratio 5 : 3 is €300, €180.

(ii) $2 + 3 + 4 = 9$ parts

$\therefore$ 1part $= \dfrac{135 \text{ kg}}{9} = 15$ kg

2 parts $= 2 \times 15$ kg $= 30$ kg

3 parts $= 3 \times 15$ kg $= 45$ kg

4 parts $= 4 \times 15$ kg $= 60$ kg

$\therefore$ 135 kg divided in the ratio 2 : 3 : 4 is 30 kg, 45 kg, 60 kg.

Sometimes we are given an equation in disguise.

Example 2

A sum of money was divided in the ratio 3 : 2. The larger amount was €39. What was the total amount of money?

Solution:

Equation given in disguise:

3 parts $= €39$

$\therefore$ 1 part $= \dfrac{€39}{3} = €13$

$3 + 2 = 5$

Thus, there are 5 parts altogether.

5 parts $= €13 \times 5 = €65$

Thus, the total amount of money was €65.

Note: In examples 3 and 4 below, equations are used. Strictly speaking, these are not equations, but writing as equations makes the working easier.

Example 3

(i) 9 metres of cloth cost €13.05. What is the cost of 5 metres of the same cloth?

(ii) A machine produces 300 bolts every 6 minutes. How many bolts will the machine produce in 7 minutes, working at the same rate?

Solution:

(i)

9 m = €13.05	(answer in euros, therefore euros on the right)
1 m = €1.45	(divide both sides by 9)
5 m = €7.25	(multiply both sides by 5)

Thus, 5 metres of the cloth will cost €7.25.

(ii)

6 minutes = 300 bolts	(answer in bolts, therefore bolts on the right)
1 minute = 50 bolts	(divide both sides by 6)
7 minutes = 350 bolts	(multiply both sides by 7)

Thus, the machine will produce 350 bolts in 7 minutes.

Sometimes we have to solve problems involving inverse proportion.
Put the required quantity on the right-hand side.

Example 4

9 men can build a wall in 20 days.

(i) How long would it take 10 men to build the same wall?

(ii) How many men are required to build the wall in 15 days?

Solution:

(i) We are looking for the number of days, so days go on the right-hand side.

9 men = 20 days	(given)
$\therefore$ 1 man = 180 days	(1 man takes 9 times as long as 9 men)
$\therefore$ 10 men = 18 days	(10 men take $\frac{1}{10}$ of the time it takes 1 man)

$\therefore$ 10 men could build the wall in 18 days.

(ii) We are looking for the number of men, so men go on the right-hand side.

20 days = 9 men (given)

$\therefore$ 1 day = 180 men (1 day requires 20 times the number of men required by 20 days)

$\therefore$ 15 days = 12 men (15 days requires $\frac{1}{15}$ the number of men required by 1 day)

$\therefore$ 12 men are required to build the wall in 15 days.

Currency Conversion

In the European Union the unit of currency is called the euro (€).

Note: When solving problems on currency, write down the equation given in disguise, putting the currency we want to find on the right-hand side.

Example 1

On a certain day €1 = ¥120. Change ¥3,000 to euros.

Solution:

Method 1:

¥120 = €1 (euros on the right, because we want our answer in euros)

¥1 = €$\frac{1}{120}$ (divide both sides by 120)

¥3,000 = €$\frac{1}{120} \times 3{,}000$ (multiply both sides by 3,000)

¥3,000 = €25 (1 [÷] 120 [×] 3,000 [=])

Method 2:

$$\text{Number of euros} = \frac{3{,}000}{120} = 25$$

Therefore ¥3,000 = €25.

Note: ¥ is the symbol for Japanese yen.

Example 2

On a certain day €1 = US$1.18.

(i) How many dollars would you get for €650?

(ii) How many euros would you get for US$885?

Solution:

(i) €1 = US$1.18 (dollars on the right, because we want our answer in dollars)

€650 = US$1.18 × 650 (multiply both sides by 650)

€650 = US$767 (simplify the right-hand side)

(ii) US$1.18 = €1 (euros on the right, because we want our answer in euros)

US$1 = €$\frac{1}{1.18}$ (divide both sides by 1.18)

US$885 = €$\frac{1}{1.18} \times 885$ (multiply both sides by 885)

US$885 = €750 (simplify the right-hand side)

Percentages

Example 1

A shopkeeper bought a table for €120 and sold it for €162.
Calculate the profit as a percentage of the cost price.

Solution:

Profit = Selling price – Cost price = €162 – €120 = €42.

Profit as a percentage of the cost price

$$= \frac{\text{Profit}}{\text{Cost price}} \times 100\% = \frac{42}{120} \times 100\% = 35\%$$

Example 2

Patrick bought a car for €14,080 and sold it for €16,000.
Calculate his profit as a percentage of the selling price.

Solution:

Profit = Selling price – Cost price = €16,000 – €14,080 = €1,920

Profit as a percentage of the selling price

$$= \frac{\text{Profit}}{\text{Selling price}} \times 100\% = \frac{1{,}920}{16{,}000} \times 100\% = 12\%$$

Example 3

A woman bought a car for €28,500 and sold it for €22,800.

Calculate her percentage loss as a percentage of **(i)** the cost price **(ii)** the selling price.

Solution:

Loss = Cost price – Selling price = €28,500 – €22,800 = €5,700

(i) Loss as a percentage of the cost price

$$= \frac{\text{loss}}{\text{cost price}} \times 100\%$$

$$= \frac{5{,}700}{28{,}500} \times 100\%$$

$$= 20\%$$

(ii) Loss as a percentage of the selling price

$$= \frac{\text{loss}}{\text{selling price}} \times 100\%$$

$$= \frac{5{,}700}{22{,}800} \times 100\%$$

$$= 25\%$$

In many questions dealing with percentages we will be given an equation in disguise.
The best way to tackle this type of problem is to write down the equation given in disguise.
From this we can find 1% and, hence, any percentage we like.

Example 4

(i) The price of a holiday is increased by 6% to €1,537.
What was the original cost of the holiday?

(ii) A bicycle was sold for €544 at a loss of 15%.
Find the original cost of the bicycle.

Solution:

(i) cost of holiday $\xrightarrow{+6\%}$ €1,537 = 106%

Think of the original cost as 100%. (100% + 6% = 106%.)

∴ 106% = €1,537 (equation given in disguise)

1% = €14.5 (divide both sides by 106)

100% = €1,450 (multiply both sides by 100)

Therefore, the original cost of the holiday was €1,450.

(ii) cost of bicycle $\xrightarrow{-15\%}$ €544 = 85%

Think of the original cost as 100%. (100% – 15% = 85%.)

∴ 85% = €544 (equation given in disguise)

1% = €6.4 (divide both sides by 85)

100% = €640 (multiply both sides by 100)

Therefore, the original cost of the bicycle was €640.

Value Added Tax (VAT)

Example 1

VAT at 15% is added to a bill of €84.60.

Calculate the total bill.

Solution:

Method 1:

$$1\% = \frac{€84.60}{100} = €0.846$$

$15\% = €0.846 \times 15 = €12.69$

Therefore, the total bill is:

$€84.60 + €12.69 = €97.29$

Method 2:

As a percentage, the new bill is:

$100\% + 15\% = 115\%$ of the bill without VAT.

Therefore, the total bill is:

$= 115\%$ of €84.60

$= €84.60 \times 1.15 = €97.29$

Example 2

An article was priced at €210 + VAT. If a person paid €247.80 for the article, calculate the rate of VAT.

Solution:

VAT added = bill including VAT − bill excluding VAT

$= €247.80 - €210 = €37.80$

$$\text{Rate of VAT} = \frac{\text{VAT added on}}{\text{bill excluding VAT}} \times 100\% = \frac{37.80}{210} \times 100\% = 18\%$$

Often a price includes VAT, and we have to work in reverse to calculate the VAT or the price before VAT was added on.

Example 3

A telephone bill, including VAT at 21%, came to €99.22. Calculate the bill without VAT.

Solution:

Bill before VAT is added on	$\xrightarrow{+21\%}$	€99.22 = 121%

Think of the bill before VAT was added on as 100%.

$100\% + 21\% = 121\%$

Therefore $121\% = €99.22$ (equation given in disguise)

$1\% = €0.82$ (divide both sides by 121)

$100\% = €82$ (multiply both sides by 100)

Therefore, the bill without VAT was €82.

Income Tax

The following is called the **income tax equation**:

Gross Tax – Tax Credits = Tax Payable

Gross tax is calculated as follows:

Standard rate on all income up to the standard rate cut-off point.	+	A higher rate on all income above the standard rate cut-off point.

Note: If a person earns less than their standard rate cut-off point, then they pay tax only at the standard (lower) rate.

Example 1

A man has a gross yearly income of €27,500. He has a standard rate cut-off point of €29,400 and a tax credit of €1,925. The standard rate of tax is 16% of income up to the standard rate cut-off point. Calculate:

(i) the amount of gross tax for the year

(ii) the amount of tax paid for the year

(iii) net income for the year.

Express tax paid for the year as a percentage of gross income for the year.

Solution:

Note: The man earns **less** than his standard rate cut-off point, therefore he pays no tax at the higher rate.

(i) Gross tax = 16% of €27,500 = €27,500 × 0.16 = €4,400

(ii) Income tax equation:

Gross Tax – Tax Credits = Tax Payable

€4,400 – €1,925 = €2,475

Therefore, the amount of tax paid = €2,475.

(iii) Net income = Gross income – Tax paid

= €27,500 – €2,475 = €25,025

$$\text{Tax paid as a percentage of gross income} = \frac{\text{Tax paid}}{\text{Gross income}} \times 100\%$$

$$= \frac{2{,}475}{27{,}500} \times 100\% = 9\%$$

Example 2

Helen's weekly wage is €850.
She pays income tax at the rate of 20% on the first €600 of her wage and income tax at the rate of 42% on the remainder of her wage.
Helen has a weekly tax credit of €54.

(i) Calculate the tax payable at the rate of 20% on the first €600 of her wage.

(ii) Calculate the tax payable at the rate of 42% on the remainder of her wage.

(iii) Hence calculate Helen's gross tax.

(iv) Calculate the tax payable by Helen

Solution:

(i) 20% of €600 = €600 × 0.2 = €120

(ii) €850 − €600 = €250 (earnings above the standard rate cut-off point of €600)

Thus, she pays tax of 42% on €250.

42% of €250 = €250 × 0.42 = €105

(iii) Gross tax = (tax paid at 20%) + (tax paid at 42%)

= €120 + €105

= €225

(iv) Gross Tax − Tax Credits = Tax Payable (income tax equation)

€225 − €54 = €171

Thus, the tax payable by Helen is €171.

Example 3

A man has a gross yearly income of €45,000. He has a standard rate cut-off point of €28,000 and a tax credit of €1,784. The standard rate of tax is 15% of income up to the standard rate cut-off point and 38% on all income above the standard rate cut-off point. Calculate:

(i) the amount of gross tax for the year

(ii) the amount of tax paid for the year.

Solution:

(i) Gross tax = 15% of €28,000 + 38% of €17,000

= €28,000 × 0.15 + €17,000 × 0.38

= €4,200 + €6,460

= €10,660

Income above the standard rate cut-off point

= €45,000 – €28,000

= €17,000

(ii) Income tax equation:

Gross Tax – Tax Credits = Tax Payable

€10,660 – €1,784 = €8,876

Thus, he paid €8,876 tax for the year.

Example 4

A woman has a gross yearly income of €26,500. She has a standard rate cut-off point of €28,700 and a tax credit of €1,825. If she pays tax of €2,680, calculate the standard rate of tax.

Solution:

Income tax equation:

Gross Tax – Tax Credits = Tax Payable

Gross tax – €1,825 = €2,680

Gross tax = €2,680 + €1,825

Gross tax = €4,505

$$\text{Standard rate of tax} = \frac{\text{Gross tax}}{\text{Gross income}} \times 100\% = \frac{4{,}505}{26{,}500} \times 100\% = 17\%$$

or the standard rate of tax is 17c in the euro.

Annual Interest

Example 1

€4,500 was invested for one year and amounted to €4,680 at the end.
Calculate the rate of interest per annum.

Solution:

Interest = €4,680 – €4,500 = €180

$$\text{Rate of interest} = \frac{\text{interest}}{\text{sum invested}} \times 100\% = \frac{180}{4,500} \times 100\% = 4\%$$

Sometimes we are given an equation in disguise.

Example 2

What sum of money will earn €37.50 interest if it is invested at 3% per annum for one year?

Solution:

Think of the sum invested as 100%. Write down the equation given in disguise.

Given: 3% = €37.50 (3% of the sum invested is €37.50)

1% = €12.50 (divide both sides by 3)

100% = €1,250 (multiply both sides by 100)

Therefore the sum of money invested is €1,250.

Example 3

A sum of money invested for a year at 4% per annum amounted to €3,640 at the year end.
Calculate the sum of money invested and the interest earned.

Solution:

sum of money at the beginning of the year —(+4%)→ €3,640 = 104%

Think of the original sum invested as 100%. (100% + 4% = 104%.)

∴ 104% = €3,640 (equation given in disguise)

1% = €35 (divide both sides by 104)

100% = €3,500 (multiply both sides by 100)

Therefore, the sum of money invested is €3,500.

Interest earned = €3,640 – €3,500 = €140.

Alternatively 1% = €35

Interest earned = 4% = €35 × 4 = €140.

Compound Interest

When dealing with interest we use the following symbols:

P = the '**principal**', the sum of money borrowed or invested.
T = the '**time**', the number of years for which the sum of money is borrowed or invested.
R = the '**rate**', the percentage rate per annum at which interest is charged.
I = the '**interest**', the sum of money paid for borrowing or lending money.
A = the '**amount**', the principal and the interest added together: $A = P + I$.

With **compound interest**, the interest earned each year is added to the principal to form a new principal. This new principal earns interest in the next year, and so on.

Method 1:

Multiply the principal at the beginning of each year by $\left(1 + \frac{R}{100}\right)$.

This will give the principal for the next year, and so on.

Method 2:

Use the formula: $A = P\left(1 + \frac{R}{100}\right)^T$

It is not necessary to memorise the formula, as compound interest problems are best solved a year at a time (as described in method 1). The examination questions will not require you to calculate compound interest beyond **three** years. Besides, the formula does **not** work if:

(a) the interest rate, R, is changed during the three years, or

(b) money is added or subtracted during the three years.

In the next examples,

$P_1 =$ principal at the beginning of year 1; $A_1 =$ amount at the end of year 1.

$P_2 =$ principal at the beginning of year 2; $A_2 =$ amount at the end of year 2.

$P_3 =$ principal at the beginning of year 3; $A_3 =$ amount at the end of year 3.

Example 1

Calculate the compound interest on €5,000 for three years at 4% per annum.

Solution:

$$1 + \frac{R}{100} = 1 + \frac{4}{100} = 1 + 0.04 = 1.04$$

Method 1:

$P_1 = 5{,}000$

$A_1 = 5{,}000 \times 1.04 = 5{,}200$

$P_2 = 5{,}200$

$A_2 = 5{,}200 \times 1.04 = 5{,}408$

$P_3 = 5{,}408$

$A_3 = 5{,}408 \times 1.04 = 5{,}624.32$

Compound interest $= A_3 - P_1 =$ €5,624.32 – €5,000 = €624.32.

The working can also be shown using a table:

Year	Principal	Amount
1	5,000	$5{,}000 \times 1.04 = 5{,}200$
2	5,200	$5{,}200 \times 1.04 = 5{,}408$
3	5,408	$5{,}408 \times 1.04 = 5{,}624.32$

Compound interest $= A_3 - P_1 =$ €5,624.32 – €5,000 = €624.32

Method 2: Using the formula

Given: $P = 5{,}000$, $R = 4$, and $T = 3$. Find A.

$$A = P\left(1 + \frac{R}{100}\right)^T$$

$A = 5{,}000\ (1.04)^3$

$A = 5{,}624.32$ (calculator: 5,000 × 1.04 [y^x] 3 [=])

Compound interest $= A - P =$ €5,624.32 – €5,000 = €624.32.

In some questions the annual interest changes each year. When this happens it is important to remember that the **formula does not work**.

Example 2

€2,500 was invested for three years at compound interest. The rate for the first year was 4%, the rate for the second year was 3%, and the rate for the third year was 2.5%. Calculate the amount after three years and the compound interest earned.

Solution:

The rate changes every year, therefore we **cannot use the formula**.

Method 1:

$P_1 = 2{,}500$

$A_1 = 2{,}500 \times 1.04 = 2{,}600 \qquad \left(1 + \frac{R_1}{100} = 1 + \frac{4}{100} = 1 + 0.04 = 1.04\right)$

$P_2 = 2{,}600$

$A_2 = 2{,}600 \times 1.03 = 2{,}678 \qquad \left(1 + \frac{R_2}{100} = 1 + \frac{3}{100} = 1 + 0.03 = 1.03\right)$

$P_3 = 2{,}678$

$A_3 = 2{,}678 \times 1.025 = 2{,}744.95 \qquad \left(1 + \frac{R_3}{100} = 1 + \frac{2.5}{100} = 1 + 0.025 = 1.025\right)$

Therefore the amount after three years is €2,744.95.

Compound interest $= A_3 - P_1 =$ €2,744.95 – €2,500 = €244.95

The working can also be shown using a table:

Year	Principal	Amount
1	2,500	$2{,}500 \times 1.04 = 2{,}600$
2	2,600	$2{,}600 \times 1.03 = 2{,}678$
3	2,678	$2{,}678 \times 1.025 = 2{,}744.95$

Compound interest $= A_3 - P_1 =$ €2,744.95 – €2,500 = €244.95

Method 2:

$P_1 = 2{,}500$

$A_3 = 2{,}500 \times 1.04 \times 1.03 \times 1.025 =$ €2,744.95

Compound interest $= A_3 - P_1 =$ €2,744.95 – €2,500 = €244.95.

In some questions money is withdrawn, or repaid, at the end of a year. Again, when this happens the **formula does not work**.

Example 3

(i) €4,000 is invested at 3% per annum.
What is the amount of the investment at the end of one year?

(ii) €1,000 is added to this amount at the beginning of the second year.
The interest rate for the second year is 2.5% per annum.
What is the amount of the investment at the end of that year?

Solution:

$P_1 = 4{,}000$ (principal at the beginning of year 1)

$A_1 = 4{,}000 \times 1.03$ $\left(1 + \frac{R}{100} = 1 + \frac{3}{100} = 1 + 0.03 = 1.03\right)$

$A_1 = 4{,}120$ (amount of the investment after one year)

$E = 1{,}000$ (extra investment of €1,000)

$P_2 = 5{,}120$ (principal at the beginning of year 2)

$A_2 = 5{,}120 \times 1.025$ $\left(1 + \frac{R}{100} = 1 + \frac{2.5}{100} = 1 + 0.025 = 1.025\right)$

$A_2 = 5{,}248$ (amount of the investment after two years)

Therefore,

(i) the amount of the investment after one year is €4,120.

(ii) the amount of the investment after two years is €5,248.

Example 4

(i) €3,000 is invested at 4% per annum.
What is the amount of the investment at the end of one year?

(ii) €500 is withdrawn from this amount at the beginning of the second year.
The interest rate for the second year is 3.6% per annum.
What is the amount of the investment at the end of that year?

Solution:

$P_1 = 3{,}000$ (principal at the beginning of year 1)

$A_1 = 3{,}000 \times 1.04$ $\left(1 + \frac{R}{100} = 1 + \frac{4}{100} = 1 + 0.04 = 1.04\right)$

$A_1 = 3{,}120$ (amount at the end of one year)

$W = 500$ (€500 is withdrawn)

$P_2 = 2{,}620$ (principal at the beginning of year 2)

$A_2 = 2{,}620 \times 1.036$ $\left(1 + \frac{R}{100} = 1 + \frac{0.36}{100} = 1 + 0.036 = 1.036\right)$

$A_2 = 2{,}714.32$ (amount at the end of two years)

Therefore,

(i) the amount of the investment at the end of one year is €3,120.

(ii) the amount of the investment at the end of two years is €2,714.32.

Chapter 5. ALGEBRA

Evaluating Expressions (Substitution)

When you are substituting numbers in an expression, it is good practice to put a bracket around the number that replaces the letter. (Remember: **BEMDAS**.)

Example 1

If $a = 2$ and $b = 7$, find the value of:

(i) $2a + 5b$ **(ii)** $3ab + 4$ **(iii)** $(b - a)^2$

Solution:

(i) $2a + 5b$

$= 2(2) + 5(7)$

$= 4 + 35$

$= 39$

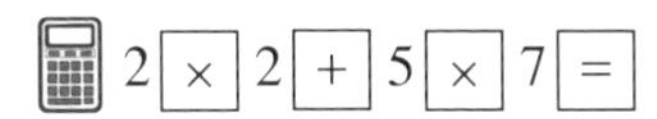

(ii) $3ab + 4$

$= 3(2)(7) + 4$

$= 42 + 4$

$= 46$

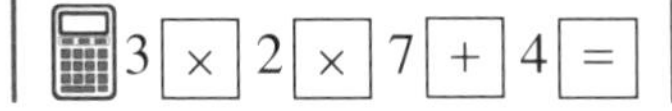

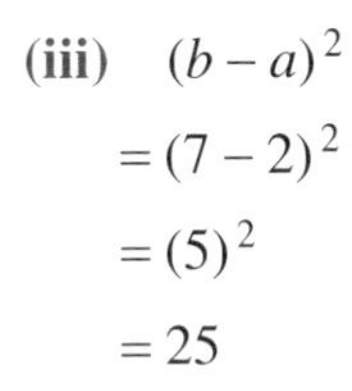

(iii) $(b - a)^2$

$= (7 - 2)^2$

$= (5)^2$

$= 25$

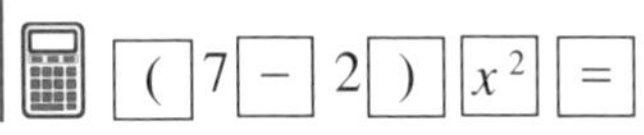

Note: $ab = a \times b$

Example 2

(i) If $x = 4$, find the value of $x^2 - x + 5\sqrt{x}$.

(ii) If $a = 3.25$ and $b = 9$, find the value of $\sqrt{a^2 - b}$.

Solution:

(i) $x^2 - x + 5\sqrt{x}$

$= (4)^2 - (4) + 5\sqrt{4}$

$= 16 - 4 + 5(2)$

$= 16 - 4 + 10$

$= 26 - 4 = 22$

4 x^2 − 4 + 5 √ 4 =

(ii) $\sqrt{a^2 - b}$

$= \sqrt{(3.25)^2 - 9}$

$= \sqrt{10.5625 - 9}$

$= \sqrt{1.5625}$

$= 1.25$

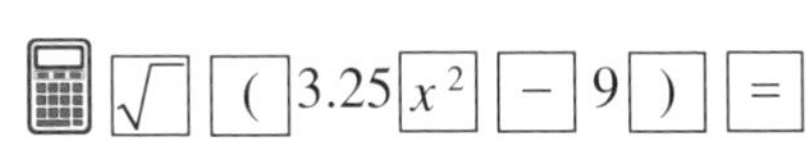

Simplifying Algebraic Expressions

Only terms that have the same power can be added or subtracted.

Example 1

Write in its simplest form:

(i) $(4x^2 - 3x + 7) + (x^2 - 2x - 8)$

(ii) $(6a - 10b) - 2(a - 5b + 1)$

Solution:

(i) $(4x^2 - 3x + 7) + (x^2 - 2x - 8)$

$= 4x^2 - 3x + 7 + x^2 - 2x - 8$

$= 4x^2 + x^2 - 3x - 2x + 7 - 8$

$= 5x^2 - 5x - 1$

(ii) $(6a - 10b) - 2(a - 5b + 1)$

$= 6a - 10b - 2a + 10b - 2$

$= 6a - 2a - 10b + 10b - 2$

$= 4a - 2$

Example 2

(i) Multiply $(3x - 2)$ by $(4x + 5)$ and write your answer in its simplest form.

(ii) Multiply $(x + 4)$ by $(x^2 + 2x - 3)$ and write your answer in its simplest form.

Solution:

(i) $(3x - 2)(4x + 5)$

$= 3x(4x + 5) - 2(4x + 5)$

$= 12x^2 + 15x - 8x - 10$

$= 12x^2 + 7x - 10$

(ii) $(x + 4)(x^2 + 2x - 3)$

$= x(x^2 + 2x - 3) + 4(x^2 + 2x - 3)$

$= x^3 + 2x^2 - 3x + 4x^2 + 8x - 12$

$= x^3 + 2x^2 + 4x^2 - 3x + 8x - 12$

$= x^3 + 6x^2 + 5x - 12$

Addition and Subtraction of Algebraic Fractions

Algebraic fractions that have numbers as denominators can be added or subtracted in exactly the same way as in arithmetic, i.e. we express the fractions using the lowest common denominator.

Algebraic fractions are added or subtracted with the following steps:

1. Put brackets on the top of each fraction.
2. Find the LCD of the numbers on the bottom.
3. Proceed in exactly the same way as in arithmetic.
4. Simplify the top (add and subtract terms that are the same).

Example

Write **(i)** $\dfrac{x-2}{2} + \dfrac{x+10}{9}$ and **(ii)** $\dfrac{4x}{3} - \dfrac{1}{6} + \dfrac{2-3x}{4}$

as a single fraction and give your answer in its simplest form.

Solution:

(i) $\dfrac{(x-2)}{2} + \dfrac{(x+10)}{9}$ (put brackets on top)
(the LCD is 18)

$= \dfrac{9(x-2)+2(x+10)}{18}$ (do the same as in arithmetic)

$= \dfrac{9x-18+2x+20}{18}$ (remove the brackets on top)

$= \dfrac{11x+2}{18}$ (simplify the top)

(ii) $\dfrac{(4x)}{3} - \dfrac{(1)}{6} + \dfrac{(2-3x)}{4}$ (put brackets on top)
(the LCD is 12)

$= \dfrac{4(4x)-2(1)+3(2-3x)}{12}$ (do the same as in arithmetic)

$= \dfrac{16x-2+6-9x}{12}$ (remove the brackets on top)

$= \dfrac{7x+4}{12}$ (simplify the top)

Chapter 6. FACTORS

Types of Factor

There are four types of factor that we will meet on our course:

	Type	Example	Factors
1.	Taking Out the HCF	$5ab - 10a^2$	$5a(b - 2a)$
2.	Factors by Grouping	$ax - bx + ay - by$	$(a - b)(x + y)$
3.	Quadratic Trinomials	$x^2 - 3x - 10$	$(x + 2)(x - 5)$
4.	Difference of Two Squares	$x^2 - 121$	$(x - 11)(x + 11)$

Note: Always look for a highest common factor first.
If there is no highest common factor, look for the following:

(i) factors by grouping (four terms)

(ii) quadratic trinomials (three terms)

(iii) difference of two squares (two terms).

1. Taking Out the Highest Common Factor (HCF)

1. Find the HCF of all the terms making up the expression.
2. Put the HCF outside the brackets.
3. Divide each term by the HCF to find the factor inside the brackets.

Note: To factorise an expression **completely** the HCF must appear outside the brackets.

Example

Factorise: **(i)** $5ab + 10b$ **(ii)** $3pq - 6pr$ **(iii)** $4xy + 12y^2$

Solution:

(i) $5ab + 10b$

The HCF is $5b$

$\therefore 5ab + 10b$ (put $5b$ outside the bracket,

$= 5b(a + 2)$ then divide each term by $5b$)

$\frac{5ab}{5b} = a$
$\frac{10b}{5b} = 2$

(ii) $3pq - 6pr$

The HCF is $3p$

$\therefore 3pq - 6pr$ (put $3p$ outside the bracket,

$= 3p(q - 2r)$ then divide each term by $3p$)

$\frac{3pq}{3p} = q$
$\frac{-6pr}{3p} = -2r$

(iii) $4xy + 12y^2$

The HCF is $4y$

$\therefore 4xy + 12y^2$ (put $4y$ outside the bracket,

$= 4y(x + 3y)$ then divide each term by $4y$)

$\frac{4xy}{4y} = x$
$\frac{12y^2}{4y} = 3y$

2. Factors by Grouping

An expression consisting of four terms with no common factor can be factorised with the following steps:

1. Group into pairs with a common factor.
2. Take out the common factor in each pair separately.
3. Take out the new common factor.

Example

Factorise: **(i)** $ab + 2ac + 5b + 10c$ **(ii)** $3x - 3y + ax - ay$ **(iii)** $xy + 4ay - xz - 4az$

Solution:

(i) $ab + 2ac + 5b + 10c$

$= (ab + 2ac) + (5b + 10c)$ (group into pairs with a common factor)

$= a(b + 2c) + 5(b + 2c)$ (take out common factor in each pair)

$= (b + 2c)(a + 5)$ (take out common factor $(b + 2c)$)

(ii) $3x - 3y + ax - ay$

$= (3x - 3y) + (ax - ay)$ (group into pairs with a common factor)

$= 3(x - y) + a(x - y)$ (take out common factor in each pair)

$= (x - y)(3 + a)$ (take out common factor $(x - y)$)

(iii) $xy + 4ay - xz - 4az$

$= (xy + 4ay) - (xz + 4az)$ (group into pairs with a common factor)

$= y(x + 4a) - z(x + 4a)$ (take out common factor in each pair)

$= (x + 4a)(y - z)$ (take out common factor $(x + 4a)$)

3. Quadratic Trinomials

Quadratic trinomials can be broken up into **two** types:

1. **Final term positive**

   When the final term is positive, the signs inside the middle of the brackets will be the **same**, either two pluses or two minuses. Keep the sign of the middle term given in the question.

Middle term plus:	$(x + \text{number})(x + \text{number})$	(two pluses)
Middle term minus:	$(x - \text{number})(x - \text{number})$	(two minuses)

2. **Final term negative**

   When the final term is negative, the signs inside the middle of the brackets will be **different**.

$(x + \text{number})(x - \text{number})$ or $(x - \text{number})(x + \text{number})$

In both cases the factors can be found by trial and improvement. The test is to multiply the inside terms, multiply the outside terms, and add the results to see if you get the middle term of the original quadratic trinomial.

Example

Factorise: **(i)** $x^2 + 6x + 8$ **(ii)** $x^2 - 9x + 14$ **(iii)** $x^2 + x - 20$ **(iv)** $x^2 - 2x - 15$

Solution:

(i) $x^2 + 6x + 8$

Factors of 8
1×8
2×4

Final term is + and middle term +,

$\therefore$ the factors are $(x + \text{number})(x + \text{number})$

$(x + 1)(x + 8)$ $x + 8x = 9x$ (no)

$(x + 2)(x + 4)$ $2x + 4x = 6x$ (yes, this is the middle term)

$\therefore\ x^2 + 6x + 8 = (x + 2)(x + 4)$

(ii) $x^2 - 9x + 14$

Factors of 14
1×14
2×7

Final term is + and middle term is −,

$\therefore$ the factors are $(x - \text{number})\ (x - \text{number})$

$(x - 1)(x - 14)$ $-x - 14x = -15x$ (no)

$(x - 2)(x - 7)$ $-2x - 7x = -9x$ (yes, this is the middle term)

$\therefore\ x^2 - 9x + 14 = (x - 2)(x - 7)$

(iii) $x^2 + x - 20$

Factors of 20
1×20
2×10
4×5

Final term −,

$\therefore$ the factors are $(x + \text{number})(x - \text{number})$

or

$(x - \text{number})(x + \text{number})$

Note: It is good practice to begin the trial and improvement with $(x + \text{number})(x - \text{number})$.

$(x + 2)(x - 10)$ $2x - 10x = -8x$ (no)

$(x + 4)(x - 5)$ $4x - 5x = -x$ (no, wrong sign)

On our second trial we have the correct number in front of x but of the wrong sign. So we just swap the signs:

$(x-4)(x+5)$ $\quad -4x+5x=x$ $\quad$ (yes, this is the middle term)

$\therefore\ x^2+x-20=(x-4)(x+5)$

(iv) $x^2-2x-15$

Factors of 15
1×15
3×5

Final term $-$,

$\therefore$ the factors are $(x+\text{number})(x-\text{number})$

or

$(x-\text{number})(x+\text{number})$

$(x+1)(x-15)$ $\quad x-15x=-14x$ $\quad$ (no)

$(x+3)(x-5)$ $\quad 3x-5x=-2x$ $\quad$ (yes, this is the middle term)

$\therefore\ x^2-2x-15=(x+3)(x-5)$

4. Difference of Two Squares

We factorise the difference of two squares with the following steps:

1. Write each term as a perfect square with brackets.
2. Use the rule $a^2-b^2=(a-b)(a+b)$.

   In words: $(\text{first})^2-(\text{second})^2=(\text{first}-\text{second})(\text{first}+\text{second})$.

Example

Factorise: **(i)** x^2-81 **(ii)** $36-y^2$ **(iii)** $1-25y^2$ **(iv)** $9a^2-4b^2$

Solution:

(i) x^2-81

$=(x)^2-(9)^2$ (write as perfect squares in brackets)

$=(x-9)(x+9)$ (apply the rule, (first – second) (first + second))

(ii) $36-y^2$

$=(6)^2-(y)^2$ (write as perfect squares in brackets)

$=(6-y)(6+y)$ (apply the rule, (first – second) (first + second))

(iii) $1 - 25y^2$

$= (1)^2 - (5y)^2$ (write as perfect squares in brackets)

$= (1 - 5y)(1 + 5y)$ (apply the rule, (first – second) (first + second))

Note: $1 = (1)^2$

(iv) $9a^2 - 4b^2$

$= (3a)^2 - (2b)^2$ (write as perfect squares in brackets)

$= (3a - 2b)(3a + 2b)$ (apply the rule, (first – second) (first + second))

Simplification Using Factors

Sometimes we have to simplify an algebraic expression using factors.

Example

Factorise: **(i)** $12ab - 6a$ **(ii)** $6b - 3$

Hence, simplify $\dfrac{12ab - 6a}{6b - 3}$

Solution:

(i) $12ab - 6a$

$= 6a(2b - 1)$

(ii) $6b - 3$

$= 3(2b - 1)$

$\therefore \dfrac{12ab - 6a}{6b - 3}$

$= \dfrac{6a(2b - 1)}{3(2b - 1)}$ (put in answers from **(i)** and **(ii)**)

$= \dfrac{6a}{3}$ (divide top and bottom by $(2b - 1)$)

$= 2a$ (divide top and bottom by 3)

Chapter 7. SIMPLE EQUATIONS

Simple Equations

When solving an equation we can:

1. **Add** or **subtract** the same quantity to or from both sides.
2. **Multiply** or **divide** both sides by the same quantity.

Remember: You must carry out the same operation on each side of the equation to keep it in **balance**. It is good practice to check your answer by substitution.

Example

Solve each of the following equations:

(i) $-2x = 6$ **(ii)** $4x + 3 = 23$ **(iii)** $7x - 1 = 2x + 9$

Solution:

(i)

$-2x = 6$

$2x = -6$ (multiply both sides by -1)

$\frac{2x}{2} = \frac{-6}{2}$ (divide both sides by 2)

$x = -3$

(ii)

$4x + 3 = 23$

$4x + 3 - 3 = 23 - 3$ (subtract 3 from both sides)

$4x = 20$

$\frac{4x}{4} = \frac{20}{4}$ (divide both sides by 4)

$x = 5$

(iii)

$7x - 1 = 2x + 9$

$7x - 1 + 1 = 2x + 9 + 1$ (add 1 to both sides)

$7x = 2x + 10$

$7x - 2x = 2x + 10 - 2x$ (subtract $2x$ from both sides)

$5x = 10$

$\frac{5x}{5} = \frac{10}{5}$ (divide both sides by 5)

$x = 2$

Equations with Brackets

Equations that contain brackets are solved with the following steps:

1. Remove the brackets.
   (Any term not in a bracket is moved down to the next line unchanged.)
2. Proceed as when solving previous equations.

Example 1

Solve the equations: **(i)** $5(2x - 1) = 35$ **(ii)** $5x - 6 = 3(x + 4)$

Solution:

(i)

$5(2x - 1) = 35$

$10x - 5 = 35$ (remove the brackets)

$10x = 40$ (add 5 to both sides)

$\frac{10x}{10} = \frac{40}{10}$ (divide both sides by 10)

$x = 4$

(ii)

$5x - 6 = 3(x + 4)$

$5x - 6 = 3x + 12$ (remove the brackets)

$5x = 3x + 18$ (add 6 to both sides)

$2x = 18$ (subtract $3x$ from both sides)

$\frac{2x}{2} = \frac{18}{2}$ (divide both sides by 2)

$x = 9$

Example 2

Solve each of the following equations:

(i) $4(x+5)-2(x+3)=12$ **(ii)** $5-4(x-3)=x-2(x-1)$

Solution:

(i) $4(x+5)-2(x+3)=12$

$4x+20-2x-6=12$ (remove the brackets)

$2x+14=12$ (simplify the left-hand side)

$2x=-2$ (subtract 14 from both sides)

$\frac{2x}{2}=\frac{-2}{2}$ (divide both sides by 2)

$x=-1$

(ii) $5-4(x-3)=x-2(x-1)$

$5-4x+12=x-2x+2$ (remove the brackets)

$-4x+17=-x+2$ (simplify both sides)

$-4x=-x-15$ (subtract 17 from both sides)

$-3x=-15$ (add x to both sides)

$3x=15$ (multiply both sides by -1)

$\frac{3x}{3}=\frac{15}{3}$ (divide both sides by 3)

$x=5$

Equations with Fractions

Equations with fractions are solved with the following steps:

1. Put brackets on top.
2. Multiply each part of the equation by the LCD of the numbers on the bottom.
3. Divide the bottom into the top (this removes all fractions).
4. Proceed as when solving previous equations.

Example 1

Solve each of the following equations:

(i) $\frac{2x}{5} - \frac{x}{4} = \frac{3}{2}$ (ii) $\frac{x+10}{9} + \frac{x-2}{2} = 5$

Solution:

(i) The LCD of 5, 4 and 2 is 20. Therefore we multiply each part of the equation by 20.

$$\frac{(2x)}{5} - \frac{(x)}{4} = \frac{(3)}{2} \quad \text{(put brackets on top)}$$

$$\frac{20(2x)}{5} - \frac{20(x)}{4} = \frac{20(3)}{2} \quad \text{(multiply each part by 20)}$$

$$4(2x) - 5(x) = 10(3) \quad \text{(divide the bottom into the top)}$$

$$8x - 5x = 30 \quad \text{(remove the brackets)}$$

$$3x = 30 \quad \text{(simplify the left-hand side)}$$

$$\frac{3x}{3} = \frac{30}{3} \quad \text{(divide both sides by 3)}$$

$$x = 10$$

(ii) The LCD of 9 and 2 is 18. Therefore we multiply each part of the equation by 18.

$$\frac{(x+10)}{9} + \frac{(x-2)}{2} = (5) \quad \text{(put brackets on top, including the 5)}$$

$$\frac{18(x+10)}{9} + \frac{18(x-2)}{2} = 18(5) \quad \text{(multiply each part by 18)}$$

$$2(x+10) + 9(x-2) = 90 \quad \text{(divide the bottom into the top)}$$

$$2x + 20 + 9x - 18 = 90 \quad \text{(remove the brackets)}$$

$$11x + 2 = 90 \quad \text{(simplify the left-hand side)}$$

$$11x = 88 \quad \text{(subtract 2 from both sides)}$$

$$\frac{11x}{11} = \frac{88}{11} \quad \text{(divide both sides by 11)}$$

$$x = 8$$

Example 2

(i) Express $\dfrac{x+5}{4} + \dfrac{x+2}{3}$ as a single fraction.

Give your answer in its simplest form.

(ii) Hence, or otherwise, solve the equation $\dfrac{x+5}{4} + \dfrac{x+2}{3} = \dfrac{5}{2}$

Solution:

(i) $\dfrac{x+5}{4} + \dfrac{x+2}{3}$

$= \dfrac{(x+5)}{4} + \dfrac{(x+2)}{3}$ (put brackets on top)
(the LCD is 12)

$= \dfrac{3(x+5)+4(x+2)}{12}$ (do the same as in arithmetic)

$= \dfrac{3x+15+4x+8}{12}$ (remove the brackets on top)

$= \dfrac{7x+23}{12}$ (simplify the top)

(ii) Method 1 (using 'hence'):

$\dfrac{x+5}{4} + \dfrac{x+2}{3} = \dfrac{5}{2}$

$\dfrac{(7x+23)}{12} = \dfrac{(5)}{2}$ (using the result from part (**i**))
(put brackets on top)

$\dfrac{12(7x+23)}{12} = \dfrac{12(5)}{2}$ (multiply each part by 12)

$1(7x+23) = 6(5)$ (divide the bottom into the top)

$7x+23 = 30$ (remove the brackets)

$7x = 7$ (subtract 23 from both sides)

$\dfrac{7x}{7} = \dfrac{7}{7}$ (divide both sides by 7)

$x = 1$

Method 2 (using 'otherwise'):

$$\frac{x+5}{4}+\frac{x+2}{3}=\frac{5}{2}$$

$$\frac{(x+5)}{4}+\frac{(x+2)}{3}=\frac{(5)}{2}$$ (put brackets on top)
(the LCD is 12)

$$\frac{12(x+5)}{4}+\frac{12(x+2)}{3}=\frac{12(5)}{2}$$ (multiply each part by 12)

$$3(x+5)+4(x+2)=6(5)$$ (divide the bottom into the top)

$$3x+15+4x+8=30$$ (remove the brackets)

$$7x+23=30$$ (simplify the left-hand side)

$$7x=7$$ (subtract 23 from both sides)

$$\frac{7x}{7}=\frac{7}{7}$$ (divide both sides by 7)

$$x=1$$

Chapter 8. SIMULTANEOUS LINEAR EQUATIONS

Simultaneous Linear Equations

Simultaneous linear equations are solved with the following steps:

1. Write both equations in the form $ax + by = k$ and label the equations ① and ②.
2. Multiply one or both of the equations by a number in order to make the coefficients of x or y the same, but of opposite sign.
3. Add to remove the variable with equal coefficients.
4. Solve the resultant equation to find the value of the remaining unknown (x or y).
5. Substitute this value in equation ① or ② to find the value of the other unknown.

Example 1

Solve, for x and y, the simultaneous equations:

$$5x + 2y = 23$$

$$x + y = 7$$

Solution:

1. Both equations are in the form $ax + by = k$. Label the equations ① and ②.
   $5x + 2y = 23$ ①
   $x + y = 7$ ②
2. Leave ① unchanged. Multiply ② by -2.
   $5x + 2y = 23$ ①
   $-2x - 2y = -14$ ② × −2
3. Add these new equations.
   $3x = 9$
4. Divide both sides by 3.
   $x = 3$
5. Put $x = 3$ into ① or ②.
   $x + y = 7$ ②
   ↓
   $3 + y = 7$

   Subtract 3 from both sides.
   $y = 4$

Therefore, the solution is $x = 3$ and $y = 4$.

Example 2

Solve, for x and y, the simultaneous equations:

$$2x + 3y = 11$$
$$x - 2y = -12$$

Solution:

1. Both equations are in the form $ax + by = k$.
Label the equations ① and ②.

$$2x + 3y = 11 \quad ①$$
$$x - 2y = -12 \quad ②$$

2. Multiply ① by 2.
Multiply ② by 3.

$$4x + 6y = 22 \quad ① \times 2$$
$$3x - 6y = -36 \quad ② \times 3$$

3. Add these new equations.

$$7x = -14 \quad \text{(add)}$$

4. Divide both sides by 7.

$$\frac{7x}{7} = \frac{-14}{7}$$
$$x = -2$$

5. Put $x = -2$ into ① or ②.

$$2x + 3y = 11 \quad ①$$
$$2(-2) + 3y = 11$$
$$-4 + 3y = 11$$

Add 4 to both sides.

$$3y = 15$$

Divide both sides by 3.

$$\frac{3y}{3} = \frac{15}{3}$$
$$y = 5$$

Therefore, the solution is $x = -2$ and $y = 5$.

Chapter 9. QUADRATIC EQUATIONS

Quadratic Equations

There are three types of quadratic equation we will meet on our course:

1.	$x^2 + bx + c = 0$	(three terms)	Example:	$x^2 - 7x + 6 = 0$
2.	$x^2 + bx = 0$	(no constant term)	Example:	$x^2 + 4x = 0$
3.	$x^2 + c = 0$	(no x term)	Example:	$x^2 - 9 = 0$

Quadratic equations are solved with the following steps:

1. Bring every term to the left-hand side.
   (If necessary multiply both sides by – 1 to make the coefficient of x^2 positive.)
2. Factorise the left-hand side.
3. Let each factor $= 0$.
4. Solve each simple equation.

Type 1

Example

Solve: **(i)** $x^2 + 2x - 8 = 0$ **(ii)** $x^2 - 7x + 6 = 0$ **(iii)** $x^2 - 3x - 10 = 0$

Solution:

(i) 1. $x^2 + 2x - 8 = 0$ (every term is on the left-hand side)

2. $(x + 4)(x - 2) = 0$ (factorise the left-hand side)

3. $x + 4 = 0$ or $x - 2 = 0$ (let each factor $= 0$)

4. $x = -4$ or $x = 2$ (solve each simple equation)

(ii) **1.** $x^2 - 7x + 6 = 0$ (every term on the left-hand side)

2. $(x - 1)(x - 6) = 0$ (factorise the left-hand side)

3. $x - 1 = 0$ or $x - 6 = 0$ (let each factor = 0)

4. $x = 1$ or $x = 6$ (solve each simple equation)

(iii) **1.** $x^2 - 3x - 10 = 0$ (every term is on the left-hand side)

2. $(x + 2)(x - 5) = 0$ (factorise the left-hand side)

3. $x + 2 = 0$ or $x - 5 = 0$ (let each factor = 0)

4. $x = -2$ or $x = 5$ (solve each simple equation)

Type 2

Example

Solve: **(i)** $x^2 + 5x = 0$ **(ii)** $x^2 - 2x = 0$

Solution:

(i) **1.** $x^2 + 5x = 0$ (every term is on the left-hand side)

2. $x(x + 5) = 0$ (factorise the left-hand side)

3. $x = 0$ or $x + 5 = 0$ (let each factor = 0)

4. $x = 0$ or $x = -5$ (solve each simple equation)

(ii) **1.** $x^2 - 2x = 0$ (every term is on the left-hand side)

2. $x(x - 2) = 0$ (factorise the left-hand side)

3. $x = 0$ or $x - 2 = 0$ (let each factor = 0)

4. $x = 0$ or $x = 2$ (solve each simple equation)

Note: It is important not to divide both sides by x, otherwise the root $x = 0$ is lost.

Type 3

Example

Solve for x: $x^2 - 16 = 0$

Solution:

We will use two methods to solve this quadratic equation.

Method 1:

1. $x^2 - 16 = 0$ (every term is on the left-hand side)

2. $(x)^2 - (4)^2 = 0$ (difference of two squares)

$(x - 4)(x + 4) = 0$ (factorise the left-hand side)

3. $x - 4 = 0$ or $x + 4 = 0$ (let each factor = 0)

4. $x = 4$ or $x = -4$ (solve each simple equation)

Method 2:

$x^2 - 16 = 0$

$x^2 = 16$ (add 16 to both sides)

$x = \pm\sqrt{16}$ (take square root of both sides)

$x = \pm 4$ ($\sqrt{16} = 4$)

$\therefore$ $x = 4$ or $x = -4$

Chapter 10. LINEAR INEQUALITIES IN ONE VARIABLE

Inequalities

The four inequality symbols:

$>$ means 'greater than'

$\geqslant$ means 'greater than or equal to'

$<$ means 'less than'

$\leqslant$ means 'less than or equal to'

Algebraic expressions that are linked by one of the four inequality symbols are called **inequalities**.

Solving inequalities is exactly the same as solving equations, with the following exception:

Multiplying or dividing both sides of an inequality by a **negative** number **reverses** the direction of the inequality.

That is:

$>$ changes to $<$ $\qquad$ $\geqslant$ changes to $\leqslant$

$<$ changes to $>$ $\qquad$ $\leqslant$ changes to $\geqslant$

The following rules apply to graphing inequalities on a number line:

Number line for $x \in \boldsymbol{N}$ or $x \in \boldsymbol{Z}$, use dots.

Number line for $x \in \boldsymbol{R}$, use 'full' heavy shading.

Example 1

Find the values of x for which $3x - 1 \leqslant 11$, $x \in \boldsymbol{N}$.

Graph your solution on the number line.

Solution:

$$3x - 1 \leqslant 11$$

$$3x \leqslant 12 \qquad \text{(add 1 to both sides)}$$

$$x \leqslant 4 \qquad \text{(divide both sides by 3)}$$

This is the set of natural numbers less than or equal to 4.
Therefore, the values of x are 0, 1, 2, 3, and 4.

Number line:

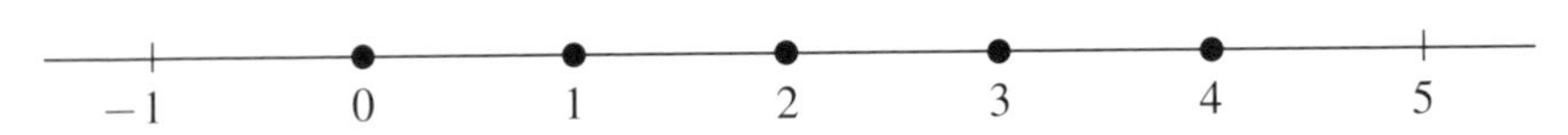

Dots are used on the number line as $x \in \boldsymbol{N}$, positive whole numbers, including 0.

Example 2

Solve $5x + 2 < 17$, $x \in \boldsymbol{Z}$.

Graph your solution on the number line.

Solution:

$$5x + 2 < 17$$

$$5x < 15 \qquad \text{(subtract 2 from both sides)}$$

$$x < 3 \qquad \text{(divide both sides by 5)}$$

This is the set of integers (whole numbers) less than 3 (3 not included).

Number line:

Dots are used on the number line as $x \in \boldsymbol{Z}$, positive or negative, whole numbers.

3 is **not** included as $<$ is used.

Example 3

(i) Solve the inequality $2(x-1)+3<13$. $x \in \boldsymbol{R}$.

(ii) Graph your solution on the number line.

Solution:

$$2(x-1)+3<13$$

$$2x-2+3<13 \qquad \text{(remove the brackets)}$$

$$2x+1<13 \qquad \text{(simplify the left-hand side)}$$

$$2x<12 \qquad \text{(subtract 1 from both sides)}$$

$$x<6 \qquad \text{(divide both sides by 2)}$$

This is the set of real numbers less than 6 (6 not included).

A circle is put around 6 to indicate that 6 is not included (as $<$ is used).
Heavy shading is used on the number line as $x \in \boldsymbol{R}$, the real numbers.

Example 4

Graph on the number line the solution set of $5-4x \leqslant 9$, $x \in \boldsymbol{R}$.

Solution:

$$5-4x \leqslant 9$$

$$-4x \leqslant 4 \qquad \text{(subtract 5 from both sides)}$$

$$4x \geqslant -4 \qquad \text{(multiply both sides by } -1 \text{ and reverse the inequality)}$$

$$x \geqslant -1 \qquad \text{(divide both sides by 4)}$$

This is the set of real numbers greater than or equal to -1.

Heavy shading is used on the number line as $x \in \boldsymbol{R}$, the real numbers.

Chapter 11. INDICES

Rules of Indices

1. $a^m \times a^n = a^{m+n}$ Example: $2^4 \times 2^5 = 2^{4+5} = 2^9$

   Multiplying powers of the same number, **add** the indices.

2. $\dfrac{a^m}{a^n} = a^{m-n}$ Example: $\dfrac{3^7}{3^2} = 3^{7-2} = 3^5$

   Dividing powers of the same number, **subtract** the index on the bottom from the index on top.

3. $(a^m)^n = a^{mn}$ Example: $(4^2)^3 = 4^{2\times 3} = 4^6$

   Raising the power of a number to a power, **multiply** the indices.

   Remember: $mn = m \times n$

Note: $a = a^1$

Example 1

(i) $2^3 \times 2^5 = 2^p$. Write down the value of p.

(ii) $\dfrac{3^8}{3^2} = 3^q$. Write down the value of q.

(iii) $(5^3)^4 = 5^k$. Write down the value of k.

Solution:

(i) $a^m \times a^n = a^{m+n}$

(add the indices)

$\therefore\ 2^3 \times 2^5$

$= 2^{3+5} = 2^8 = 2^p$

Thus, $p = 8$.

(ii) $\dfrac{a^m}{a^n} = a^{m-n}$

(subtract the index on the bottom from the index on top)

$\therefore\ \dfrac{3^8}{3^2}$

$= 3^{8-2} = 3^6 = 3^q$

Thus, $q = 6$.

(iii) $(a^m)^n = a^{mn}$

(multiply the indices)

$\therefore\ (5^3)^4$

$= 5^{3\times 4} = 5^{12} = 5^k$

Thus, $k = 12$.

Example 2

(i) Simplify $\frac{2^5 \times 2^6}{2^2 \times 2^5}$, giving your answer in the form 2^n, $n \in \mathbf{N}$.

(ii) Simplify $\frac{a^4 \times a^{10}}{a^5 \times a^3}$, giving your answer in the form a^n, $n \in \mathbf{N}$.

Solution:

(i) $\frac{2^5 \times 2^6}{2^2 \times 2^5}$

$= \frac{2^{5+6}}{2^{2+5}}$ $\left(\text{add the indices on the top and the bottom}\right)$

$= \frac{2^{11}}{2^7}$

$= 2^{11-7}$ (subtract the index on the bottom from the index on top)

$= 2^4$

(ii) $\frac{a^4 \times a^{10}}{a^5 \times a^3}$

$= \frac{a^{4+10}}{a^{5+3}}$ $\left(\text{add the indices on the top and the bottom}\right)$

$= \frac{a^{14}}{a^8}$

$= a^{14-8}$ (subtract the index on the bottom from the index on top)

$= a^6$

Example 3

Simplify $\frac{a^7 \times a}{a^6 \times a^5}$, giving your answer in the form a^n, $n \in \mathbf{Z}$.

Solution:

$\frac{a^7 \times a}{a^6 \times a^5}$

$\frac{a^7 \times a^1}{a^6 \times a^5}$ $(a = a^1)$

$= \frac{a^{7+1}}{a^{6+5}}$ (add the indices on the top and the bottom)

$= \frac{a^8}{a^{11}}$

$= a^{8-11}$ (subtract the index on the bottom from the index on top)

$= a^{-3}$ $(8 - 11 = -3)$

Chapter 12. INDEX NOTATION

Index Notation

Index notation is a shorthand way of writing very large numbers.

Index notation gives a number in two parts:

Number between 1 and 10 (but not 10)	×	power of 10

This is often written as $a \times 10^n$, where $1 \leqslant a < 10$ and $n \in \boldsymbol{N}$.

This way of writing a number is called **index notation** or **exponential notation**, or sometimes **standard form**.

Example 1

Express the numbers **(i)** 370,000 **(ii)** 8,260,000

in the form $a \times 10^n$, where $1 \leqslant a < 10$, $n \in \boldsymbol{N}$.

Solution:

(i) 370,000. (put in the decimal point)

3.70000 (move the decimal point **five** places to give a number between 1 and 10)

$\therefore$ $370{,}000 = 3.7 \times 10^5$

Alternatively, $370{,}000 = 3.7 \times 100{,}000 = 3.7 \times 10^5$

(ii) 8,260,000. (put in the decimal point)

8.260000 (move the decimal point **six** places to give a number between 1 and 10)

$\therefore$ $8{,}260{,}000 = 8.26 \times 10^6$

Alternatively, $8{,}260{,}000 = 8.26 \times 1{,}000{,}000 = 8.26 \times 10^6$

Notice that in each case the index of the power of 10 is equal to the number of decimal places moved.

Example 2

(i) Multiply 560,000 by 0.3 (ii) Divide 61,920 by $(1.2)^2$

In each case, write your answer in the form $a \times 10^n$, where $1 \leqslant a < 10$, and $n \in N$.

Solution:

(i) $560,000 \times 0.3$

$= 168,000$

(calculator: 560,000 [×] 0.3 [=])

$= 1.68 \times 10^5$

(ii) $61,920 \div (1.2)^2$

$= 43,000$

(calculator: 61,920 [÷] 1.2 [x^2] [=])

$= 4.3 \times 10^4$

Keying in Numbers in Index Notation into a Calculator

Numbers given in index notation can be keyed into your calculator by using the 'exponent key'. It is marked [EXP] or [EE] or [E].

To key in a number in index notation do the following:

1. Key in 'a', the 'number part', first.
2. Press the exponent key next.
3. Key in the index of the power of 10.

To enter 2.8×10^6, for example, you key in 2.8 [EXP] 6

Note: If you press [=] at the end, the calculator will write the number as a natural number, provided the index of the power of 10 is not too large.

Addition and Subtraction

To add or subtract two numbers in index notation, do the following:

1. Write each number as a natural number.
2. Add or subtract these numbers.
3. Write your answer in index notation.

Alternatively, you can use your calculator by keying in the numbers in index notation.

Example

Express **(i)** $3.52 \times 10^4 + 2.8 \times 10^3$ **(ii)** $2.348 \times 10^5 - 4.8 \times 10^3$
in the form $a \times 10^n$, where $1 \leqslant a < 10$ and $n \in N$.

Solution:

(i) $3.52 \times 10^4 = 35{,}200$

$2.8 \times 10^3 = \underline{2{,}800}$

$38{,}000$

$= 3.8 \times 10^4$

(3.52 [EXP] 4 [+] 2.8 [EXP] 3 [=])

$= 38{,}000$ (on the display)

$= 3.8 \times 10^4$

(ii) $2.348 \times 10^5 = 234{,}800$

$4.8 \times 10^3 = \underline{4{,}800}$

$230{,}000$

$= 2.3 \times 10^5$

(2.348 [EXP] 5 [−] 4.8 [EXP] 3 [=])

$= 230{,}000$ (on the display)

$= 2.3 \times 10^5$

Multiplication and Division

To multiply or divide two numbers in index notation, do the following:

1. Multiply or divide the 'a' parts (the number parts).
2. Multiply or divide the powers of 10 (add or subtract the indices).
3. Write your answer in index notation.

Alternatively, you can use your calculator by keying in the numbers in index notation and multiplying or dividing as required.

Example

Express **(i)** $(4.8 \times 10^3) \times (1.5 \times 10^2)$ **(ii)** $(3.91 \times 10^8) \div (1.7 \times 10^5)$
in the form $a \times 10^n$, where $1 \leqslant a < 10$, and $n \in \boldsymbol{N}$.

Solution:

(i) $(4.8 \times 10^3) \times (1.5 \times 10^2)$

$= 4.8 \times 10^3 \times 1.5 \times 10^2$

$= 4.8 \times 1.5 \times 10^3 \times 10^2$

$= 7.2 \times 10^{3+2}$

$= 7.2 \times 10^5$

(Calculator: 4.8 [EXP] 3 [×] 1.5 [EXP] 2 [=])

$= 720{,}000$ (on the display)

$= 7.2 \times 10^5$

(ii) $(3.91 \times 10^8) \div (1.7 \times 10^5)$

$$= \frac{3.91 \times 10^8}{1.7 \times 10^5}$$

$$= \frac{3.91}{1.7} \times \frac{10^8}{10^5}$$

$= 2.3 \times 10^{8-5}$

$= 2.3 \times 10^3$

(Calculator: 3.91 [EXP] 8 [÷] 1.7 [EXP] 5 [=])

$= 2{,}300$ (on the display)

$= 2.3 \times 10^3$

Chapter 13. USING EQUATIONS TO SOLVE PROBLEMS

Forming Expressions

Statements in words can be translated into algebraic expressions. It is common to let x represent the unknown number, usually the smallest, in a problem given in words. However, any other letter would do.

For example, if x represents an unknown number, then:

Words	Expression
7 more than the number	$(x+7)$
5 less than the number	$(x-5)$
4 times the number	$4x$
3 times the number, less 2	$(3x-2)$
one-fifth of the number	$\frac{1}{5}x$ *or* $\frac{x}{5}$
the number subtracted from 9	$9-x$
the difference between two numbers is 6	x and $(x+6)$
two numbers add up to 8	x and $(8-x)$
the number plus 3, then divided by 4	$\frac{x+3}{4}$

Steps in Constructing an Equation in Solving a Practical Problem

A numerical problem given in words can often be translated into an equation. The solution of this equation will give the answer to the problem.

To solve a practical problem by constructing an equation, do the following:

Step 1: Read the question carefully a few times.

Step 2: Let x equal the unknown number that is required.

Step 3: Write each statement in the problem in terms of x. Use a diagram if necessary.

Step 4: Use the information in the problem to **link** the parts in step 3 to form an equation. Make sure both sides are measured in the same units.

Step 5: Solve the equation (find the unknown number).

Step 6: Test your solution in the problem itself – **not in your equation**, as your equation may be wrong.

Note: If the problem requires simultaneous equations to be solved, then step 2 becomes, 'Let x and y equal the unknown numbers that are required.'

When an equation is constructed from a problem given in words, it may lead to any one of three types of equation:

1. simple linear equation **2.** simultaneous linear equations **3.** quadratic equation.

1. Using Simple Equations to Solve Problems

Example 1

Two cylindrical buckets hold 18 litres and 6 litres of liquid, respectively. To each bucket are now added another $2x$ litres of liquid, so that the larger one now holds twice as much as the smaller one.

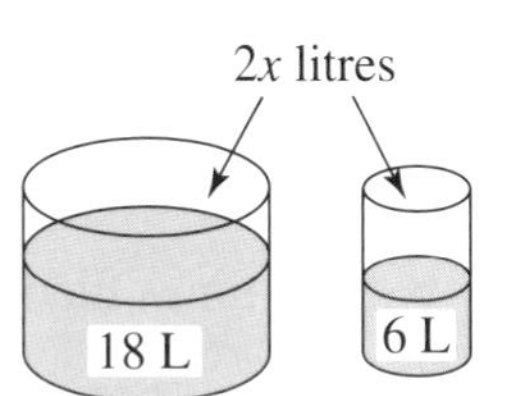

(i) Express the volume of liquid in each bucket in terms of x.

(ii) Form an equation in x.

(iii) Solve the equation to find the value of x.

Solution:

(i) Volume of liquid in the larger bucket = $(2x + 18)$ litres.

Volume of liquid in the smaller bucket = $(2x + 6)$ litres.

(ii) Link used to form the equation:

Given: (volume of liquid in larger bucket) = 2 (volume of liquid in smaller bucket)

Equation: $(2x + 18) = 2(2x + 6)$

(iii)

$$2x + 18 = 4x + 12$$

$$2x - 4x = 12 - 18$$

$$-2x = -6$$

$$2x = 6$$

$$\frac{2x}{2} = \frac{6}{2}$$

$$x = 3$$

Example 2

x is a number. A second number is 5 greater than x.

(i) Write down the second number in terms of x.

(ii) Twice the first number added to three times the second number is equal to 35. Write down an equation in x to represent this information.

(iii) Solve your equation for x and state what the two numbers are.

(iv) Verify your result.

Solution:

(i) x = first (smaller) number

Then $(x + 5)$ is the second (larger) number (5 more than x)

(ii) x = first (smaller) number $x + 5$ = second (larger) number

Link used to form the equation:

Given: 2(first number) + 3(second number) = 35

$$\therefore \quad 2(x) + 3(x+5) = 35$$

Equation: $2x + 3(x + 5) = 35$

(iii)

$$2x + 3(x + 5) = 35 \quad \text{(equation from part (ii))}$$

$$2x + 3x + 15 = 35 \quad \text{(remove brackets)}$$

$$5x + 15 = 35 \quad \text{(simplify the left-hand side)}$$

$$5x = 20 \quad \text{(subtract 15 from both sides)}$$

$$\frac{5x}{5} = \frac{20}{5} \quad \text{(divide both sides by 5)}$$

$$x = 4$$

(iv) Thus $x = 4$ = first (smaller) number

and $x + 5 = 4 + 5 = 9$ = second (larger) number.

Given: twice first number + three times second number = 35

Check:

$$2(4) + 3(9) = 35$$

$$8 + 27 = 35$$

$$35 = 35 \quad \text{(correct)}$$

Thus, our answer is verified.

Example 3

A rectangle has a length $(x + 6)$ cm and width x cm, as in the diagram.

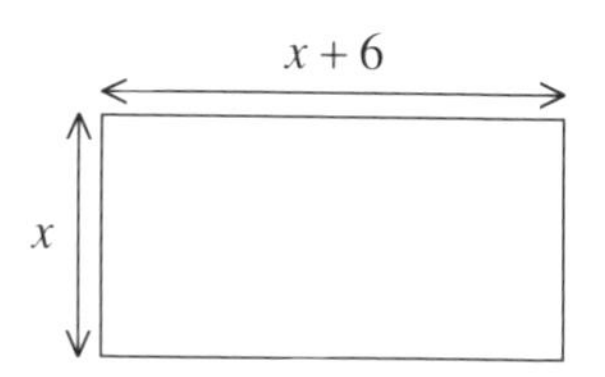

(i) Find the perimeter of this rectangle in terms of x.

(ii) If the perimeter of the rectangle is 40 cm, write down an equation in x to represent this information.

(iii) Solve the equation that you formed in part **(ii)** above, for x.

(iv) Find the area of the square with the same perimeter as the given rectangle. Give your answer in cm^2.

Solution:

(i) Perimeter = Distance around the 4 sides

$$= x + (x + 6) + x + (x + 6)$$
$$= x + x + 6 + x + x + 6$$
$$= 4x + 12$$

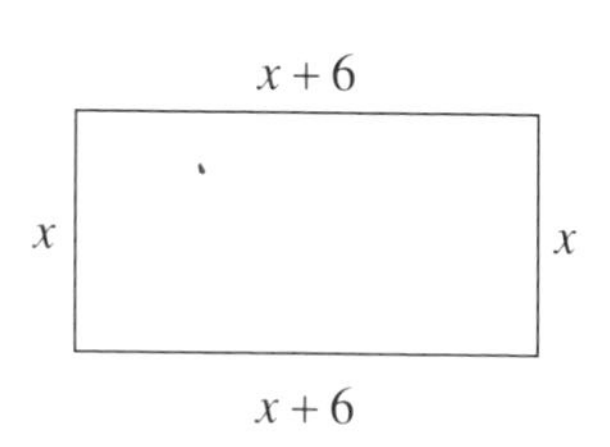

(ii) **Link used to form the equation:**

Given: Perimeter = 40 cm

$\therefore \quad 4x + 12 = 40 \qquad$ (from part **(i)**)

(iii)

$4x + 12 = 40 \qquad$ (equation from part **(ii)**)

$4x = 28 \qquad$ (subtract 12 from both sides)

$\dfrac{4x}{4} = \dfrac{28}{4} \qquad$ (divide both sides by 4)

$x = 7$

(iv) Let the length of a side of the square $= a$ cm

Given: Perimeter of square = 40 cm (same as rectangle)

$\therefore \quad a + a + a + a = 40$

$4a = 40$

$a = 10$

Area of square $= a \times a = 10 \times 10 = 100 \text{ cm}^2$.

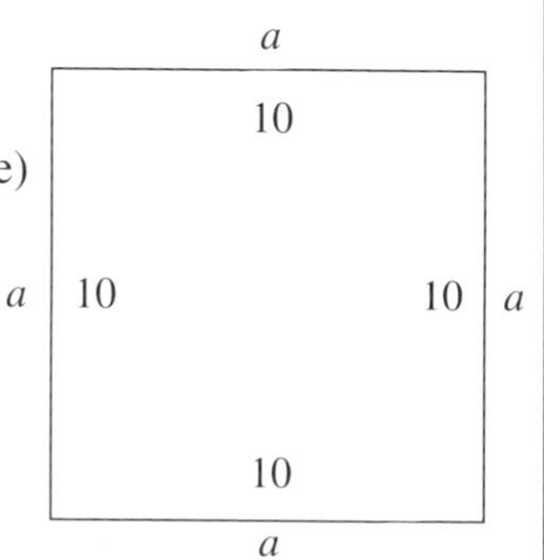

2. Using Simultaneous Equations to Solve Problems

Example 1

The cost of cinema tickets for two adults and three children is €38.
The cost of cinema tickets for one adult and two children is €22.

Let €x be the cost of a cinema ticket for an adult and let €y be the cost of a cinema ticket for a child.

(i) Write down two equations, each in x and y, to represent the above information.

(ii) Solve these equations to find the cost of a cinema ticket for an adult and the cost of a cinema ticket for a child.

Solution:

(i) **First fact that links *x* and *y*:**

Given: The cost of cinema tickets for two adults and three children is €38.

Equation: $2x + 3y = 38$ ①

Second fact that links *x* and *y*:

Given: The cost of cinema tickets for one adult and two children is €22.

Equation: $x + 2y = 22$ ②

(ii) Now solve the simultaneous equations ① and ②.

$$2x + 3y = 38 \quad ①$$
$$x + 2y = 22 \quad ②$$
$$4x + 6y = 76 \quad ① \times 2$$
$$-3x - 6y = -66 \quad ② \times -3$$
$$x = 10 \quad \text{(add)}$$

Put $x = 10$ into ① or ②.

$$x + 2y = 22 \quad ②$$
$$\downarrow$$
$$10 + 2y = 22 \quad (x = 10)$$
$$2y = 12$$
$$\frac{2y}{2} = \frac{12}{2}$$
$$y = 6$$

Therefore:

The cost of an adult cinema ticket = €10.

The cost of a children's cinema ticket = €6.

Example 2

The cost of five books and one magazine is €32.

The cost of eight books and three magazines is €54.

Let €x be the cost of a book and let €y be the cost of a magazine.

(i) Write down two equations, each in x and y, to represent the above information.

(ii) Solve these equations to find the cost of a book and the cost of magazine.

Solution:

(i) **First fact that links x and y:**

Given: The cost of five books and one magazine is €32.

Equation: $5x + y = 32$ ①

Second fact that links x and y:

Given: The cost of eight books and three magazines is €54.

Equation: $8x + 3y = 54$ ②

(ii) Now solve the simultaneous equations ① and ②.

$5x + y = 32$ ①

$8x + 3y = 54$ ②

$15x + 3y = 96$ ① × 3

$-8x - 3y = -54$ ② × −1

$7x = 42$ (add)

$$\frac{7x}{7} = \frac{42}{7}$$

$x = 6$

Put $x = 6$ into ① or ②

$5x + y = 32$ ①

$5(6) + y = 32$ $(x = 6)$

$30 + y = 32$

$y = 2$

Therefore:

The cost of a book = €6.

The cost of a magazine = €2.

3. Using Quadratic Equations to Solve Problems

When we use an equation to solve a practical problem, the equation often turns out to be a quadratic equation. These equations usually have two solutions. If one of these makes no sense, for example, producing a negative number of people, we reject it. Again, always look for the link in the question to set up the equation.

Example 1

A square has a length of x cm.
A rectangle has a length of 5 cm and a width of x cm.
Write, in terms of x, an expression for the area of:

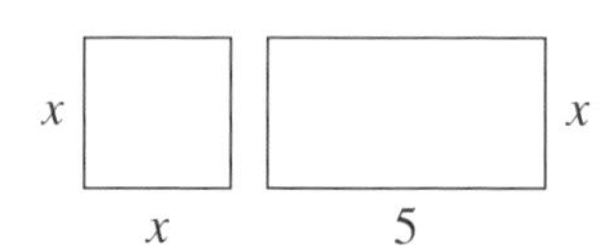

(i) the square **(ii)** the rectangle.

If the area of the square added to the area of the rectangle is 14 cm^2,

(iii) use this information to form an equation

(iv) solve the equation to find x.

Solution:

(i) Area of square $= x \times x = x^2$

(ii) Area of rectangle $= 5 \times x = 5x$

(iii) **Link used to form the equation:**

Given: (Area of square) + (Area of rectangle) = 14 cm^2

Equation: $x^2 \quad + \quad 5x \quad = 14$

(iv)

$$x^2 + 5x - 14 = 0$$

$$(x - 2)(x + 7) = 0$$

$$x - 2 = 0 \quad \text{or} \quad x + 7 = 0$$

$$x = 2 \quad \text{or} \quad x = -7$$

The negative value, $x = -7$, is not possible, therefore $x = -7$ is rejected.

Therefore, $x = 2$.

Example 2

One positive number is 3 greater than another positive number.

(i) If the smaller number is x, write the larger number in terms of x.

(ii) Write, in terms of x, an expression for the product of the two numbers.

If the product is 40,

(iii) use this information to form an equation

(iv) solve the equation to find x.

What are the two numbers?

Solution:

(i) x = smaller number

Then $(x + 3)$ is the larger number (3 more than x)

(ii) **Note:** 'product' means 'the result from multiplying'.

Product of the two numbers

= (smaller number) × (larger number)

$= (x)(x + 3)$

$= x^2 + 3x$

(iii) **Link used to form the equation:**

Given: Product of the two numbers is 40

Equation: $x^2 + 3x = 40$

(iv)

$$x^2 + 3x - 40 = 0$$

$$(x - 5)(x + 8) = 0$$

$$x - 5 = 0 \quad \text{or} \quad x + 8 = 0$$

$$x = 5 \quad \text{or} \quad x = -8$$

The negative value, $x = -8$, is rejected, as we are told x is a positive number.

Therefore, $x = 5$.

$x + 3 = 5 + 3 = 8$

Thus, the two numbers are 5 and 8.

Chapter 14. FUNCTIONS

Functions

A function is a rule that changes one number (input) into another number (output). Functions are usually represented by the letter f. We can think of a function, f, as a number machine which changes an input, x, into an output, $f(x)$.

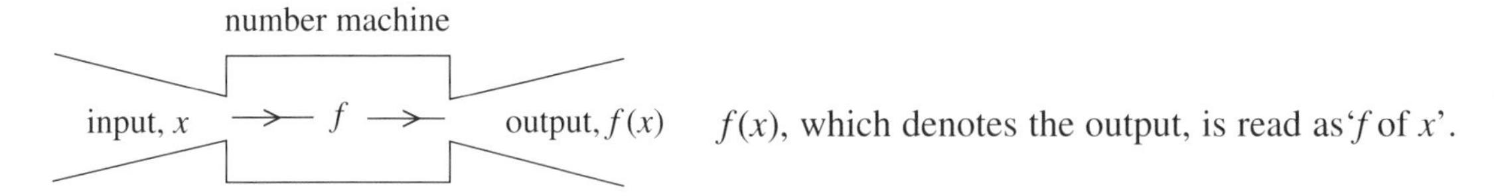

$f(x)$, which denotes the output, is read as 'f of x'.

Note: A function is also called a **mapping** or simply a **map**.
One number is **mapped** onto another number.
The set of numbers that are put into a function is called the **domain**.
The set of numbers that comes out of a function is called the **range**.
A function connects **every** input in the domain to an input in the range.
A function is another way of writing an algebraic formula that links input to output.

Example 1

$f(x) = 5x - 6$. Find **(i)** $f(3)$ **(ii)** $f(1)$ **(iii)** $f(-2)$.

Solution:

$f(x) = 5x - 6$

(i) $f(3) = 5(3) - 6$
$= 15 - 6$
$= 9$

(ii) $f(1) = 5(1) - 6$
$= 5 - 6$
$= -1$

(iii) $f(-2) = 5(-2) - 6$
$= -10 - 6$
$= -16$

Example 2

Given that $f(x) = 3x - 5$, find **(i)** $f(4)$ **(ii)** $f(-1)$ **(iii)** $f(2) + f(0)$.

Find the value of x for which $f(x) = 16$.

Solution:

$f(x) = 3x - 5$

(i) $f(4) = 3(4) - 5$
$= 12 - 5$
$= 7$

(ii) $f(-1) = 3(-1) - 5$
$= -3 - 5$
$= -8$

(iii) $f(2) = 3(2) - 5$
$= 6 - 5$
$= 1$

$f(0) = 3(0) - 5$
$= 0 - 5$
$= -5$

$\therefore\ f(2) + f(0) = 1 - 5 = -4$

$f(x) = 16$ (this is an equation in disguise)

$3x - 5 = 16$ ($f(x) = 3x - 5$)

$3x = 21$ (add 5 to both sides)

$\frac{3x}{3} = \frac{21}{3}$ (divide both sides by 3)

$x = 7$

Therefore, the value of x for which $f(x) = 16$ is 7.

Example 3

(i) Given that $f(x) = x^2 - 2x - 8$, find **(a)** $f(5)$ **(b)** $f(-1)$.

(ii) Find the values of x for which $f(x) = 0$.

Solution:

(i) $f(x) = x^2 - 2x - 8$

(a)
$$\begin{aligned} f(5) &= (5)^2 - 2(5) - 8 \\ &= 25 - 10 - 8 \\ &= 25 - 18 \\ &= 7 \end{aligned}$$

(b)
$$\begin{aligned} f(-1) &= (-1)^2 - 5(-1) - 8 \\ &= 1 + 5 - 8 \\ &= 6 - 8 \\ &= -2 \end{aligned}$$

(ii) Given: $f(x) = 0$ (equation)

$\therefore$ $x^2 - 2x - 8 = 0$ $(f(x) = x^2 - 2x - 8)$

$(x + 2)(x - 4) = 0$ (factorise the left-hand side)

$x + 2 = 0$ or $x - 4 = 0$ (let each factor $= 0$)

$x = -2$ or $x = 4$ (solve each simple equation)

Domain = set of inputs (x values) **Range** = set of outputs (y values)

Example 4

P = {(1, 5), (2, 5), (3, 6), (4, 6)}.

Write out the domain and range of P.

Solution:

Domain = set of inputs (x values) = {1, 2, 3, 4}

Range = set of outputs (y values) = {5, 6}

Note: Never repeat an element in a set.

Example 5

R = {(0, 1), (1, 3), (2, 3), (3, 4)}

Write out the domain and range of R.

Solution:

Domain = set of inputs (x values) = {0, 1, 2, 3}

Range = set of outputs (y values) = {1, 3, 4}

Example 6

Given $f(x) = 4x - 3$, $-2 \leqslant x \leqslant 3$, $x \in \mathbf{Z}$:

(i) represent f with a mapping diagram

(ii) represent f as a set of couples

(iii) write out the domain and range of f.

If $f(k) = 17$, find the value of k.

Solution:

A table is very useful to calculate the set of couples for the mapping diagram.

x	$4x - 3$	$f(x)$
−2	−8 − 3	−11
−1	−4 − 3	−7
0	0 − 3	−3
1	4 − 3	1
2	8 − 3	5
3	12 − 3	9

(i) Mapping diagram

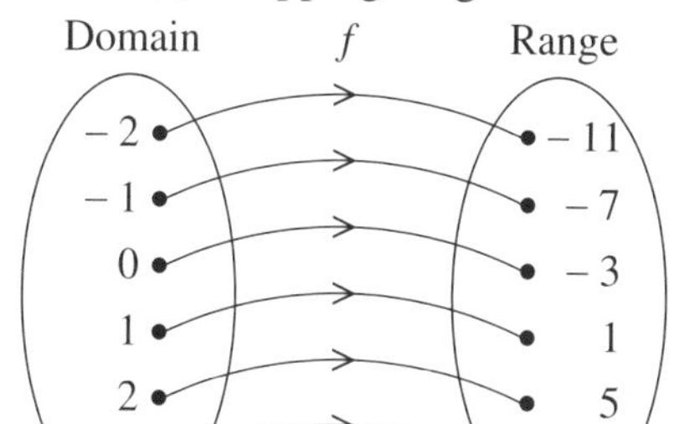

(ii) $f = \{(-2, -11), (-1, -7), (0, -3), (1, 1), (2, 5), (3, 9)\}$

(iii) Domain = {−2, −1, 0, 1, 2, 3} (the set of inputs)

Range = {−11, −7, −3, 1, 5, 9} (the set of outputs)

If $f(x) = 4x - 3$, then $f(k) = 4k - 3$, i.e. replace x with k.

Given: $f(k) = 17$ (this is an equation in disguise)

$\therefore$ $4k - 3 = 17$ $(f(k) = 4k - 3)$

$4k = 20$ (add 3 to both sides)

$\frac{4k}{4} = \frac{20}{4}$ (divide both sides by 4)

$k = 5$

Sometimes we are given a function, with a mapping diagram where parts of the domain and the range are missing.

Example 7

A function f is defined as $f: x \rightarrow 2x - 1$.

Copy the mapping diagram and find

(i) the value of p **(ii)** the value of q **(iii)** the value of r.

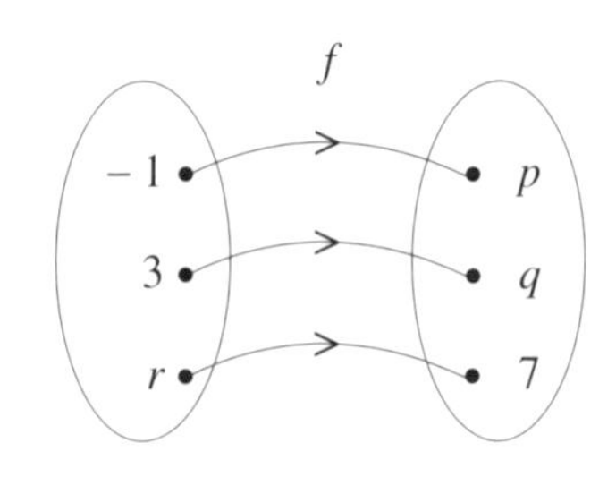

Solution:

$$f(x) = 2x - 1$$

(i) $f(-1) = 2(-1) - 1$

$= -2 - 1$

$= -3$

$\therefore \quad p = -3$

(ii) $f(3) = 2(3) - 1$

$= 6 - 1$

$= 5$

$\therefore \quad q = 5$

(iii) Given: Output = 7; find input, r.

$\therefore$ $f(x) = 7$

$2x - 1 = 7$

$2x = 8$

$\frac{2x}{2} = \frac{8}{2}$

$x = 4$

$\therefore$ $r = 4$

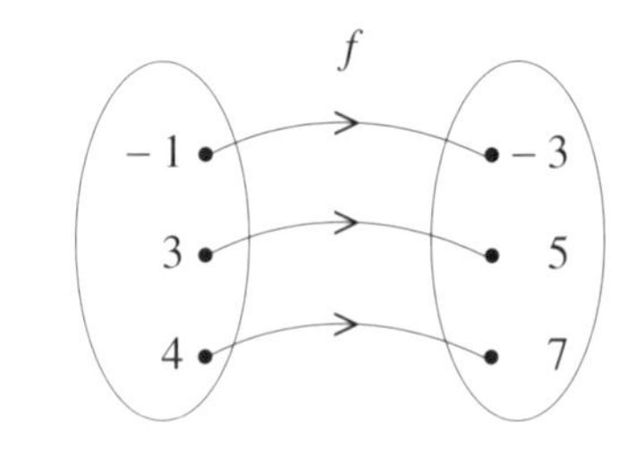

Chapter 15. GRAPHING FUNCTIONS

Notation

The notation $y = f(x)$ means 'the value of the output y depends on the value of the input x, according to some rule called f. Hence, y and $f(x)$ are interchangeable, and the y-axis can also be called the $f(x)$-axis.

Note: It is very important not to draw a graph outside the given values of x.

Graphing Linear Functions

The first four letters in the word **linear** spell **line**. Therefore the graph of a linear function will be a straight line. A linear function is usually given in the form $f: x \rightarrow ax + b$, where $a \neq 0$ and a, b are constants. For example, $f: x \rightarrow 2x + 5$. As the graph is a straight line, two points are all that is needed to graph it. In the question, you will always be given a set of inputs, x, called the domain.

To graph a linear function do the following:

1. Choose two suitable values of x, in the given domain. (Two suitable values are the **smallest** and **largest** values of x.)
2. Substitute these into the function to find the two corresponding values of y.
3. Plot the points and draw the line through them.

Example

Graph the function $g: x \rightarrow 2x + 1$, in the domain $-2 \leqslant x \leqslant 3$, $x \in \mathbf{R}$.

Solution:

Let $x = -2$ and $x = 3$.

Let $y = g(x) \Rightarrow y = 2x + 1$

x	$2x + 1$	y
-2	$-4 + 1$	-3
3	$6 + 1$	7

Plot the points $(-2, -3)$ and $(3, 7)$ and join them with a straight line.

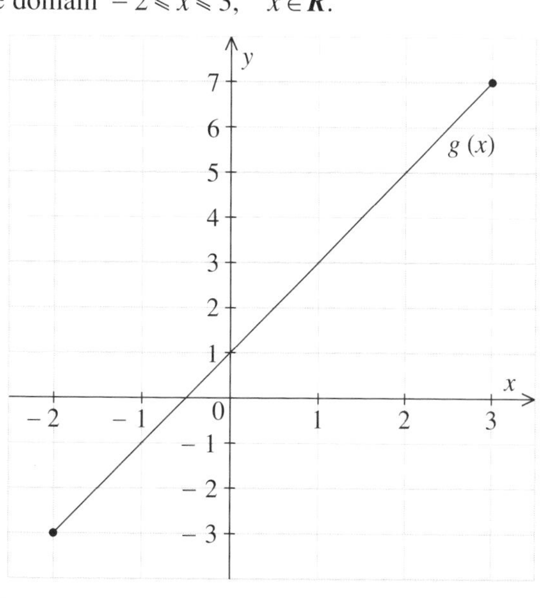

Graphing Quadratic Functions

A **quadratic** function is usually given in the form $f: x \to ax^2 + bx + c$, $a \neq 0$, and a, b, c are constants. For example, $f: x \to 2x^2 - x + 3$. Because of its shape, quite a few points are needed to plot the graph of a quadratic function. In the question, you will always be given a set of inputs, x, called the domain. With these inputs, a table is used to find the corresponding set of outputs, y or $f(x)$, called the range. When the table is completed, plot the points and join them with a **smooth curve**.

Notes on making out the table:

1. Work out each column separately, i.e. all the x^2 values first, then all the x values, and finally the constant. (Watch for patterns in the numbers.)
2. Work out each corresponding value of y.
3. The **only** column that changes sign is the x-term (middle) column.
   If the given values of x contain 0, then the x-term column will make one sign change, either from $+$ to $-$ or from $-$ to $+$, where $x = 0$.
4. The other two columns **never** change sign. They remain either all pluses or all minuses. These columns keep the sign given in the question.

Note: Decide where to draw the x- and y-axes by looking at the table to see what the largest and smallest values of x and y are. In general, the units on the x-axis are larger than the units on the y-axis. Try to make sure that the graph extends almost the whole width and length of the page.

Using Graphs

Once we have drawn the graph, we are usually asked to use the graph to answer some questions. Below are examples of the general types of problem where graphs are used.

Notes: **1.** $y = f(x)$, so $f(x)$ can be replaced by y.

2. In general, if given x find y, and vice versa.

Examples of the main problems, once the graph is drawn:

1. **Find the values of x for which $f(x) = 0$.**

   This question is asking:

   'Where does the curve meet the x-axis?'

   Solution:

   Write down the values of x where the graph meets the x-axis.

   From the graph: $x = -1$ or $x = 2$.

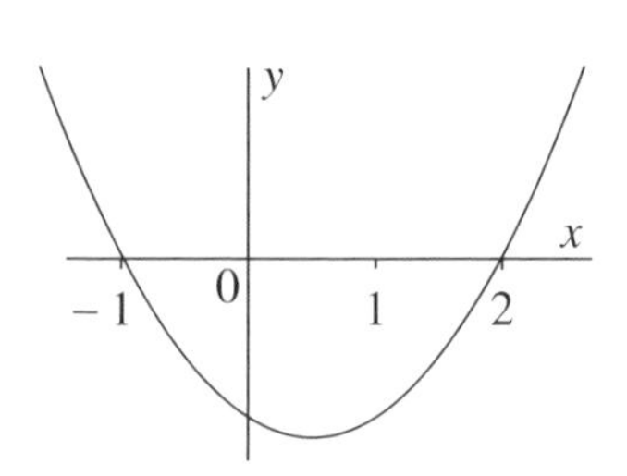

2. Find the values of x for which $f(x) = 2$.

This question is asking:

'When $y = 2$, what are the values of x?'

Solution:

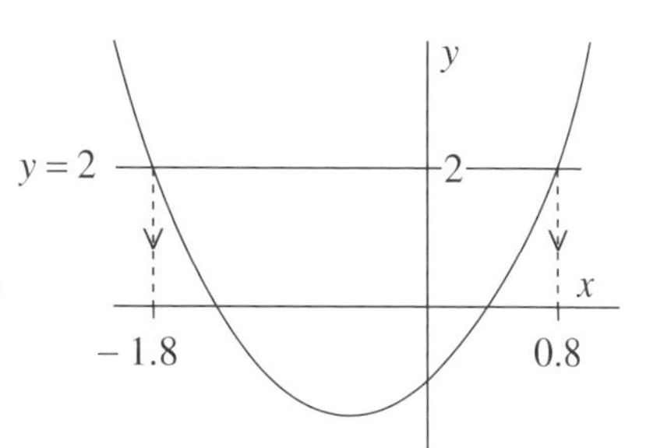

Draw the line $y = 2$. Where this line meets the curve, draw broken perpendicular lines onto the x-axis. Write down the values of x where these broken lines meet the x-axis.

From the graph:

When $y = 2$, $x = -1.8$, or $x = 0.8$.

3. Find the value of $f(-1.5)$.

This question is asking:

'When $x = -1.5$, what is the value of y?'

Solution:

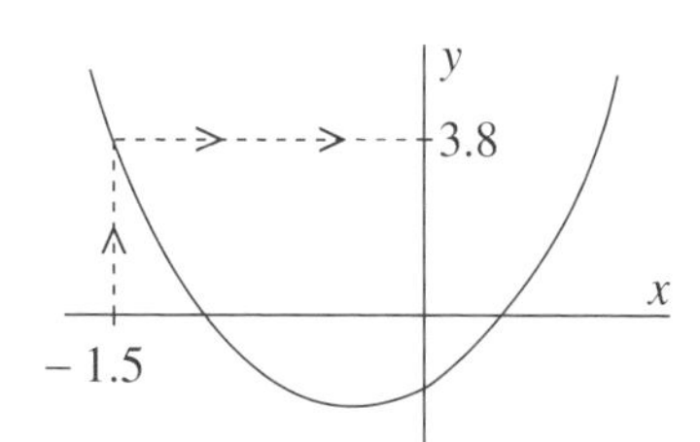

From $x = -1.5$ on the x-axis, draw a broken perpendicular line to meet the curve. From this, draw a broken horizontal line to meet the y-axis. Write down the value of y where this line meets the y-axis.

From the graph:

$f(-1.5) = 3.8$

4. Maximum point and maximum value

Solution:

Consider the graph on the right. The maximum point is (2, 4). The maximum value is found by drawing a horizontal line from the maximum point to the y-axis and reading the value where this line meets the y-axis. The maximum value is 4 (the same as the y-coordinate of the maximum point).

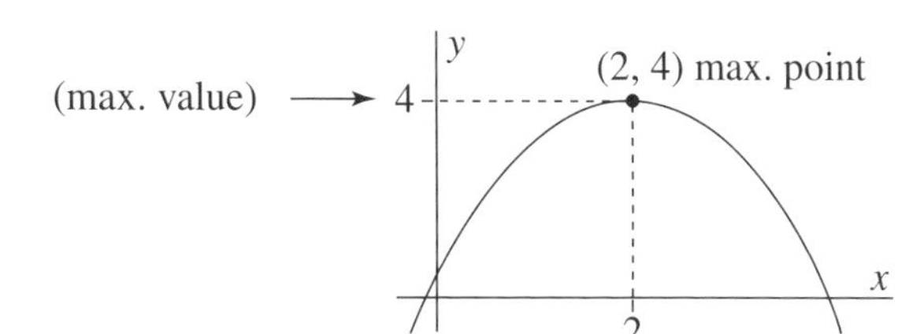

5. Minimum point and minimum value

Solution:

Consider the graph on the right. The minimum point is $(-1, -3)$. The minimum value is found by drawing a horizontal line from the minimum point to the y-axis and reading the value where this line meets the y-axis.
The minimum value is -3 (the same as the y-coordinate of the minimum point).

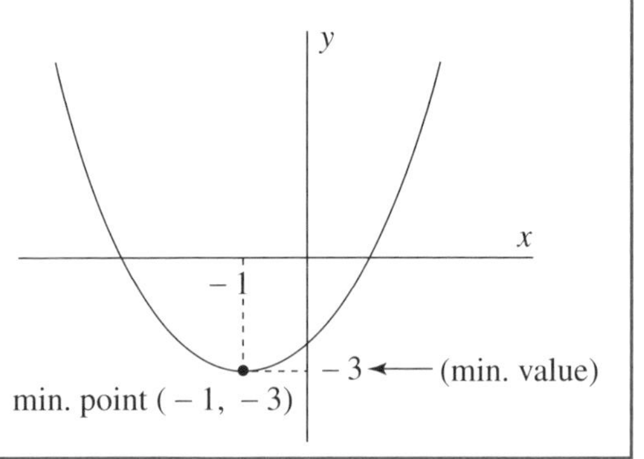

6. Axis of symmetry

Graphs of quadratic functions are symmetrical about a line that passes through the middle of the curve (and also through the maximum and minimum points). The line is called the 'axis of symmetry'.

Solution:

From the graph:

The equation of the axis of symmetry is $x = 3$.

3 is where the line meets the x-axis.

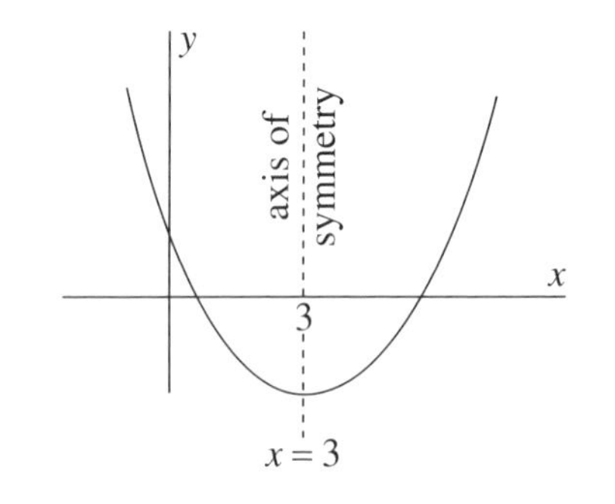

Example 1

Draw the graph of the function $f: x \rightarrow x^2 - 2x - 4$ in the domain $-2 \leqslant x \leqslant 4, \quad x \in \boldsymbol{R}$.

Use your graph to:

(i) estimate the values of x for which $f(x) = 0$

(ii) estimate the values of x for which $f(x) = -2$

(iii) estimate the value of $f(1.7)$

(iv) find the minimum point of the graph.

Draw the axis of symmetry of the graph of $f(x)$ and write down its equation.

Solution:

$$\text{Let } y = f(x) \Rightarrow y = x^2 - 2x - 4$$

x	$x^2 - 2x - 4$	y
-2	$4 + 4 - 4$	4
-1	$1 + 2 - 4$	-1
0	$0 + 0 - 4$	-4
1	$1 - 2 - 4$	-5
2	$4 - 4 - 4$	-4
3	$9 - 6 - 4$	-1
4	$16 - 8 - 4$	4

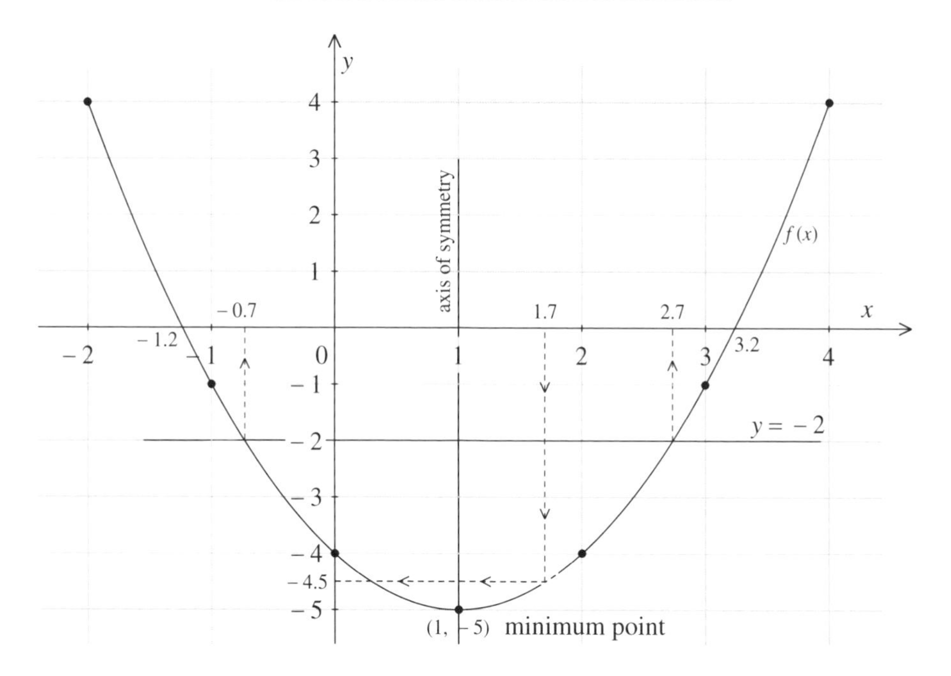

(i) Estimate the values of x for which $f(x) = 0$

This question is asking, 'Where does the graph cut the x-axis?'
The graph cuts the x-axis at -1.2 and 3.2.
Therefore $f(x) = 0$ for $x = -1.2$ and $x = 3.2$.

Note: Another way of asking the same question is,
'Estimate the values of x for which $x^2 - 2x - 4 = 0$.'

(ii) Estimate the values of x for which $f(x) = -2$

This question is asking, 'When $y = -2$ what are the values of x?'

Draw the line $y = -2$. Where this line meets the curve, draw broken perpendicular lines to meet the x-axis. These lines meet the x-axis at -0.7 and 2.7.

Therefore $f(x) = -2$ for $x = -0.7$ and $x = 2.7$.

Note: Another way of asking the same question is,
'Estimate the values of x for which $x^2 - 2x - 4 = -2$.'

(iii) Estimate the value of $f(1.7)$

This question is asking, 'When $x = 1.7$, what is the value of y?'

From $x = 1.7$ on the x-axis, draw a broken perpendicular line to meet the curve.

From this, a broken horizontal line is drawn to meet the y-axis.

This line meets the y-axis at -4.5.

Therefore $f(1.7) = -4.5$.

Note: Another way of asking the same question is,
'Estimate the value of $f(x)$ when $x = 1.7$', or
'Estimate the value of $x^2 - 2x - 4$ when $x = 1.7$.'

(iv) Find the minimum point of the graph

From the graph, the minimum point is $(1, -5)$.

Note: A point must have an x value and a y value.

Draw the axis of symmetry of the graph of $f(x)$ and write down its equation.

Through the minimum point $(1, -5)$, draw a line parallel to the y-axis.

This is the axis of symmetry.

As can be seen from the graph, the axis of symmetry meets the x-axis at 1.

Therefore $x = 1$ is the equation of the axis of symmetry of the graph of $f(x)$.

Example 2

Draw the graph of the function $f: x \rightarrow 4 + 3x - x^2$ in the domain $-2 \leqslant x \leqslant 5$, $x \in \mathbf{R}$.

Use your graph to:

(i) find the values of x for which $f(x) = 0$

(ii) find the values of x for which $f(x) = f(5)$

(iii) estimate the value of $f(-0.6)$

(iv) estimate the maximum value of f.

Solution:

$$\text{Let } y = f(x) \Rightarrow y = -x^2 + 3x + 4$$

x	$-x^2 + 3x + 4$	y
-2	$-4 - 6 + 4$	-6
-1	$-1 - 3 + 4$	0
0	$-0 + 0 + 4$	4
1	$-1 + 3 + 4$	6
2	$-4 + 6 + 4$	6
3	$-9 + 9 + 4$	4
4	$-16 + 12 + 4$	0
5	$-25 + 15 + 4$	-6

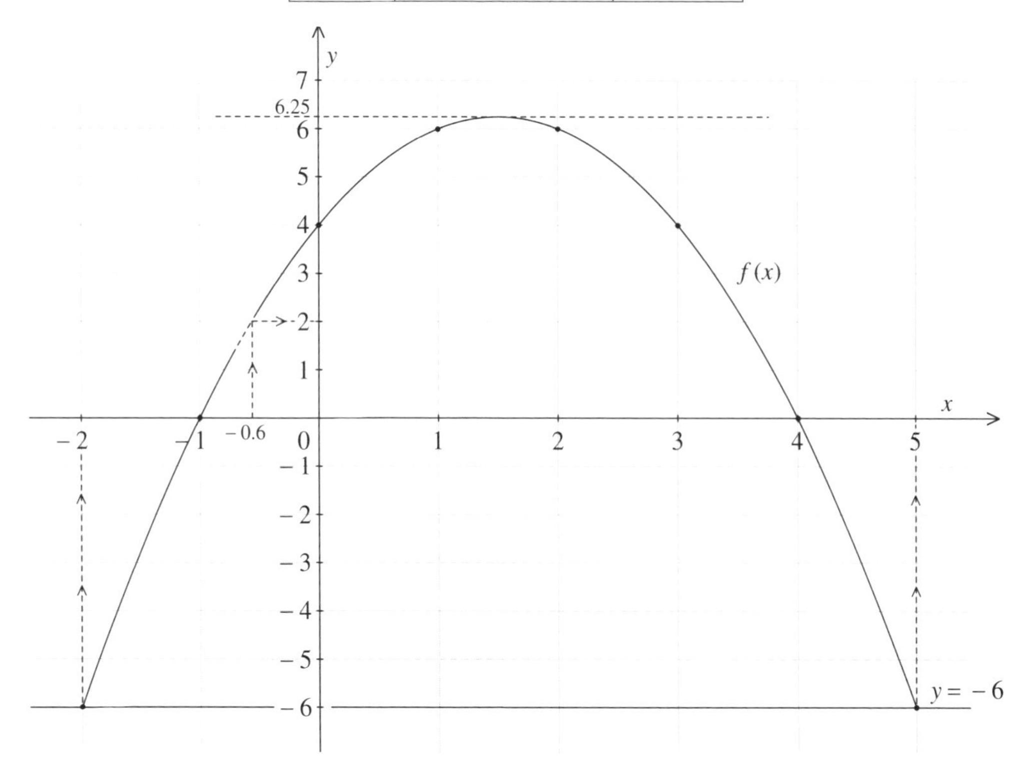

Solution:

(i) **Find the values of x for which $f(x) = 0$**

This question is asking, 'Where does the graph cut the x-axis?'
The graph cuts the x-axis at -1 and 4.
Therefore $f(x) = 0$ for $x = -1$ and $x = 4$.

Note: Another way of asking the same question is,
'Find the values of x for which $4 + 3x - x^2 = 0$.'

(ii) Find the values of x for which $f(x) = f(5)$

From the table, $f(5) = -6$ (i.e. when $x = 5$, $y = -6$)

$$f(x) = f(5)$$
$$f(x) = -6$$

This question is asking, 'When $y = -6$, what are the values of x?'

Draw the line $y = -6$. Where this line meets the curve, draw broken perpendicular lines to meet the x-axis. These lines meet the x-axis at $x = -2$ and $x = 5$.

Therefore $f(x) = f(5)$ for $x = -2$ and $x = 5$.

Note: Another way of asking the same question is,
'Find the values of x for which $4 + 3x - x^2 = -6$.'

(iii) Estimate the value of $f(-0.6)$

This question is asking, 'When $x = -0.6$, what is the value of y?'

From $x = -0.6$ on the x-axis, draw a broken perpendicular line to meet the curve.

From this, a broken horizontal line is drawn to meet the y-axis.

This line meets the y-axis at 2.

Therefore $f(-0.6) = 2$.

Note: Another way of asking the same question is,
'Estimate the value of $4 + 3x - x^2$ when $x = -0.6$.'

(iv) Estimate the maximum value of $f(x)$

From the maximum (highest) point on the graph, draw a broken horizontal line to meet the y-axis. This line meets the y-axis at 6.25.

Therefore, the maximum value of $f(x)$ is 6.25.

Example 3

Draw the graph of the function $f: x \to x^2 - 5x + 8$ in the domain $0 \leqslant x \leqslant 5$, $x \in \boldsymbol{R}$.

The graph shows the wind speed at hourly intervals.

The x-axis shows one-hour intervals: for example, $x = 0$ means 1200 hrs, $x = 1$ means 1300 hrs, etc.

The y-axis shows wind speed in kilometres per hour: $y = 0$ means 0 km/h, $y = 1$ means 10 km/h, $y = 2$ means 20 km/h, etc.

Use your graph to estimate:

(i) the times when the wind speed was 33 km/h

(ii) the speed of the wind at 1645 hrs

(iii) the time when the wind speed was at its lowest and the wind speed at this time.

Solution:

$$y = f(x) \Rightarrow y = x^2 - 5x + 8$$

x	$x^2 - 5x + 8$	y
0	$0 - 0 + 8$	8
1	$1 - 5 + 8$	4
2	$4 - 10 + 8$	2
3	$9 - 15 + 8$	2
4	$16 - 20 + 8$	4
5	$25 - 25 + 8$	8

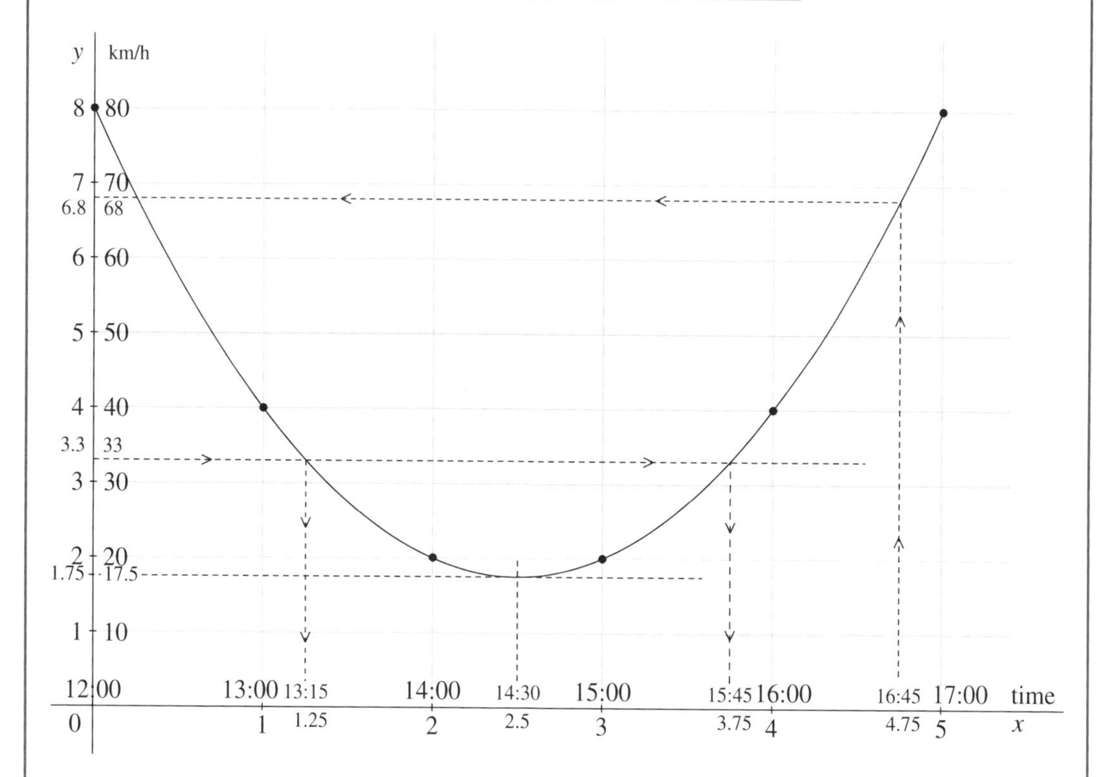

The x-axis measures time, t, in hourly intervals from 1200 hrs to 1700 hrs.

The y-axis measures wind speed in km/h.

Each interval on the y-axis represents 10 km/h.

Note: If we are given the time, we are required to find the wind speed.
If we are given the wind speed, we are required to find the time.

(i) Find the times when the wind speed was 33 km/h

Given that the wind speed is 33 km/h, find the time.

When wind speed = 33 km/h, $y = 3.3$.

From 3.3 on the y-axis (speed axis), draw a broken horizontal line to meet the curve at two places. Where this line meets the curve, draw broken perpendicular lines to meet the x-axis (time axis). These lines meet the x-axis at 1.25 and 3.75.

When $x = 1.25$, $t = 1315$ hrs, and when $x = 3.75$, $t = 1545$ hrs.

Therefore the wind speed was 33 km/h at 1315 hrs and 1545 hrs.

(ii) Find the speed of the wind at 1645 hrs

Given that the time is 1645 hrs, find the wind speed.

When $t = 1645$ hrs, $x = 4.75$.

From 4.75 on the x-axis (time axis), draw a broken vertical line to meet the curve. Where this line meets the curve, draw a broken horizontal line to meet the y-axis (speed axis). This line meets the y-axis at 6.8.

When $y = 6.8$, speed = 68 km/h.

Therefore at 1645 hrs the wind speed was 68 km/h.

(iii) Find the time when the wind speed was at its lowest and the wind speed at this time

From the minimum (lowest) point on the graph, draw a broken vertical line to meet the the x-axis (time axis) and also from this point draw a broken horizontal line to meet the y-axis (speed axis). The vertical line meets the x-axis at 2.5, or 1430 hrs on the time axis. The horizontal line meets the y-axis at 1.75, or 17.5 km/h on the speed axis.

Therefore, the wind speed was at its lowest at 1430 hrs and the wind speed at this time was 17.5 km/h.

Chapter 16. METRIC SYSTEM AND DISTANCE, SPEED AND TIME

Metric System

Example 1

(i) Add 2,437 g to 624 g and give your answer in kg.

(ii) Subtract 500 g from 5,640 g, and give your answer in kg.

Solution:

(i)

$$\begin{array}{r} 2{,}437 \text{ g} \\ +\ 624 \text{ g} \\ \hline = 3{,}061 \text{ g} \end{array}$$

$$3{,}061 \text{ g} = \frac{3{,}061}{1{,}000} \text{ kg} = 3.061 \text{ kg}$$

(To change g to kg divide by 1,000.)

Note : 1 kg = 1,000 g

(ii)

$$\begin{array}{r} 5{,}640 \text{ g} \\ -\ 500 \text{ g} \\ \hline = 5{,}140 \text{ g} \end{array}$$

$$5{,}140 \text{ g} = \frac{5{,}140}{1{,}000} \text{ kg} = 5.14 \text{ kg}$$

(5140 ÷ 1000 =)

(To change g to kg divide by 1,000.)

Example 2

(i) A swimming pool is 50 m in length. Mary swims 25 lengths of the pool. What distance, in kilometres, does Mary swim?

(ii) A ribbon of length 2.5 m is cut into two pieces. One piece measures 97 cm. What is the length of the other piece?

Solution:

(i) Distance Mary swims

= (number of lengths she swims) × (length of the pool)

= 25 × 50 m

= 1,250 m

$= \frac{1,250}{1,000}$ km $\left(\begin{array}{l}\text{To change m to km} \\ \text{divide by 1,000.}\end{array}\right)$

= 1.25 km

Note : 1 km = 1,000 m

(ii) Change 2.5 m to cm

2.5 m = 2.5 × 100 cm = 250 cm

(To change m to cm multiply by 100.)

One piece measures 97 cm

∴ length of the other piece

= 250 cm − 97 cm

= 153 cm or 1.53 m

(To change cm to m divide by 100.)

Note : 1 m = 100 cm

Converting minutes to hours

To convert minutes to hours **divide by 60**.

For example, 48 minutes $= \frac{48}{60}$ h $= \frac{4}{5}$ h or 0.8 h.

However, the following occur quite often and are easy to memorise:

30 minutes $= \frac{1}{2}$ hour	20 minutes $= \frac{1}{3}$ hour	50 minutes $= \frac{5}{6}$ hour
15 minutes $= \frac{1}{4}$ hour	40 minutes $= \frac{2}{3}$ hour	12 minutes $= \frac{1}{5}$ hour
45 minutes $= \frac{3}{4}$ hour	10 minutes $= \frac{1}{6}$ hour	24 minutes $= \frac{2}{5}$ hour

Converting fractions, or decimals, of an hour to minutes.

To convert fractions, or decimals, of an hour to minutes **multiply by 60**.

For example,

$\frac{1}{3}$ hour $= \frac{1}{3} \times 60$ minutes = 20 minutes (calculator: 1 [$a\frac{b}{c}$] 3 [×] 60 [=])

0.7 hour = 0.7 × 60 minutes = 42 minutes (calculator: 0.7 [×] 60 [=])

Example 3

Express in hours and minutes (i) $2\frac{3}{4}$ hours (ii) 5.2 hours.

Solution:

(i) $2\frac{3}{4}$ hours

$\frac{3}{4}$ hours $= \frac{3}{4} \times 60$ minutes $= 45$ minutes

$\therefore$ $2\frac{3}{4}$ hours = 2 hours 45 minutes

(ii) 5.2 hours

0.2 hours = 0.2×60 minutes = 12 minutes

$\therefore$ 5.2 hours = 5 hours 12 minutes

Distance, Speed and Time

There are three formulas to remember when dealing with problems involving distance (D), speed (S), and time (T). It can be difficult to remember these formulas; however, the work can be made easier using a triangle and the memory aid 'Dad's Silly Triangle'.

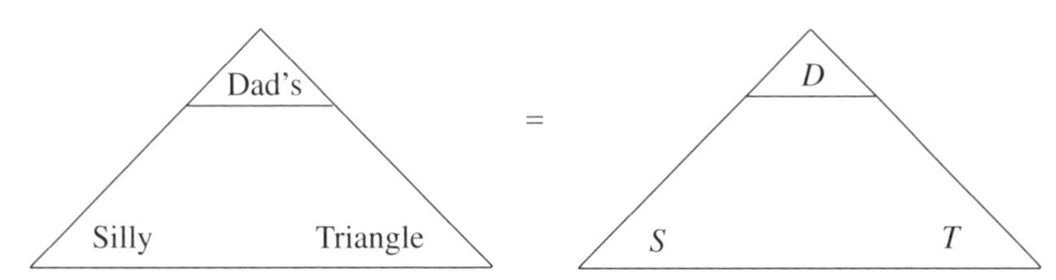

1. Speed = $\frac{\text{Distance}}{\text{Time}}$ 2. Time = $\frac{\text{Distance}}{\text{Speed}}$ 3. Distance = Speed × Time

Consider the triangle on the right. By covering the quantity required, D, S or T, any of the three formulas above can be found by inspection. Speed here means 'average speed'.

Example 1

(i) A train takes 3 hours and 30 minutes to travel a distance 280 km. Calculate the average speed in km/h.

(ii) How long, in hours and minutes, does it take a bus to travel 168 km at an average speed of 96 km/h?

(iii) A car travelled at an average speed of 120 km/h between 1255 hrs and 1410 hrs. What distance did it travel?

Solution:

(i) Time has to be expressed in hours.
3 hours and 30 minutes $= 3\frac{1}{2}$ hours

$$\text{Speed} = \frac{\text{Distance}}{\text{Time}}$$
$$= \frac{280}{3\frac{1}{2}}$$
$$= 80 \text{ km/h}$$

(280 [÷] 3 [$a\frac{b}{c}$] 1 [$a\frac{b}{c}$] 2 [=])

(ii) $\text{Time} = \frac{\text{Distance}}{\text{Speed}}$
$$= \frac{168}{96}$$
$$= 1.75 \text{ hours}$$
$$= 1 \text{ hour and } 45 \text{ minutes}$$

(0.75 hour $= 0.75 \times 60 = 45$ minutes)

(0.75 [×] 60 [=])

(iii) Distance = Speed × Time
$$= 120 \times 1\frac{1}{4}$$
$$= 150 \text{ km}$$

(120 [×] 1 [$a\frac{b}{c}$] 1 [$a\frac{b}{c}$] 4 [=])

1410 hrs − 1255 hrs
= 1 hour and 15 minutes
$= 1\frac{1}{4}$ hours

Example 2

The distance, by rail, between Galway and Dublin is 240 km.

On Tuesday, a train left Galway at 1305 and travelled to Dublin.
The average speed for this journey of 240 km was 100 km/hr.
At what time did the train arrive in Dublin?

Solution:

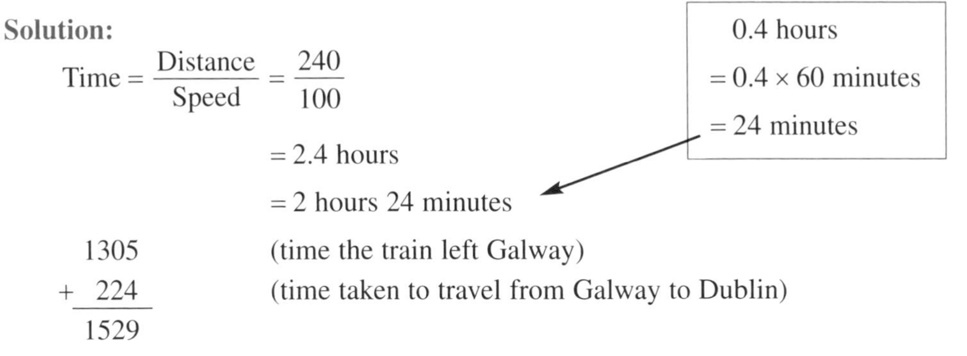

$$\text{Time} = \frac{\text{Distance}}{\text{Speed}} = \frac{240}{100}$$

$= 2.4$ hours

$= 2$ hours 24 minutes

0.4 hours
$= 0.4 \times 60$ minutes
$= 24$ minutes

```
  1305      (time the train left Galway)
+  224      (time taken to travel from Galway to Dublin)
  ----
  1529
```

$\therefore$ the train arrived in Dublin at 1529 hrs.

Example 3

Cormac went by car from Limerick to Cork, a journey of 100 km.
He travelled at an average speed of 80 km/h.

(i) How many hours and minutes did it take Cormac to complete the journey?

(ii) Cormac left Limerick at 1115. At what time did he arrive in Cork?

(iii) Cormac's car used 1 litre of petrol for every 16 km travelled. On that day petrol cost €1.24 per litre. Find the cost of the petrol used on Cormac's journey from Limerick to Cork.

Solution:

(i) Distance = 100 km Speed = 80 km/h

$$\text{Time} = \frac{\text{Distance}}{\text{Speed}} = \frac{100}{80}$$

$= 1.25$ hours

$= 1$ hour 15 minutes

0.25 hours
$= 0.25 \times 60$ minutes
$= 15$ minutes

(ii)

```
  1115      (time Cormac left Limerick)
+  115      (time taken for journey)
  ----
  1230
```

$\therefore$ Cormac arrives in Cork at 1230 hrs.

(iii) Cormac's car uses 1 litre of petrol to travel 16 km.

$\therefore$ Number of litres of petrol used $= \dfrac{\text{Distance}}{16}$

$= \dfrac{100}{16} = 6.25$ (calculator: 100 ÷ 16 =)

1 litre = €1.24 (cost of one litre of petrol)

$\therefore$ 6.25 litres = €1.24 × 6.25 (multiply both sides by 6.25)

$\therefore$ 6.25 litres = €7.75 (calculator: 1.24 × 6.25 =)

The cost of petrol used on Cormac's journey from Limerick to Cork was €7.75.

Note: Strictly speaking, these are not equations, but using equations makes the working easier.

Chapter 17. PERIMETER, AREA AND VOLUME

Perimeter and Area

Formulas required:

1. Rectangle

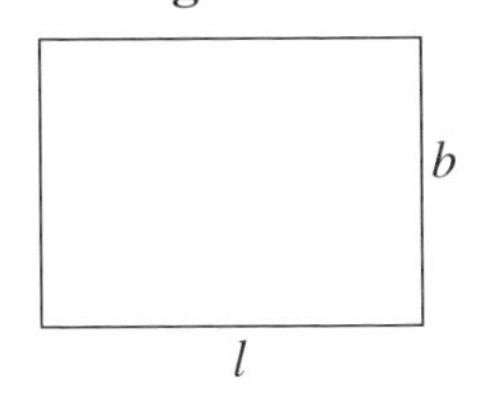

Area, $A = lb$
Perimeter, $P = 2l + 2b = 2(l + b)$

2. Square

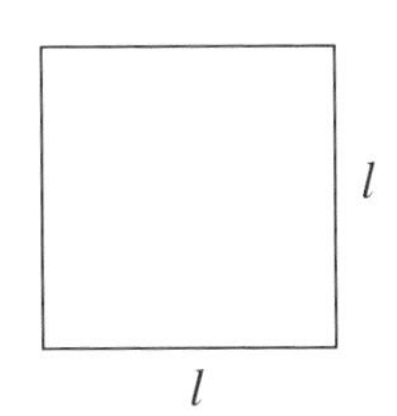

Area, $A = l^2$
Perimeter, $P = 4l$

3. Triangle

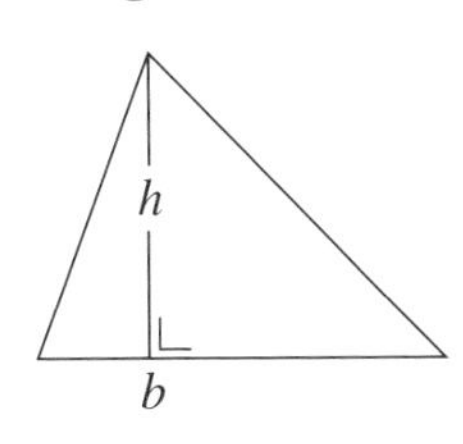

Area, $A = \frac{1}{2}bh$

4. Parallelogram

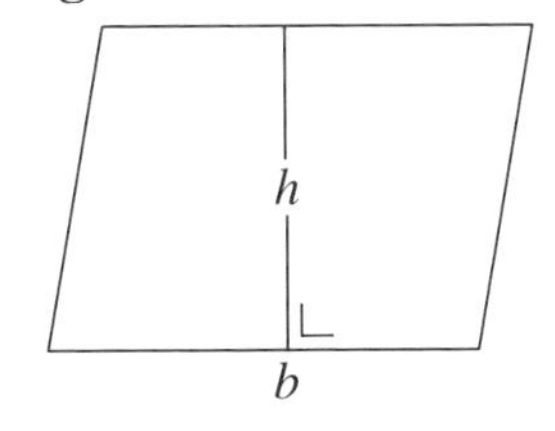

Area, $A = bh$

5. Circle (Disc)

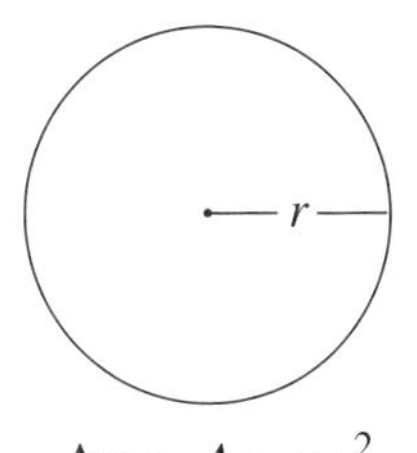

Area, $A = \pi r^2$
Circumference, $C = 2\pi r$

6. Sector of a circle

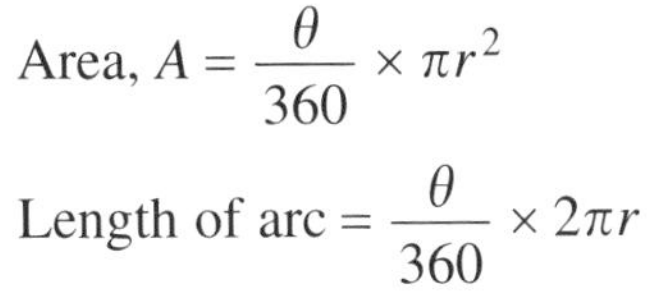

Area, $A = \dfrac{\theta}{360} \times \pi r^2$

Length of arc $= \dfrac{\theta}{360} \times 2\pi r$

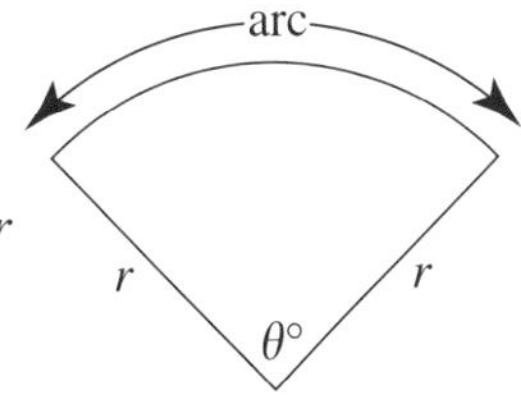

$\left(\text{similar to circle with } \dfrac{\theta}{360} \text{ in front of formulas}\right)$

Notes: **1.** When using $\pi = \frac{22}{7}$, it is good practice to write the radius as a fraction.

For example, $21 = \frac{21}{1}$ or $10.5 = \frac{21}{2}$.

2. If a question says 'give your answer in terms of π', then leave π in the answer: do **not** put 3.14 or $\frac{22}{7}$.

3. If no approximation is given for π, then you must use the value for π given by your calculator.

Example 1

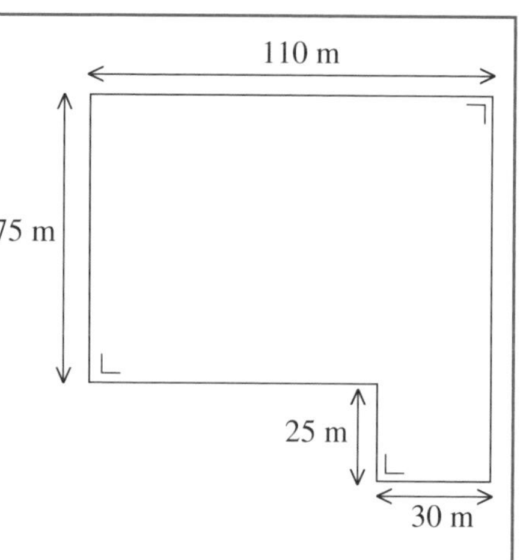

A field has shape and measurements as shown in the diagram.

(i) Find, in metres, the length of the perimeter of the field.

(ii) Find, in m^2, the area of the field.

(iii) Mary bought the field at a cost of €20,000 per hectare. How much did Mary pay for the field?

Solution:

(i) Perimeter = Distance around the edges.

There are two missing lengths:

$110 - 30 = 80$ m

$75 + 25 = 100$ m

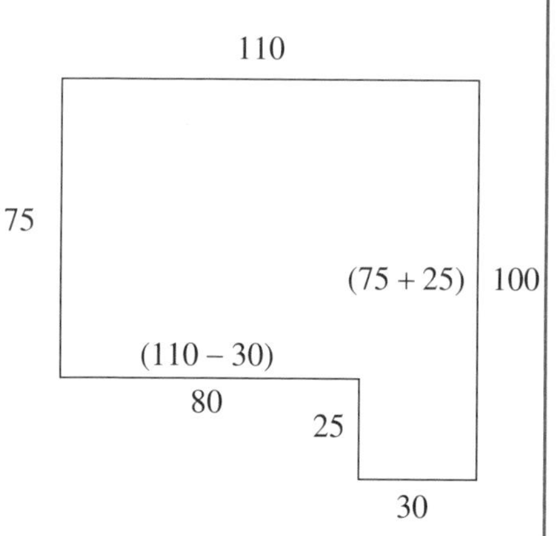

$\therefore$ Length of the perimeter of the field

$= 110 + 100 + 30 + 25 + 80 + 75$

$= 420$ m

(ii) To find the area of the field we split it up into two rectangles, A and B, as shown.

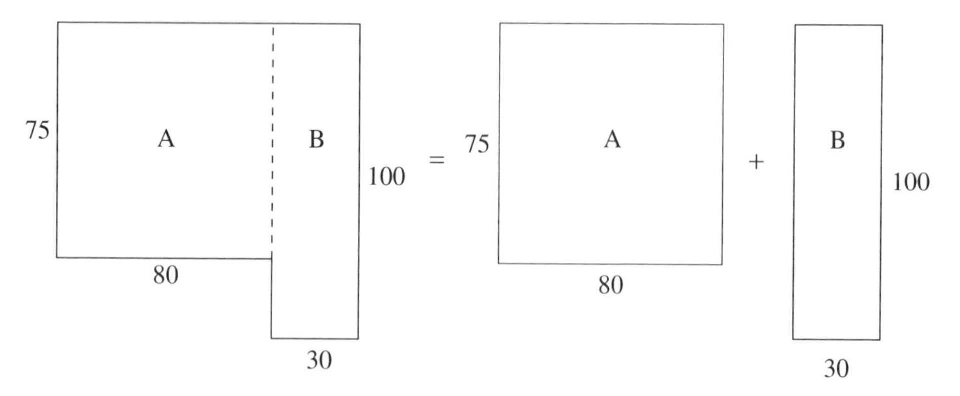

Area of field = (Area of rectangle A) + (Area of rectangle B)

$= 80 \times 75 + 30 \times 100$

$= 6{,}000 + 3{,}000$

$= 9{,}000 \text{ m}^2$

(iii) **Note:** 1 hectare = 10,000 m^2

Given: 1 hectare = €20,000 (euros on the right, as we want our answer in euros)

$\therefore$ 10,000 m^2 = €20,000 (1 hectare = 10,000 m^2)

1 m^2 = €2 (divide both sides by 10,000)

9,000 m^2 = €18,000 (multiply both sides by 9,000)

$\therefore$ Cost of the field is €18,000.

Note: Strictly speaking, these are not equations, but using equations makes the working easier.

Example 2

A garden is made up of a rectangular lawn that is surrounded by a path.

The garden is 16 m long and 10 m wide.
The path is 2 m wide.

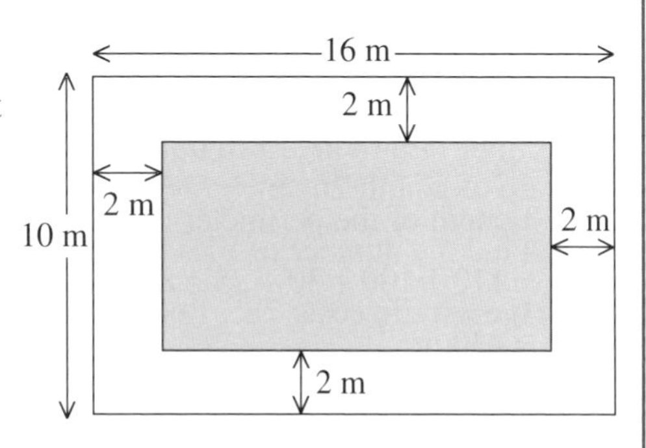

(i) Find, in m^2, the area of the garden.

(ii) Find, in m^2, the area of the lawn.

(iii) Find, in m^2, the area of the path.

Solution:

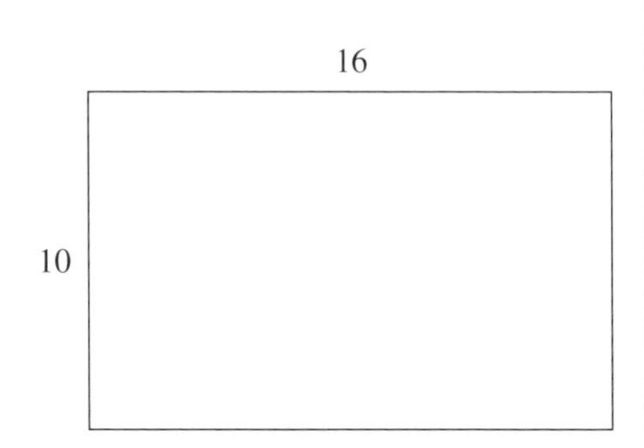

(i) Area of garden

= length × width

= 16 × 10

= 160 m^2

(ii) Length of the lawn = 16 – 2 – 2 = 12 m

Width of the lawn = 10 – 2 – 2 = 6 m

Area of lawn

= length × width

= 12 × 6

= 72 m^2

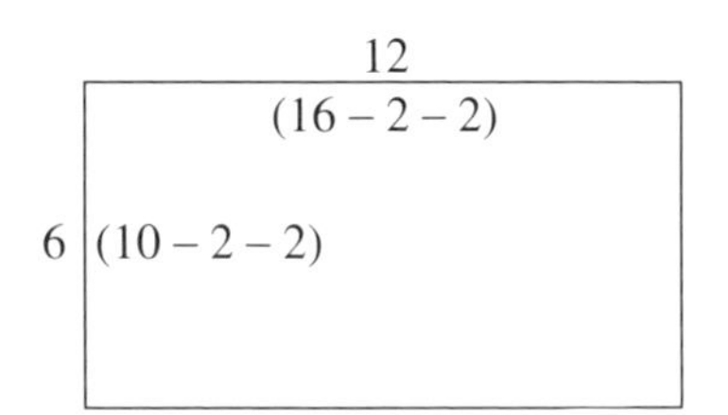

(iii) The path is the shaded region below:

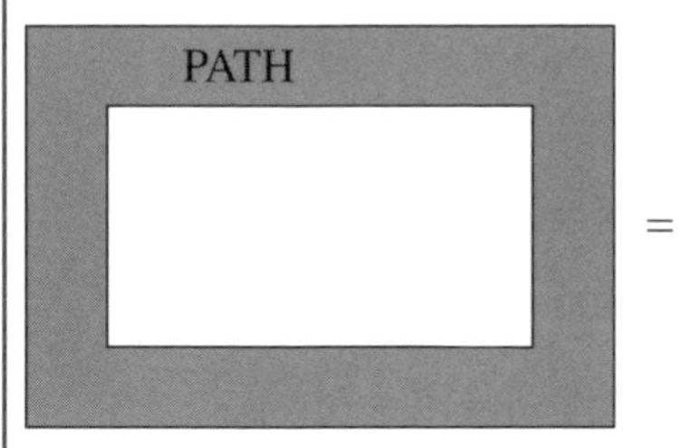

= Garden Area = 160 m^2 − Lawn Area = 72 m^2

Area of the path = Area of the garden − Area of the lawn

= 160 − 72

= 88 m^2

Example 3

The floor of a room 15 m long by 12 m wide is to be covered with tiles. Each tile is a square of length 20 cm.

(i) Find the number of tiles required to cover the floor.

(ii) If each tile costs 28c, find the cost of the tiles.

Solution:

Change all dimensions to the smaller unit, centimetres.

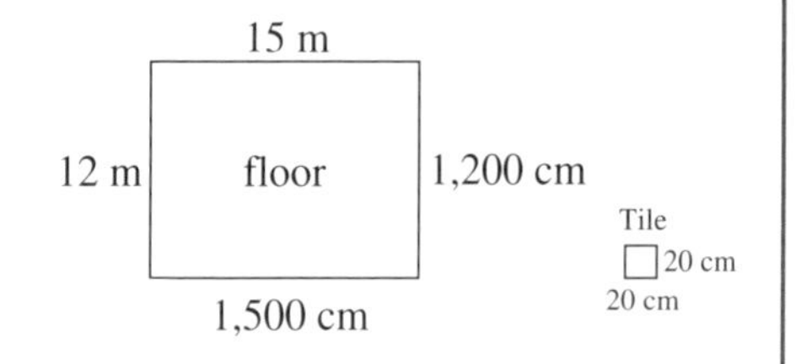

15 m = 15 × 100 cm = 1,500 cm

12 m = 12 × 100 cm = 1,200 cm

(i) Area of floor = 1,500 × 1,200 = 1,800,000 cm^2

Area of one tile = 20 × 20 = 400 cm^2

Number of tiles required to cover the floor $= \dfrac{\text{Area of floor}}{\text{Area of one tile}}$

$= \dfrac{1,800,000}{400}$

= 4,500

(ii) Cost of the tiles = number of tiles × cost of one tile

= 4,500 × 28c = 126,000c = €1,260

Example 4

The front wheel of a bicycle has a diameter of 56 cm.

(i) Calculate, in cm, the length of the radius of the wheel.

(ii) Calculate, in cm, the length of the circumference of the wheel.
Assume $\pi = \frac{22}{7}$.

(iii) How far does the bicycle travel when the wheel makes 250 complete turns?
Give your answer in metres.

Solution:

d = diameter $\quad\quad r$ = radius

(i) **Given:** $d = 56$

$r = \frac{1}{2}$ d

$\therefore \quad r = \frac{1}{2} \times 56$

$r = 28$ cm

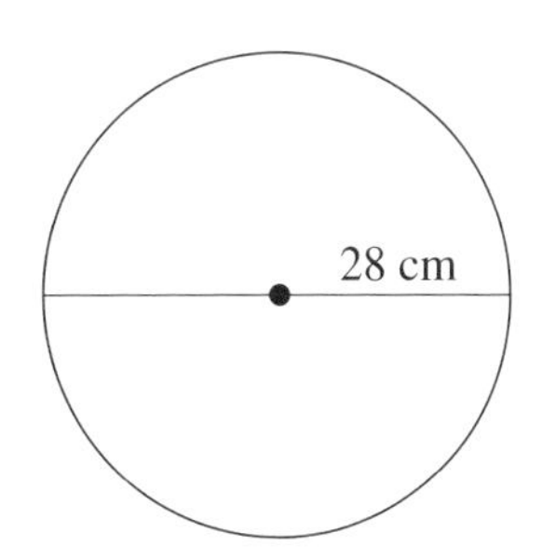

(ii) $C = 2\pi r$ (C = circumference = length of a circle)

$C = 2 \times \frac{22}{7} \times 28$ $\quad$ ($\pi = \frac{22}{7}$ and $r = 28$)

$C = 176$ cm $\quad$ (calculator: 2 [×] 22 [$a\frac{b}{c}$] 7 [×] 28 [=])

(iii) 1 complete turn = length of the circumference of the wheel

1 complete turn = 176 cm

250 complete turns = 250 × 176 $\quad$ (multiply both sides by 250)

= 44,000 cm $\quad$ (calculator: 250 [×] 176)

= 440 m $\quad$ (to change cm to m 'divide by 100')

Thus, the bicycle would travel 440 m when the wheel makes 250 complete turns.

Example 5

(i) Calculate the area enclosed by a circle of radius 3.5 cm (assume $\pi = \frac{22}{7}$).

(ii) A rectangular piece of cardboard measures 14 cm by 7 cm. Two circular pieces, each of radius 3.5 cm, are cut out from this rectangular piece of cardboard, as shown.

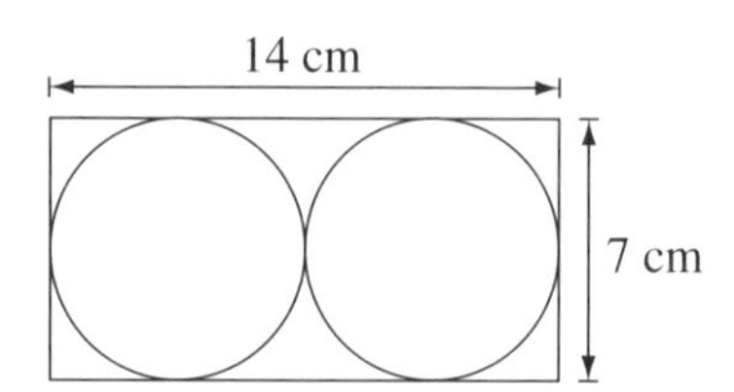

(a) Calculate the area of the remaining piece of cardboard.

(b) Express the area of the remaining piece of cardboard as a percentage of the area of the original rectangular piece.

Give your answer correct to two places of decimals.

Solution:

(i) Area of circle $= \pi r^2$

$= \frac{22}{7} \times (3.5)^2 \qquad \left(\pi = \frac{22}{7}, r = 3.5\right)$

$= 38.5 \text{ cm}^2 \qquad$ (calculator: 22 $a\frac{b}{c}$ 7 × (3.5) x^2 =)

(ii) (a) Area of remaining piece of cardboard

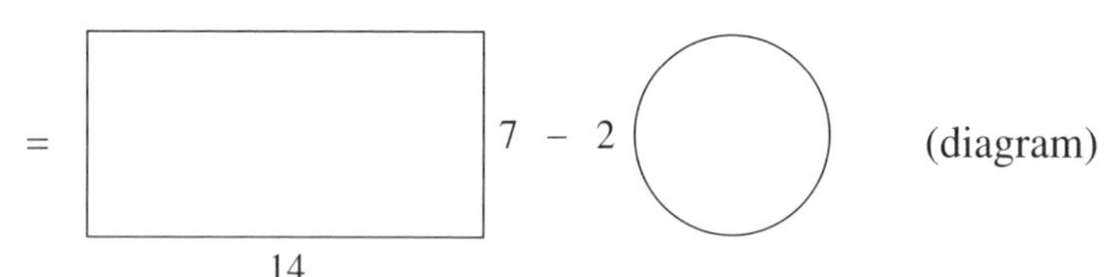

(diagram)

= Area of rectangle − Area of 2 circular pieces

$= 14 \times 7 - 2\,(38.5)$ (area of circular piece = 38.5 from part **(i)** above)

$= 98 - 77$

$= 21 \text{ cm}^2$

(b) Area of remaining piece of cardboard as a percentage of the original piece of cardboard.

$= \frac{\text{Area of remaining piece of cardboard}}{\text{Area of original piece of cardboard}} \times 100\%$

$= \frac{21}{98} \times 100\%$

$= 21.42857143\% \qquad$ (calculator: 21 $a\frac{b}{c}$ 98 × 100 =)

$= 21.43\%$ (correct to two places of decimals)

Example 6

A running track has two equal parallel sides $[pq]$ and $[sr]$ and two equal semicircular ends with diameters $[ps]$ and $[qr]$.

$|pq| = |sr| = 90$ metres, and $|ps| = |qr| = 70$ metres.

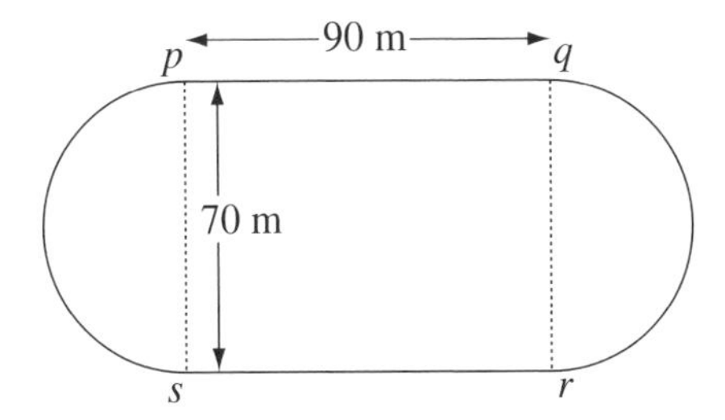

(i) Calculate the total length of one lap of the track. (Assume $\pi = \frac{22}{7}$.)

(ii) How many laps of the track would an athlete have to complete in a 10,000 metres race?

Solution:

(i) Total length of one lap of the track

= two straight lengths of 90 m each + two semicircular ends of radius 35 m.

$= 2(90) + 2(\pi r)$

$= 2(90) + 2(110)$

$= 180 + 220$

$= 400$

Therefore, the total length of one lap of the track is 400 m.

$r = \frac{1}{2}(70) = 35$
length of semi-circle $= \frac{1}{2}(2\pi r) = \pi r$ $\pi r = \frac{22}{7} \times 35 = 110$

(ii) $\text{Number of laps in a 10,000 m race} = \dfrac{10{,}000}{\text{total length of one lap}} = \dfrac{10{,}000}{400} = 25.$

Example 7

The diagram shows a sector *opq* of a circle of radius 9 cm.

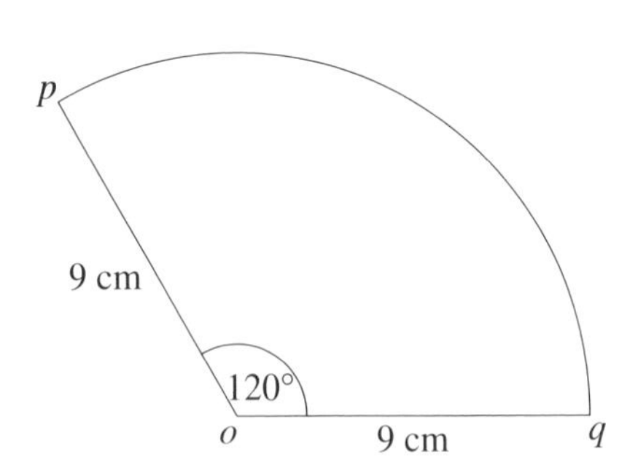

Calculate:

(i) the area of the sector *opq*

(ii) the length of the arc *pq*.

(Assume $\pi = 3.14$.)

Solution:

(i) Area of sector

$$= \frac{\theta}{360}\pi r^2$$

$$= \frac{120}{360} \times 3.14 \times 9 \times 9$$

(fraction) × (area of full circle)

$= 84.78$

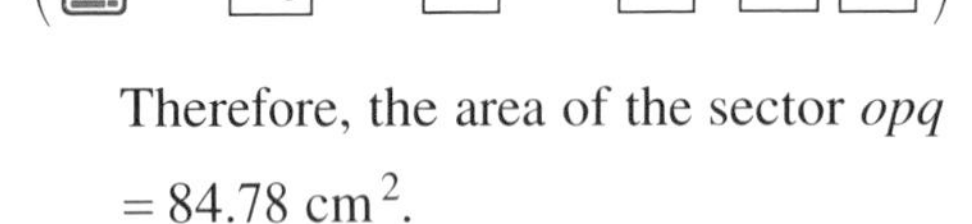

Therefore, the area of the sector *opq* $= 84.78 \text{ cm}^2$.

(ii) Length of the arc *pq*

$$= \frac{\theta}{360} 2\pi r$$

$$= \frac{120}{360} \times 2 \times 3.14 \times 9$$

(fraction) × (full circumference)

$= 18.84$

(120 [$a\frac{b}{c}$] 360 [×] 2 [×] 3.14 [×] 9 [=])

Therefore, the length of the arc *pq* $= 18.84$ cm.

Given the Perimeter and Area

In some questions we are given an **equation in disguise**.

Example 1

(i) The area of a rectangle is 240 cm^2. If its length is 40 cm, calculate its breadth.

(ii) The perimeter of a square is 60 cm. Calculate its area.

Solution:

(i) Draw a diagram, and let $b =$ the breadth.

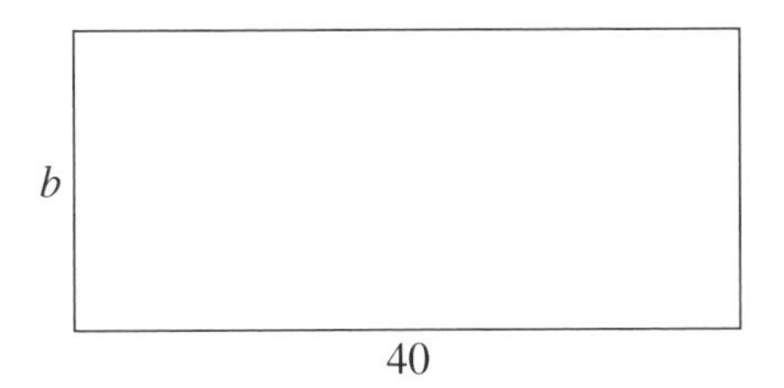

Equation given in disguise:

$$A = 240$$

$$lb = 240$$

$$(40)\,b = 240$$

$$40b = 240$$

$$b = 6$$

Therefore, the breadth is 6 cm.

(ii) Draw a diagram, and let $l =$ the length.

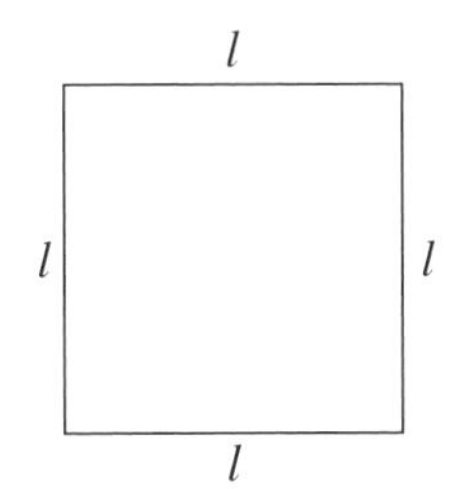

Equation given in disguise:

$$P = 60$$

$$4l = 60$$

$$l = 15$$

$$A = l^2 = 15 \times 15 = 225 \text{ cm}^2$$

Therefore, area of square is 225 cm^2.

Example 2

The area of a triangle is 150 cm^2. If its base is 25 cm, calculate its perpendicular height.

Solution:

Draw a rough diagram and let the perpendicular height $= h$.

Equation given in disguise:

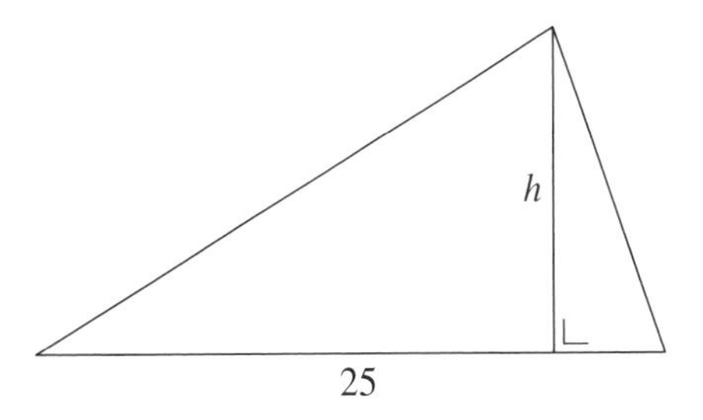

$$A = 150$$

$$\frac{1}{2}bh = 150$$

$$\frac{1}{2}(25)\,h = 150 \quad \text{(put in } b = 25\text{)}$$

$$25h = 300 \quad \text{(multiply both sides by 2)}$$

$$h = 12 \quad \text{(divide both sides by 25)}$$

Therefore, the perpendicular height of the triangle is 12 cm.

Example 3

(i) The area of a circle is 706.5 cm^2. Calculate the radius (assume $\pi = 3.14$).

(ii) The circumference of a circle is 16π cm. Calculate the radius.

(iii) The area of a circle is 616 cm^2. Calculate the radius (assume $\pi = \frac{22}{7}$).

Solution:

(i) Equation given in disguise:

$A = 706.5$ (area of circle is 706.5 cm^2)

$\pi r^2 = 706.5$ ($A = \pi r^2$)

$3.14r^2 = 706.5$ (put in 3.14 for π)

$r^2 = 225$ (divide both sides by 3.14)

$r = \sqrt{225}$ (take the square root of both sides)

$r = 15$

Therefore, the radius is 15 cm.

(ii) Equation given in disguise:

$C = 16\pi$ (circumference of circle is 16π cm)

$2\pi r = 16\pi$ ($C = 2\pi r$)

$\pi r = 8\pi$ (divide both sides by 2)

$r = 8$ (divide both sides by π)

Therefore, the radius is 8 cm.

(iii) Equation given in disguise:

$A = 616$ (area of circle is 616 cm^2)

$\pi r^2 = 616$ ($A = \pi r^2$)

$\frac{22}{7} r^2 = 616$ (put in $\frac{22}{7}$ for π)

$22r^2 = 4{,}312$ (multiply both sides by 7)

$r^2 = 196$ (divide both sides by 22)

$r = \sqrt{196}$ (take the square root of both sides)

$r = 14$

Therefore, the radius is 14 cm.

Example 4

A garden in the shape of a rectangle has a semicircular lawn of radius r metres. The shaded area is covered by trees and shrubs.

The perimeter of the garden is 90 m.

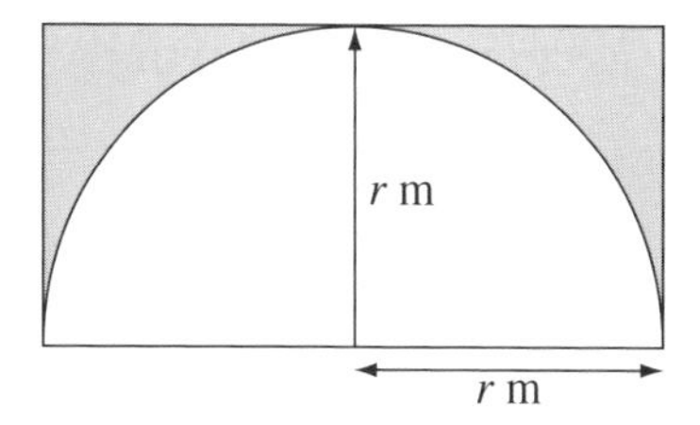

Calculate:

(i) the value of r

(ii) the area covered by trees and shrubs.

(Assume $\pi = 3.14$.)

Solution:

(i) Equation given in disguise:

Perimeter = 90 m

$\therefore \quad 6r = 90$

$r = 15$ m

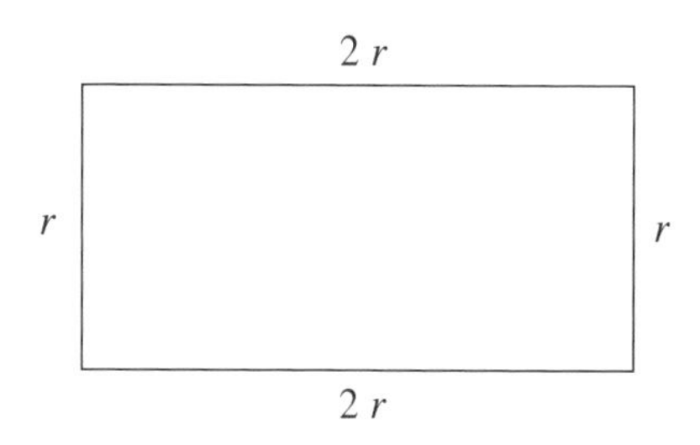

Perimeter $= 2r + r + 2r + r = 6r$

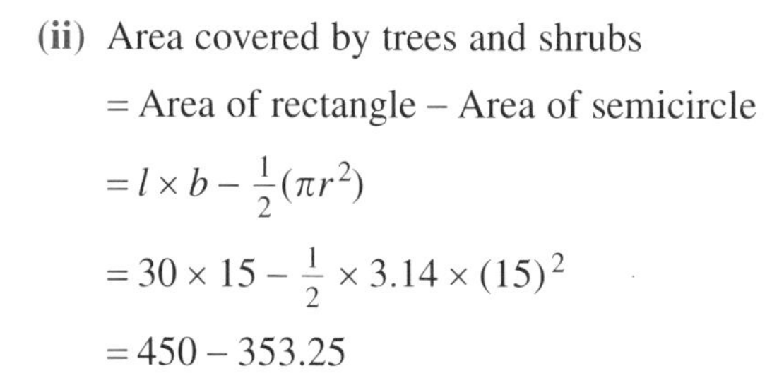

(ii) Area covered by trees and shrubs

= Area of rectangle – Area of semicircle

$= l \times b - \frac{1}{2}(\pi r^2)$

$= 30 \times 15 - \frac{1}{2} \times 3.14 \times (15)^2$

$= 450 - 353.25$

$= 96.75 \text{ m}^2$

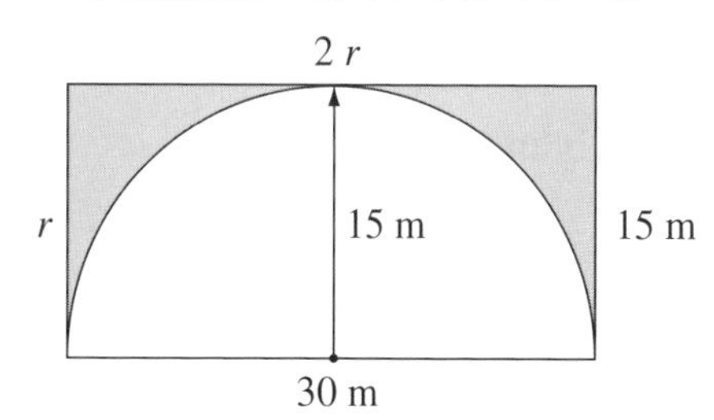

Volume and Surface Area

Formulas required:

1. Rectangular solid (cuboid):

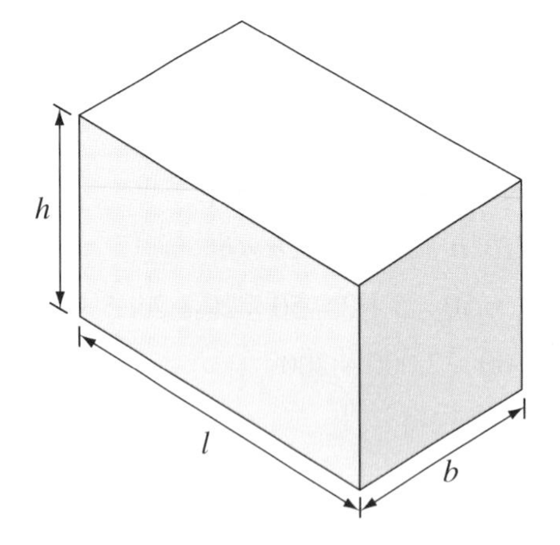

Volume, $V = lbh$

Surface Area, $SA = 2lb + 2lh + 2bh$

2. Cube:

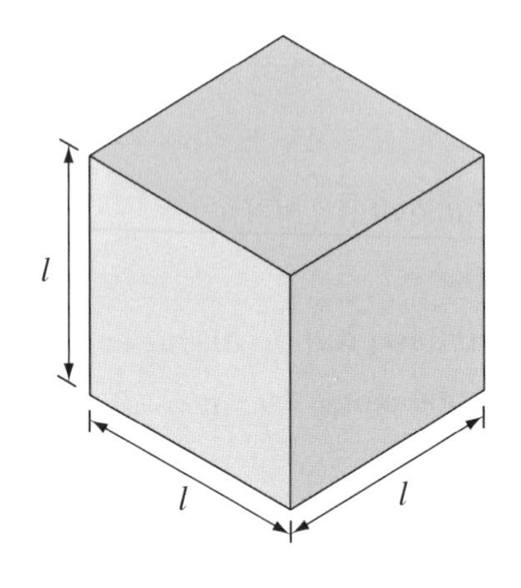

Volume, $V = l^3$

Surface Area, $SA = 6l^2$

3. Cylinder:

Volume, $V = \pi r^2 h$

Curved Surface Area, $CSA = 2\pi rh$

Total Surface Area, $TSA = 2\pi rh + 2\pi r^2$

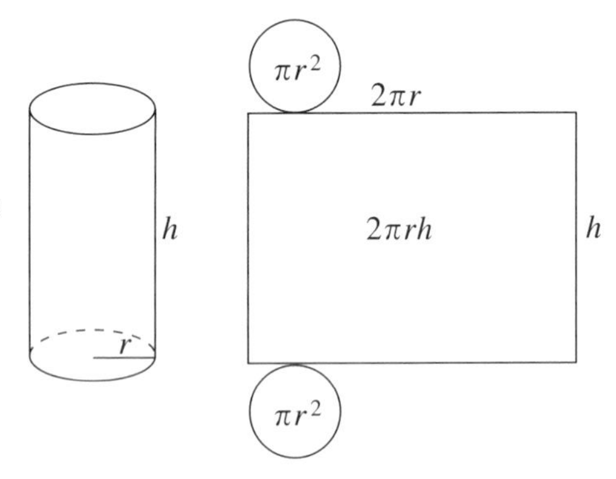

4. Sphere:

Volume, $V = \frac{4}{3}\pi r^3$

Curved Surface Area, $CSA = 4\pi r^2$

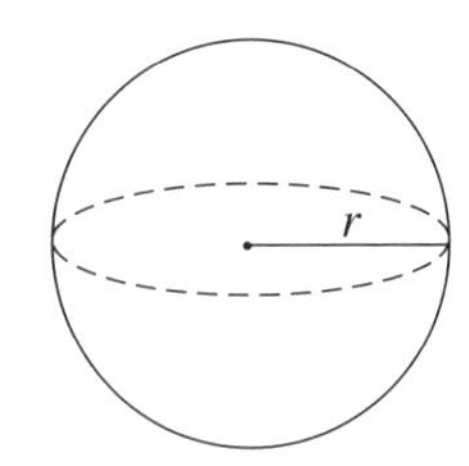

Example 1

A solid rectangular block has measurements as shown.

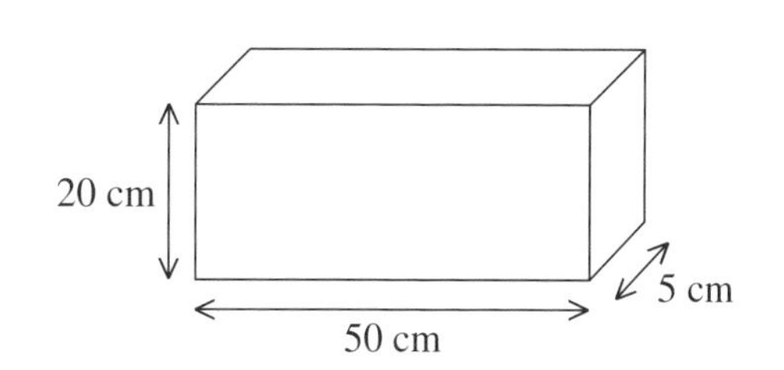

Find:

(i) the volume of the block in cm^3

(ii) the surface area of the block in cm^2.

Solution:

(i) Volume of the block

$= l \times b \times h$

$= 50 \times 5 \times 20$

$= 5{,}000\ \text{cm}^3$

(ii) Surface area of the block

$= 2l \times b + 2l \times h + 2b \times h$

$= 2 \times 50 \times 5 + 2 \times 50 \times 20 + 2 \times 5 \times 20$

$= 500 + 2{,}000 + 200$

$= 2{,}700\ \text{cm}^2$

Example 2

A ball, in the shape of a sphere, has radius 10.5 cm.

Taking π as $\frac{22}{7}$, calculate:

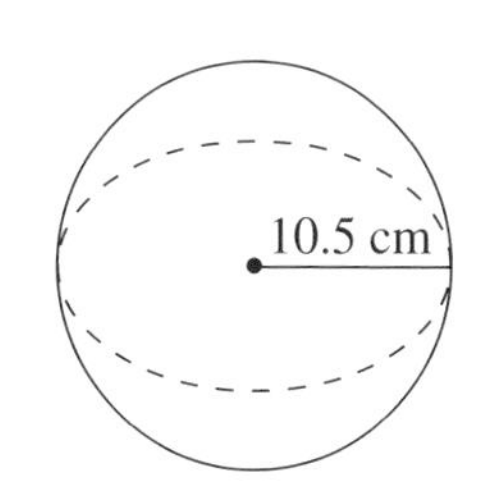

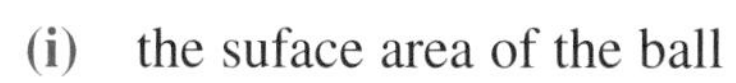

(i) the suface area of the ball

(ii) the volume of the ball.

Solution:

(i) Surface area of a sphere $= 4\pi r^2$ (page 7 of the tables)

$= 4 \times \frac{22}{7} \times 10.5^2$

$= 1{,}386\ \text{cm}^2$ (calculator: 4 [×] 22 [$a\frac{b}{c}$] 7 [×] 10.5 [x^2] [=])

(ii) Volume of a sphere $= \frac{4}{3}\pi r^3$ (page 7 of the tables)

$= \frac{4}{3} \times \frac{22}{7} \times (10.5)^3$

$= 4{,}851\ \text{cm}^3$ (calculator: 4 [$a\frac{b}{c}$] 3 [×] 22 [$a\frac{b}{c}$] 7 [×] 10.5 [y^x] 3 [=])

Example 3

A closed cylindrical metal can has external radius 7 cm and height 10 cm.

(i) Assuming $\pi = \frac{22}{7}$, calculate:

(a) the volume of the can

(b) the curved surface area of the can

(c) the total surface area of the can.

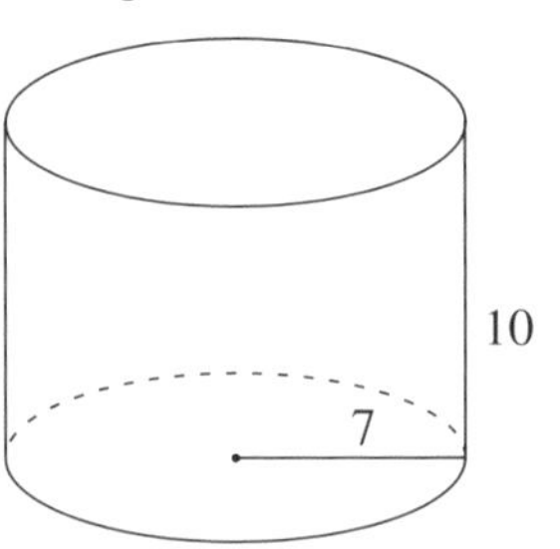

(ii) A rectangular sheet of metal measuring 50 cm by 25 cm was used to make the can. What area of the metal sheet was left over?

Solution:

(i) **(a)** $V = \pi r^2 h$

$= \frac{22}{7} \times 7^2 \times 10$

$= 1{,}540 \text{ cm}^3$

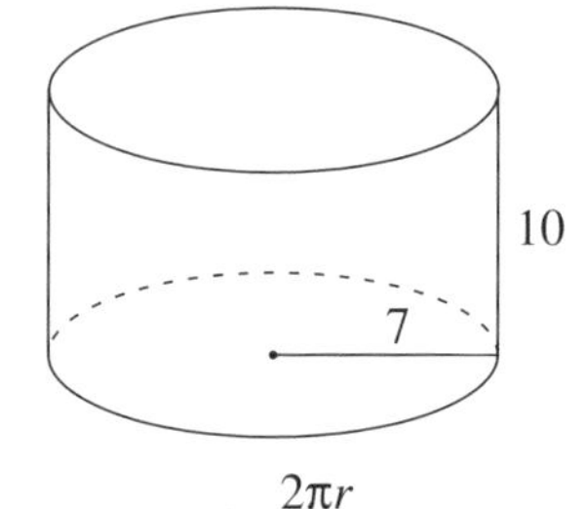

(b) $CSA = 2\pi rh$

$= \frac{2}{1} \times \frac{22}{7} \times 7 \times 10$

$= 440 \text{ cm}^2$

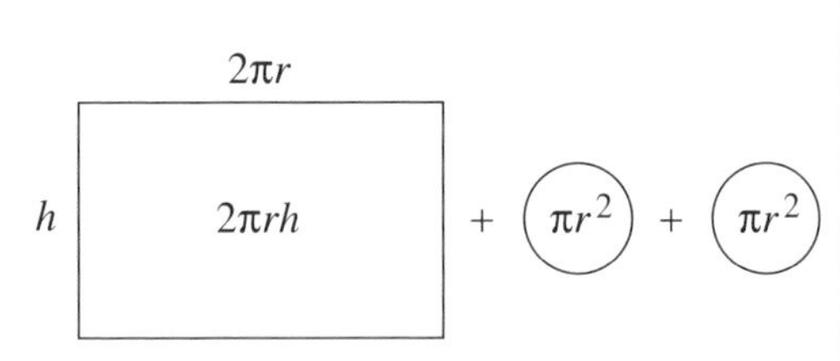

(c) $TSA = 2\pi rh + 2\pi r^2$

$\downarrow$

$= 440 + 2 \times \frac{22}{7} \times 7 \times 7$

$= 440 + 308$

$= 748 \text{ cm}^2$

2πr

h 2πrh + πr² + πr²

(ii) Area of rectangular sheet

$= l \times b$

$= 50 \times 25$

$= 1{,}250 \text{ cm}^2$

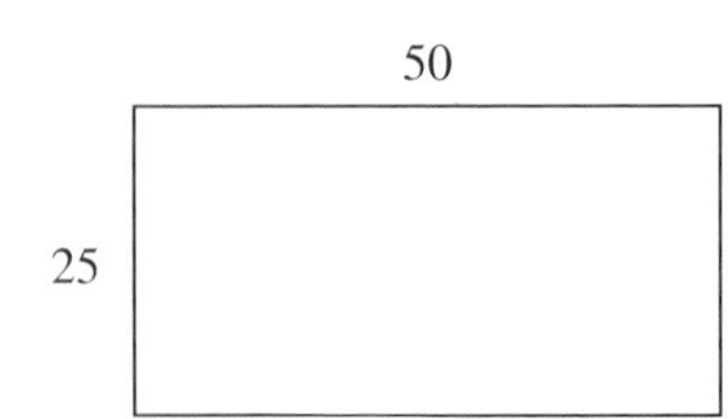

Area of metal left over

= Area of rectangular metal sheet – Total surface area of the closed metal can

$= 1{,}250 - 748 = 502 \text{ cm}^2$

Example 4

(i) Calculate, in terms of π, the volume of a sphere of radius 4.5 cm.

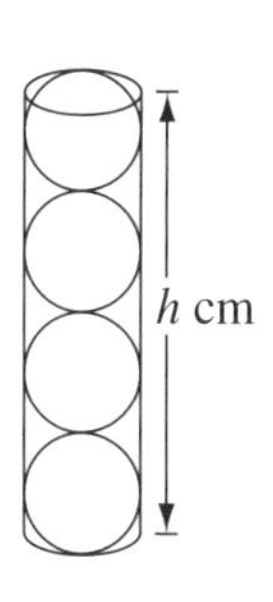

Four of these spheres exactly fit into a cylinder of radius 4.5 cm and of height h cm, as shown. Calculate:

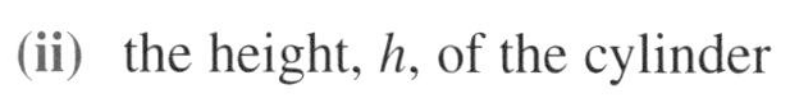

(ii) the height, h, of the cylinder

(iii) the volume of the cylinder, in terms of π

(iv) the fraction of the volume of the cylinder taken up by the four spheres.

Solution:

(i) $V = \frac{4}{3}\pi r^3$

$= \frac{4}{3} \times \pi \times (4.5)^3$ $\quad$ $(r = 4.5)$

$= 121.5\,\pi$ $\quad$ (leave π in the answer)

Therefore, the volume of the sphere is $121.5\,\pi$ cm^3.

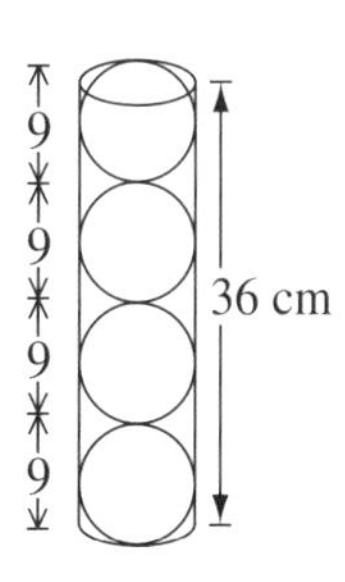

(ii) $h = 4$ (diameter of a sphere of radius 4.5)

$= 4(9)$ $\quad$ (diameter of sphere $= 2 \times 4.5 = 9$ cm)

$= 36$

Therefore, the height of the cylinder is 36 cm.

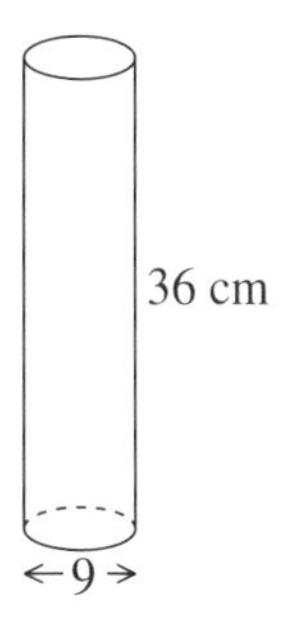

(iii) $V = \pi r^2 h$

$= \pi \times (4.5)^2 \times 36$ $\quad$ $(r = 4.5,\ h = 36)$

$= 729\,\pi$ $\quad$ (leave π in the answer)

Therefore, the volume of the cylinder is 729π cm^3.

(iv) Fraction of the volume of the cylinder taken up by the four spheres

$$= \frac{\text{Volume of four spheres}}{\text{Volume of the cylinder}} = \frac{4(121.5\pi)}{729\pi} = \frac{486\pi}{729\pi} = \frac{486}{729} = \frac{2}{3}$$

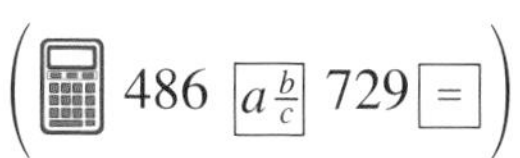

Example 5

(i) Calculate the volume of a solid cylinder of diameter 10 cm and height 14 cm (assume $\pi = \frac{22}{7}$).

(ii) Two such identical cylinders fit exactly into a rectangular box. Find:

(a) the dimensions of the box

(b) the internal volume of the box

(c) the volume of air in the box when the two cylinders are placed inside it.

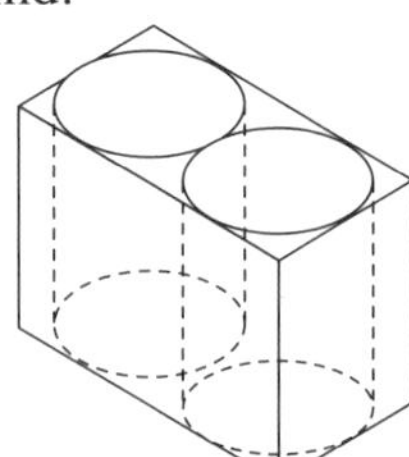

Solution:

(i) $V = \pi r^2 h$

$= \frac{22}{7} \times (5)^2 \times 14 \qquad (\pi = \frac{22}{7}, r = 5, h = 14)$

$= 1{,}100 \qquad$ (22 $a\frac{b}{c}$ 7 × 5 x^2 × 14 =)

Therefore, the volume of the cylinder is 1,100 cm^3.

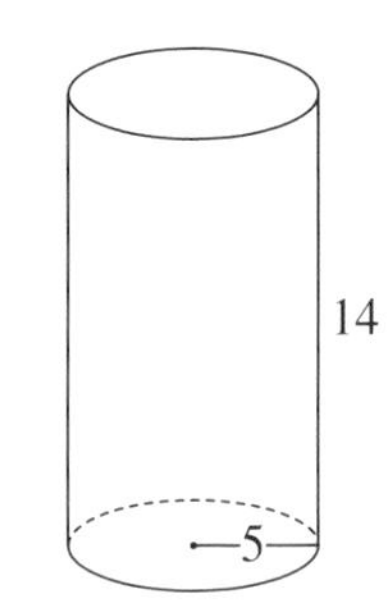

(ii) (a) Length of the box = twice the diameter of the cylinder = 2(10) = 20 cm

Width of the box = diameter of the cylinder = 10 cm

Height of the box = height of the cylinder = 14 cm

Thus the dimensions of the box are 20 cm by 10 cm by 14 cm.

(b) Volume of the box = $l \times b \times h$

$= 20 \times 10 \times 14$

$= 2{,}800$ cm^3.

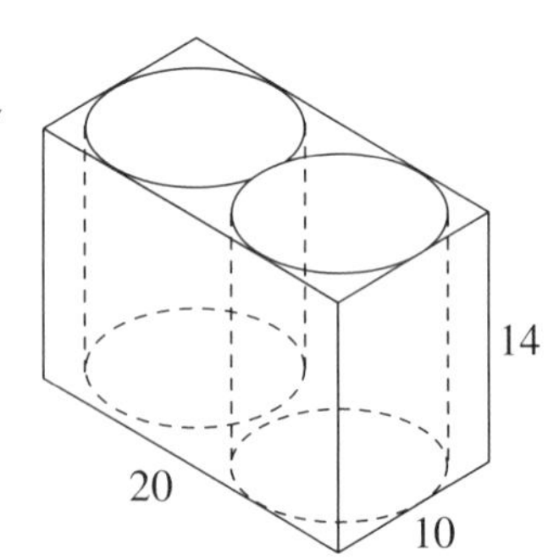

(c) Volume of air in the box when the two cylinders are placed inside it

= volume of the box – volume of two cylinders

$= 2{,}800 - 2(1{,}100) = 2{,}800 - 2{,}200 = 600$ cm^3.

Given the Volume or Surface Area of Rectangular Solids, Cylinders and Spheres

In some questions we are given the volume or surface area and asked to find a missing dimension. As before, write down the **equation given in disguise**, and solve this equation to find the missing dimension.

Notes:

1. **Moving liquids**

   In many questions we have to deal with moving liquid from one container to another container of different dimensions or shape. To help us solve the problem we use the following fact:

The volume of the moved liquid does not change.

2. **Recasting**

   Many of the questions we meet require us to solve a recasting problem. What happens is that a certain solid object is melted down and its shape is changed. We use the following fact:

The volume remains the same after it is melted down.

3. **Displaced liquid**

   In many questions we have to deal with situations where liquid is displaced by immersing, or removing, a solid object. In all cases the following principle helps us to solve these problems:

Volume of displaced liquid = volume of immersed, or removed, solid object

In problems on moving or displaced liquids and recasting, it is good practice not to put in a value for π (i.e. do **not** put in $\pi = \frac{22}{7}$ or $\pi = 3.14$), as the π's normally cancel when you write down the equation given in disguise.

Example 1

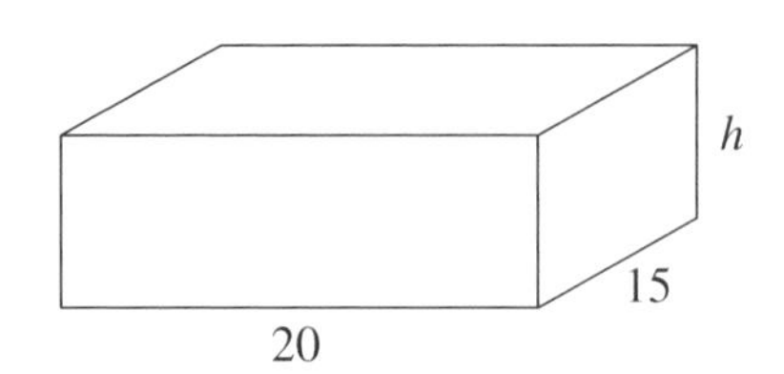

The volume of a rectangular block is 2.4 litres. If its length is 20 cm and its breadth is 15 cm, find **(i)** its height and **(ii)** its surface area.

Solution:

(i) **Equation given in disguise:**

$$\text{Volume} = 2{,}400 \text{ cm}^3$$
$$(20)(15)h = 2{,}400$$
$$300\,h = 2{,}400$$
$$h = 8$$

Therefore, height of block is 8 cm.

(ii) Surface area $= 2lb + 2lh + 2bh$

$$= 2(20)(15) + 2(20)(8) + 2(15)(8)$$
$$= 600 + 320 + 240$$
$$= 1{,}160$$

Therefore, the surface area is 1,160 cm^2.

Note: 1 litre = 1,000 cm^3. Therefore 2.4 litres = $2.4 \times 1{,}000$ cm^3 = 2,400 cm^3.

Example 2

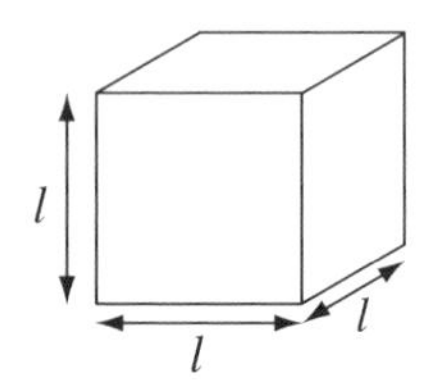

The surface area of a cube is 96 cm^2.

Calculate its volume.

Solution:

Let the length of one side of the cube be l cm.

Equation given in disguise:

$$\text{Surface area} = 96 \text{ cm}^2$$
$$\therefore \quad 6l^2 = 96$$
$$l^2 = 16$$
$$l = 4 \text{ cm}$$

$$\text{Volume} = l^3$$
$$= 4^3$$
$$= 64 \text{ cm}^3$$

Therefore the volume of the cube is 64 cm^3.

Example 3

(i) The curved surface area of a sphere is 81π cm^2. Calculate its radius.

(ii) The curved surface area of a cylinder is 264 cm^2 and its radius is 3.5 cm.

Calculate its height (assume $\pi = \frac{22}{7}$).

(iii) A cylinder has a volume of 196.25 m^3. If its height is 10 m, calculate its radius. (Assume $\pi = 3.14$.)

Solution:

(i) **Given:** Curved surface area $= 81\pi$ cm^2

$\therefore \quad 4\pi r^2 = 81\pi$ (curved surface area $= 4\pi r^2$)

$4r^2 = 81$ (divide both sides by π)

$r^2 = 20.25$ (divide both sides by 4)

$r = \sqrt{20.25}$ (take the square root of both sides)

$r = 4.5$

The radius is 4.5 cm.

(ii) **Given:** Curved surface area $= 264$ cm^2

$\therefore \quad 2\pi rh = 264$ (curved surface area $= 2\pi rh$)

$2 \times \frac{22}{7} \times 3.5 \times h = 264$ (put in $\pi = \frac{22}{7}$ and $r = \frac{7}{2}$)

$22h = 264$ (simplify left-hand side)

$h = 12$ (divide both sides by 22)

The height is 12 cm.

(iii) **Given:** Volume of cylinder $= 196.25$ m^3

$\therefore \quad \pi r^2 h = 196.25$ (volume of cylinder $= \pi r^2 h$)

$3.14 \times r^2 \times 10 = 196.25$ (put in $\pi = 3.14$ and $h = 10$)

$31.4r^2 = 196.25$ ($3.14 \times 10 = 31.4$)

$r^2 = 6.25$ (divide both sides by 31.4)

$r = \sqrt{6.25}$ (take the square root of both sides)

$r = 2.5$

The radius is 2.5 m.

Example 4

A solid sphere made of lead has radius 6 cm.

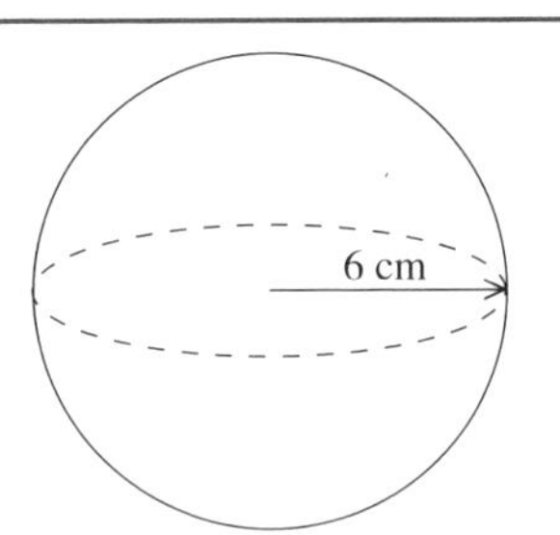

(i) Find the volume of the sphere in terms of π.

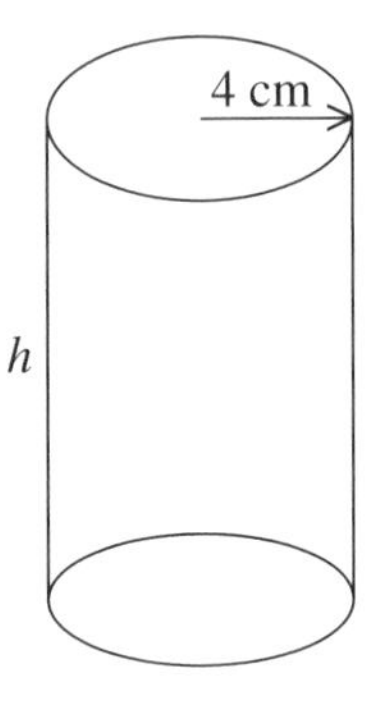

(ii) This sphere is melted down and all the lead is used to make a lead cylinder with radius 4 cm.
Find h, the height of the lead cylinder.

Solution:

(i) Volume of sphere $= \frac{4}{3}\pi r^3$ (page 7 of the tables)

$= \frac{4}{3} \times \pi \times 6^3$ ($r = 6$; leave π in your answer)

$= 288\pi \text{ cm}^3$ (4 $a\frac{b}{c}$ 3 × 6 y^x 3 =)

(ii) **Equation given in disguise:**

Volume of cylinder = Volume of sphere

Diagram of the situation

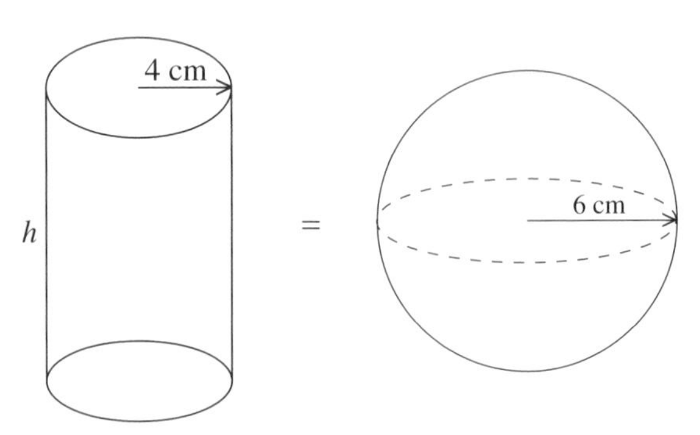

$\pi r^2 h = 288\pi$

$r^2 h = 288$ (divide both sides by π)

$4^2 h = 288$ (put in $r = 4$)

$16h = 288$ ($4^2 = 16$)

$h = 18$ (divide both sides by 16)

Chapter 18. STATISTICS

Mean and Mode

Mean

The **mean** is the proper name for what most people call the average.

The mean of a set of values is the sum of all the values divided by the number of values.

That is,

$$\text{mean} = \frac{\text{sum of all the values}}{\text{number of values}}$$

The formula is often written as:

$$\bar{x} = \frac{\sum x}{n}$$

where

(i) $\bar{x}$ (read as 'x bar') is the symbol for the mean

(ii) $\sum$ (the Greek capital letter *sigma*) means 'the sum of'
(i.e. $\sum x$ means 'add up all the x values')

(iii) n is the number of values of x.

Mode

The **mode** is the value that occurs most often.

In other words, the mode is the value with the highest frequency, or the most popular value.

Example 1

(i) Find the mean of the numbers: 0, 6, 8, 10 and 16.

(ii) Three children are aged 2, 5 and 11 years. Calculate their average age.

Solution:

(i) 0, 6, 8, 10, 16

$$\text{Mean} = \frac{0+6+8+10+16}{5}$$

$$= \frac{40}{5}$$

$$= 8$$

(ii) 2, 5, 11

$$\text{Average age} = \frac{2+5+11}{3}$$

$$= \frac{18}{3}$$

$$= 6 \text{ years}$$

Example 2

Find the mode of the following list of values: 3, 1, 2, 1, 3, 2, 4, 3, 5, 3, 2, 3, 4, 3.

Solution:

The mode is the value which occurs most often.

It can help to find the mode if the values are written in order.

Writing the values in order: 1, 1, 2, 2, 2, 3, 3, 3, 3, 3, 3, 4, 4, 5.

The number which occurs most often is 3.

Therefore, the mode is 3.

(mode = 3, occurs most often)
↓

The values can also be put in a table.

Values	1	2	3	4	5
Frequency	2	3	6	2	1

↑
(highest frequency)

The number which occurs most often is 3.

Therefore, the mode is 3.

Example 3

The mean of the five numbers 7, 3, 2, x and 6 is 4. Calculate the value of x.

Solution:

Method 1:

Equation given in disguise:

$$\text{Mean} = 4$$

$$\therefore \quad \frac{7+3+2+x+6}{5} = 4$$

$$\frac{x+18}{5} = 4$$

$$x + 18 = 20$$

(multiply both sides by 5)

$$x = 2$$

Method 2:

The mean of the five numbers is 4.

$\therefore$ the numbers must add up to 20.

$\left(\text{because } 5 \times 4 = 20 \quad \text{or} \quad \frac{20}{5} = 4\right)$

$$\therefore \quad 7+3+2+x+6 = 20$$

$$x + 18 = 20$$

$$x = 2$$

Example 4

The table shows the number of compact discs sold per day in a shop from Monday to Friday of a particular week.

Day	Monday	Tuesday	Wednesday	Thursday	Friday
No. of compact discs sold	25	20	50	35	50

(i) Calculate the mean number of compact discs sold per day from Monday to Friday.

(ii) The shop was also open on the Saturday of that particular week. The mean number of compact discs sold per day from Monday to Saturday was 40.

Calculate the number of compact discs sold on that Saturday.

Solution:

(i) Mean number of discs sold per day from Monday to Friday

$$= \frac{\text{Total no. of compact discs sold during the week}}{\text{No. of days from Monday to Friday}}$$

$$= \frac{25 + 20 + 50 + 35 + 50}{5}$$

$$= \frac{180}{5}$$

$$= 36$$

(ii) **Old Situation**

Number of discs sold from Monday to Friday $= 180$ (from part (**i**))

New Situation

Average number of discs sold per day from Monday to Saturday $= 40$

$\therefore$ the number of discs sold from Monday to Saturday $= 40 \times 6 = 240$

$240 - 180 = 60$

Thus, the shop sold 60 compact discs on that Saturday.

Bar Charts and Trend Graphs

Example 1

All students in a certain class sat a test. The grades that they obtained in the test are shown in the following bar chart.

Grades obtained in a Class Test

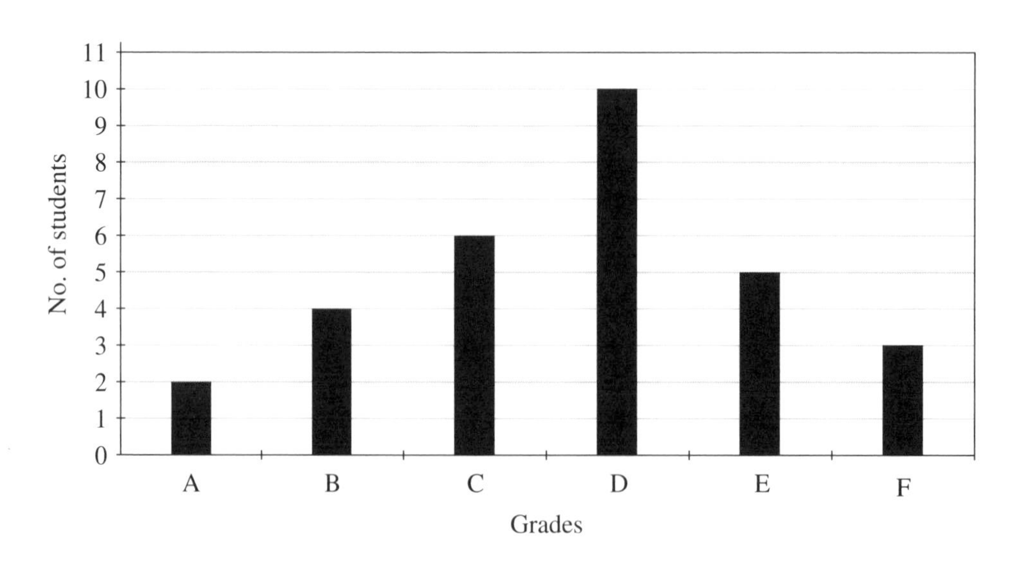

How many students were in the class?

How many students achieved a grade lower than a grade D?

Express the number of students, who achieved a grade A or a grade B, as a percentage of the total number of students in the class.

Using the bar chart above:

Number of students in the class

$= 2 + 4 + 6 + 10 + 5 + 3$

$= 30$

Number of students achieving lower than a grade D

= Number of students achieving a grade E or F

$= 5 + 3$

$= 8$

Number of students who achieved a grade A or B $= 5 + 3 = 8$.

Percentage of students who achieved a grade A or B

$$= \frac{\text{Number of students who achieved a grade A or B}}{\text{Number of students in the class}} \times 100\%$$

$$= \frac{8}{40} \times 100\%$$

$= 20\%$

(calculator: 8 $a\frac{b}{c}$ 40 × 100 =)

The table shows the rainfall, in millimetres, recorded for a number of months during 2006 at a weather station.

Month	May	June	July	Aug.	Sept.	Oct.
Rainfall in mm	35	40	25	30	50	60

Draw a trend graph of the data, putting months (May, June, etc.) on the horizontal axis.

Which month had the greatest rainfall?

Calculate, in mm, the mean rainfall per month.

Name the months in which the rainfall was greater than the mean.

The rainfall for the above six-month period represents 40% of the total rainfall recorded at the weather station during all of 2006. Calculate, in mm, the total rainfall recorded at the weather station during all of 2006.

Solution:

(i) Rainfall, in mm, at a weather station in 2006

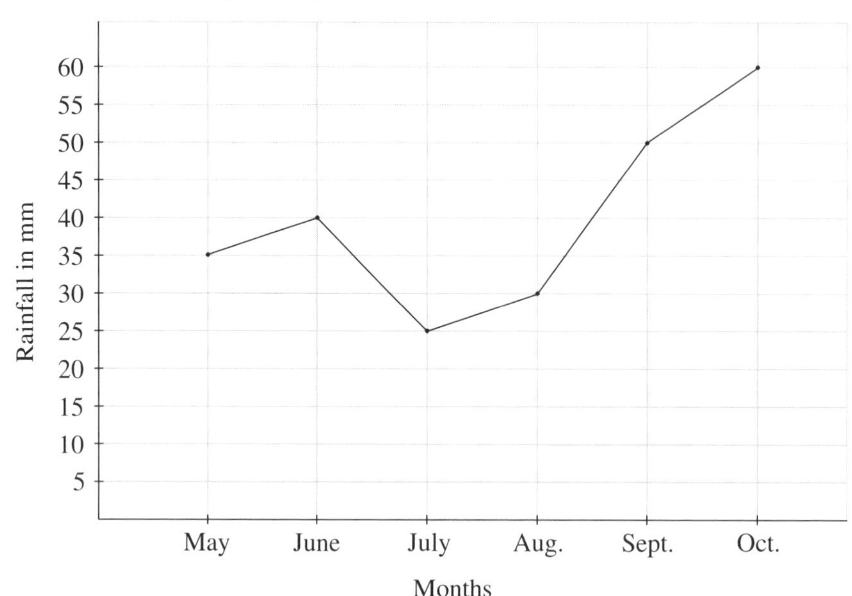

(ii) By reading the table, or the trend graph: October, with 60 mm of rain, was the month with the greatest rainfall.

(iii) Mean rainfall per month $= \dfrac{\text{total rainfall}}{\text{number of months}}$

$$= \frac{35+40+25+30+50+60}{6} = \frac{240}{6} = 40 \text{ mm}$$

(iv) In September the rainfall was 50 mm and in October the rainfall was 60 mm. Therefore, in September and October the rainfall was greater than the mean rainfall of 40 mm.

(v) **Equation given in disguise:**

40% of the rainfall for the year $= 240$ mm

1% of the rainfall for the year $= 6$ mm (divide both sides by 40)

100% of the rainfall for the year $= 600$ mm (multiply both sides by 100)

Therefore, the total rainfall recorded for the year was 600 mm.

Pie Charts

A pie chart is a circle divided into sectors in proportion to the frequency of the information. It displays the proportions as angles, measured from the centre of the circle.

Steps in drawing a pie chart:

1. Add up all the frequencies.
2. Divide this total into 360°.
3. Multiply the answer in step 2 by each individual frequency. (This gives the size of the angle for each sector.)
4. Draw the pie chart, label each sector, and give it a title. (It is a good idea to write the size of each angle on the pie chart.)

Note: It is good practice to check that all your angles add up to 360° before drawing the pie chart.

Example

24 fifth-year pupils were asked to choose from an option of 4 subjects.
The results are in the table below:

Accounting	Applied maths	Physics	French
5	8	7	4

Illustrate the data with a pie chart.

Solution:

24 pupils are to be represented by 360°.

Thus, 24 pupils = 360° (degrees on the right, because we want our answer in degrees)

$\therefore$ 1 pupil = 15° (divide both sides by 24)

In other words, one pupil will take up 15° on the pie chart.
We make up a table to work out the angle for each sector.

Sector	Number of pupils	Angle
Accounting	5	$5 \times 15° = 75°$
Applied maths	8	$8 \times 15° = 120°$
Physics	7	$7 \times 15° = 105°$
French	4	$4 \times 15° = 60°$
Total	24	360°

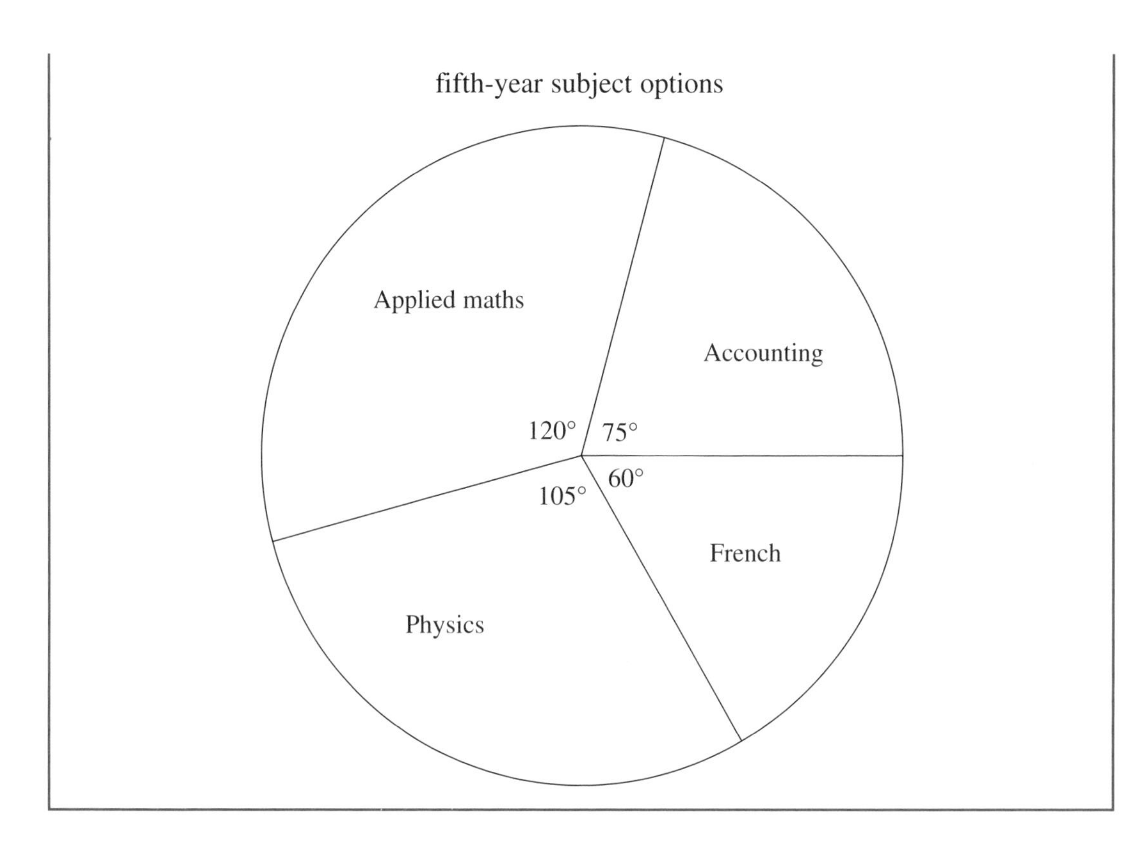

Given the Pie Chart

In some questions we are given the pie chart, or the angles in a pie chart, and we have to work backwards to calculate the numbers in each category.
In each question we are given an equation in disguise, and from this we can work out the number represented by 1°, or any other degree. It is not always necessary to calculate the number represented by 1°.

Example

A survey was taken of the people entering a supermarket during a certain hour.
The results are shown in the pie chart.

36 women were counted in the survey.

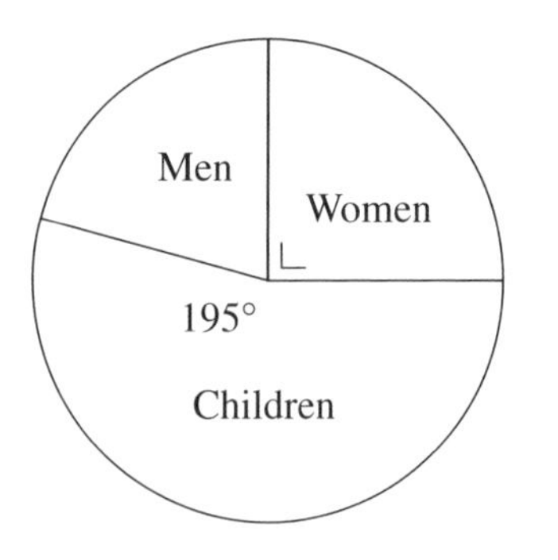

(i) What was the total number of people counted entering the supermarket?

(ii) How many men were counted entering the supermarket?

Solution:

(i) We are given that 90° represents 36 people (or 36 women).

Thus, $90° = 36$ people (people on the right, because we want our answer in the number of people)

$1° = 0.4$ people (divide both sides by 90)

$360° = 144$ people (multiply both sides by 360)

Therefore, the total number of people counted entering the supermarket was 144.

(ii) The number of degrees representing men on the pie chart $= 360 - 90 - 195 = 75$

$1° = 0.4$ people (from part **(i)**)

$75° = 30$ people (multiply both sides by 75)

Therefore, the number of men counted entering the supermarket was 30.

Mean and Mode of a Frequency Distribution

To find the mean of a frequency distribution, do the following:

1. Multiply each value by its corresponding frequency.
2. Sum all these products.
3. Divide this sum by the total number of frequencies.

That is,

$$\bar{x} = \frac{\sum fx}{\sum f}$$

where

(i) x is the value of each measurement

(ii) f is the frequency of each measurement

(iii) $\sum fx$ is the sum of all the fx values

(iv) $\sum f$ is the sum of all the frequencies.

The mode can be read directly from the table. The mode is the value with the highest frequency (most common value).

Note: Remember that the mode is the value, **not** the frequency.

Example 1

In a survey, the number of people travelling in each car which crossed a certain bridge between 0800 hours and 0815 hours on a particular day was recorded. The results of the survey are contained in the following frequency table:

Number of people per car	1	2	3	4	5
Number of cars	25	15	5	10	5

(i) Write down the modal number of people per car.

(ii) Draw a bar chart to illustrate the data given in the frequency table. Put the number of people per car on the horizontal axis.

(iii) How many cars were involved in the survey?

(iv) Calculate the mean number of cars which crossed the bridge per minute while the survey was taking place.

(v) Calculate the mean number of people per car.

Solution:

(i) (mode = 1, occurs most often) ↓

Number of people per car	1	2	3	4	5
Number of cars	25	15	5	10	5

↑ (highest frequency)

From the table, we can see that 1 occurs more than any other value.
Therefore, the modal number of people per car is 1.

(ii) **Number of people per car crossing a bridge**

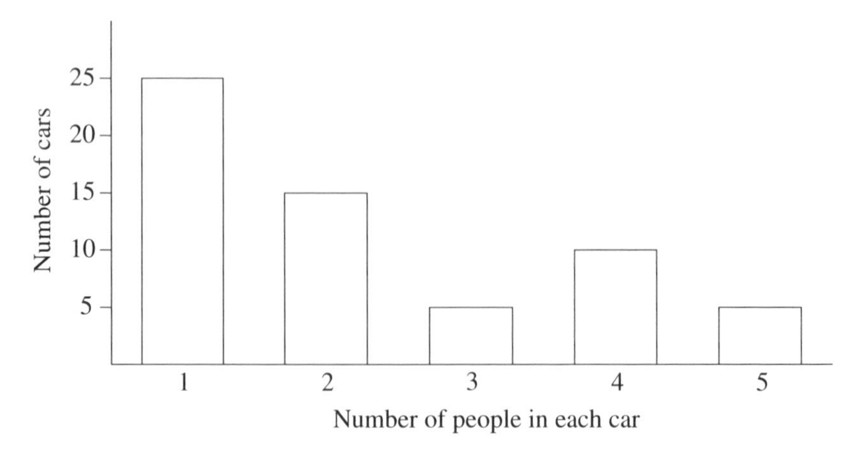

(iii) Number of cars in the survey $= 25 + 15 + 5 + 10 + 5 = 60$

(iv) Mean number of cars which crossed the bridge per minute $= \dfrac{\text{Total number of cars}}{\text{Number of minutes}} = \dfrac{60}{15} = 4$

(v) Mean number of people per car

$$= \frac{\text{total number of people}}{\text{total number of cars}}$$

$$= \frac{25(1) + 15(2) + 5(3) + 10(4) + 5(5)}{25 + 15 + 5 + 10 + 5}$$

$$= \frac{25 + 30 + 15 + 40 + 25}{60} = \frac{135}{60} = 2.25$$

Example 2

A die was thrown 30 times. The score of each throw was recorded as follows:

2, 1, 3, 5, 2, 4, 4, 1, 2, 3
2, 4, 2, 6, 1, 5, 2, 3, 6, 1
1, 5, 1, 2, 4, 6, 6, 1, 3, 2

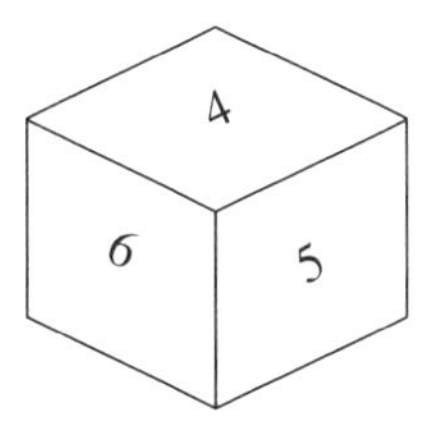

(i) Complete the following frequency distribution table:

Score	1	2	3	4	5	6
Frequency			4			

(ii) Write down the modal score.

(iii) Calculate the mean score per throw.

(iv) The die was then thrown 20 times. The mean of these 20 throws was 3.5. Calculate the overall mean score for all 50 throws.

Note: A 'die' is what most people call a dice. Dice is plural for a die.

Solution:

(i) Completed table:

Score	1	2	3	4	5	6
Frequency	7	8	4	4	3	4

(ii) From the table we see that the score 2 occurs more than any other score. Therefore, the modal score is 2.

(iii) Mean score per throw $= \dfrac{\text{total of all the scores}}{\text{total number of throws}}$

$$= \frac{7(1) + 8(2) + 4(3) + 4(4) + 3(5) + 4(6)}{7 + 8 + 4 + 4 + 3 + 4}$$

$$= \frac{7 + 16 + 12 + 16 + 15 + 24}{30} = \frac{90}{30} = 3$$

(iv) The mean of the 20 throws was 3.5 (given). Therefore, these scores must add up to 70.

$\left(\text{because } 20 \times 3.5 = 70 \quad \text{or} \quad \frac{70}{20} = 3.5\right)$

Mean score for the 50 throws $= \dfrac{\text{total score for all 50 throws}}{50}$

$$= \frac{90 + 70}{50} \qquad \left(\begin{array}{c}\text{total score for first 30 throws was 90;} \\ \text{total score for the next 20 throws was 70}\end{array}\right)$$

$$= \frac{160}{50} = 3.2$$

Chapter 19. ANGLES

Parallel Lines, Triangles and Quadrilaterals

Example 1

Calculate the value of:

(i) x (ii) y

giving a reason for each answer.

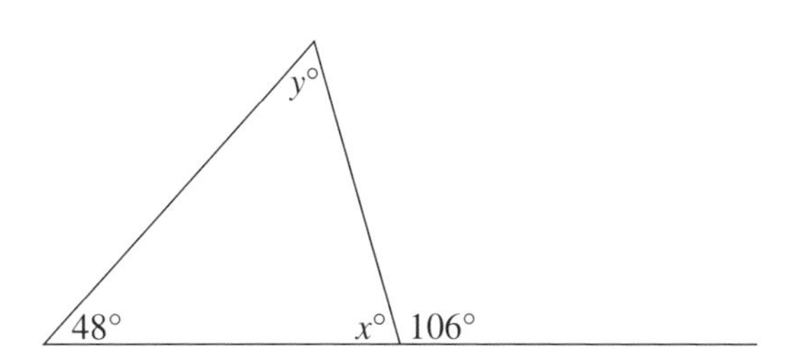

Solution:

(i) $x° + 106° = 180°$ *straight angle*

$x + 106 = 180$

$x = 74$ (subtract 106 from both sides)

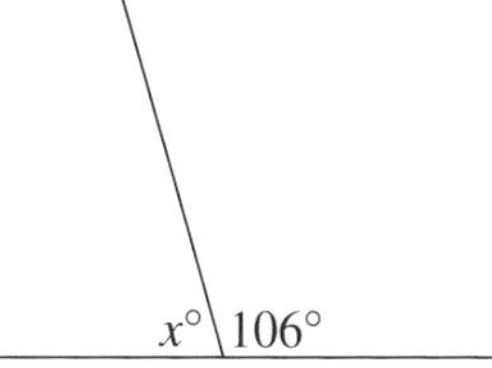

(ii) $x° + y° + 48° = 180°$ *three angles in a triangle*

$74 + y + 48 = 180$ (put in $x = 74$)

$y + 122 = 180$

$y = 58$ (subtract 122 from both sides)

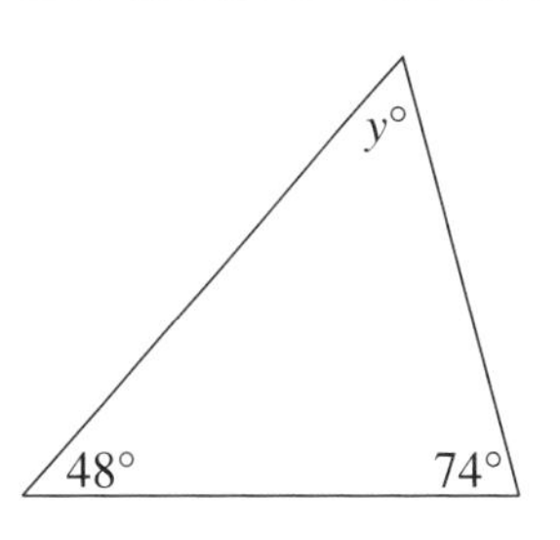

Example 2

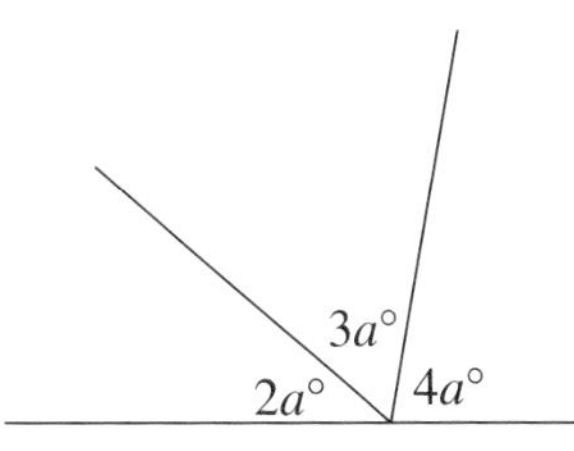

(i) Calculate the value of a in the diagram.

(ii) Calculate the value of p in the diagram.

In each case give a reason for your answer.

Solution:

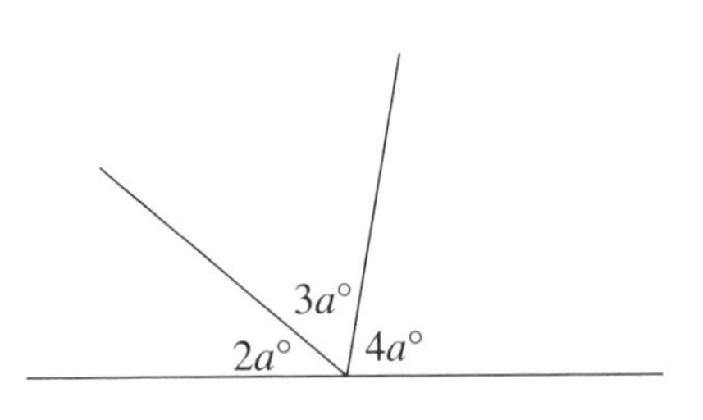

(i) $2a° + 3a° + 4a° = 180°$ *straight angle*

$$2a + 3a + 4a = 180$$

$$9a = 180$$

$$a = 20 \quad \text{(divide both sides by 9)}$$

(ii) The marks indicate that the triangle is isosceles.

Therefore, the two base angles are equal to $p°$.

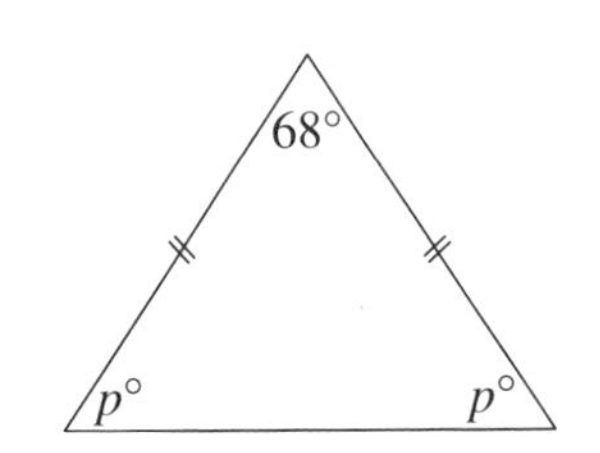

$p° + p° + 68° = 180°$ *three angles in a triangle*

$$p + p + 68 = 180$$

$$2p + 68 = 180$$

$$2p = 112 \quad \text{(subtract 68 from both sides)}$$

$$p = 56 \quad \text{(divide both sides by 2)}$$

Example 3

In the diagram, $L \parallel M$ and $|\angle abq| = 72°$.

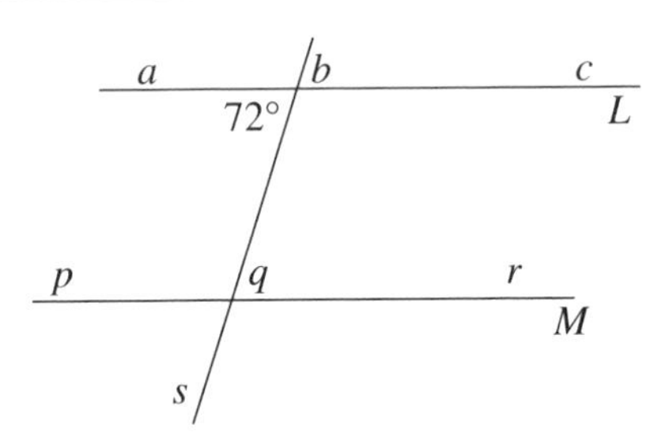

(i) Name the angle corresponding to $\angle abq$.

(ii) Find $|\angle pqs|$.

(iii) Name the angle vertically opposite to $\angle sqr$.

(iv) Find $|\angle sqr|$.

Solution:

(i)

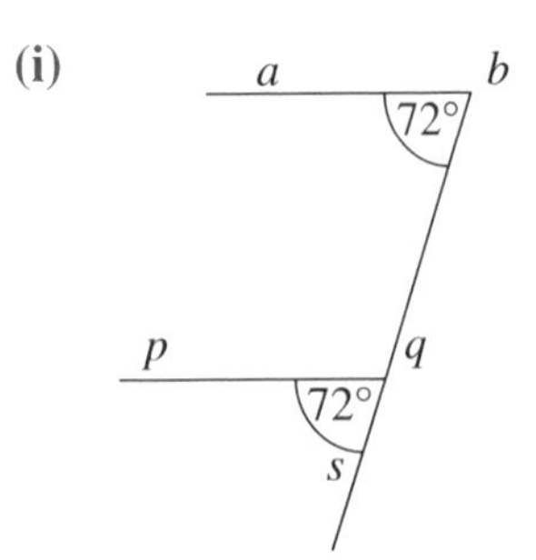

$\angle pqs$ corresponds to $\angle abq$

(ii) $|\angle pqs| = 72°$

(iii)

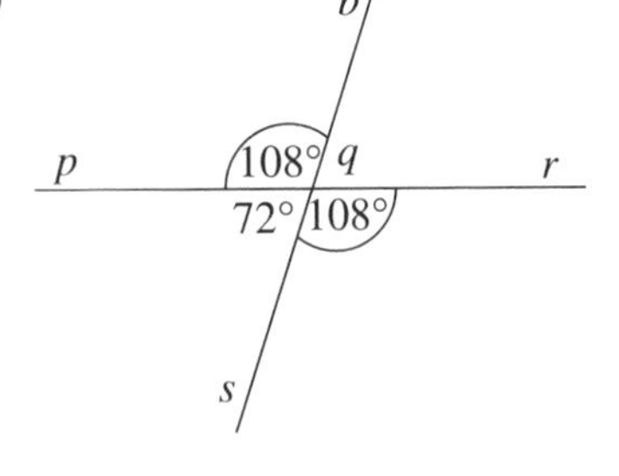

$\angle pqb$ is vertically opposite to $\angle sqr$

(iv) $|\angle pqs| + |\angle sqr| = 180°$

$$72° + |\angle sqr| = 180°$$

$$|\angle sqr| = 108°$$

Example 4

$ab \parallel cd$, $|\angle abc| = 40°$ and $|pc| = |pd|$.

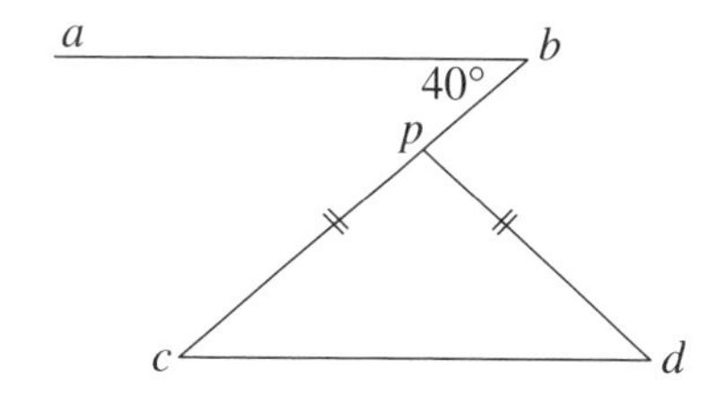

(i) Name the angle that is alternate to $\angle abc$.

Find **(ii)** $|\angle pdc|$ **(iii)** $|\angle cpd|$ **(iv)** $|\angle dpb|$.

Solution:

(i)

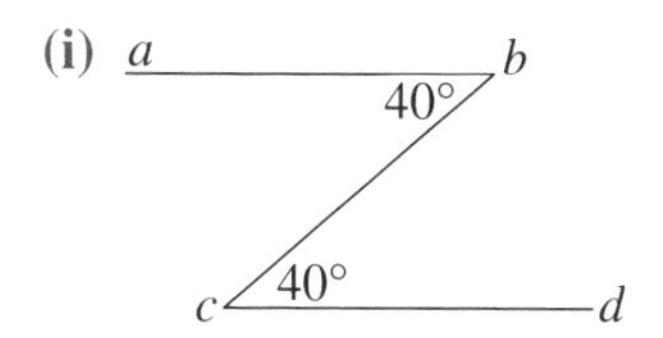

$\angle dcb$ is alternate to $\angle abc$

$\therefore\ |\angle dcb| = |\angle abc| = 40°$

(ii) and **(iii)**

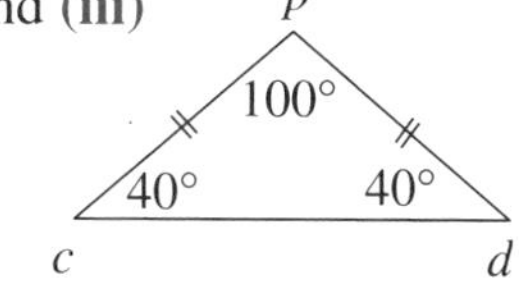

$\triangle pcd$ is isosceles (given)

$\therefore\ |\angle pcd| = |\angle pdc| = 40°$

$\therefore\ |\angle cpd| = 180° - 80°$

$= 100°$

(iv)

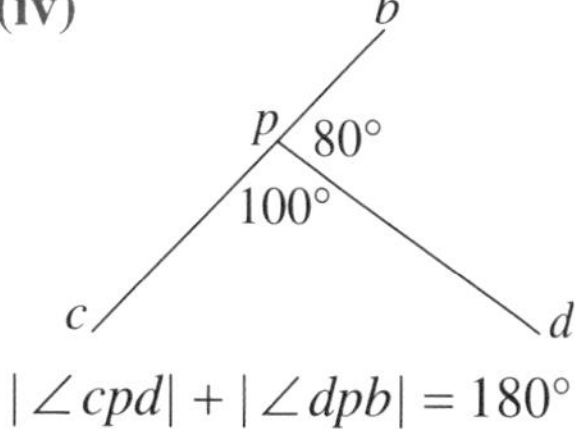

$|\angle cpd| + |\angle dpb| = 180°$

$100° + |\angle dpb| = 180°$

$\therefore\ |\angle dpb| = 80°$

Example 5

abcd is a parallelogram, with $|\angle bad| = 125°$ and $|\angle cbd| = 25°$.

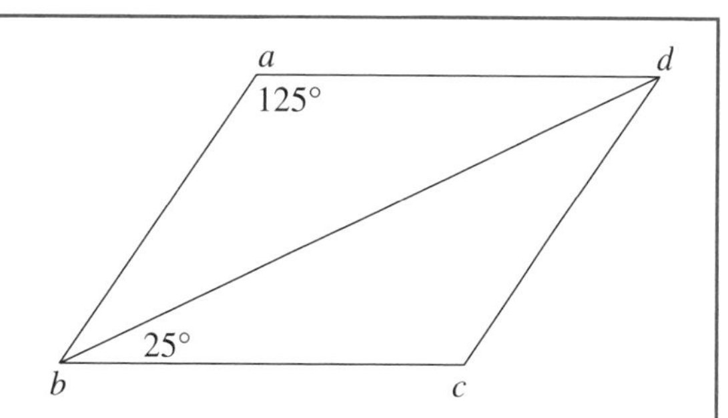

Find **(i)** $|\angle bcd|$ **(ii)** $|\angle adb|$ **(iii)** $|\angle abd|$ **(iv)** $|\angle cdb|$.

In each case give a reason for your answer.

Solution:

(i)

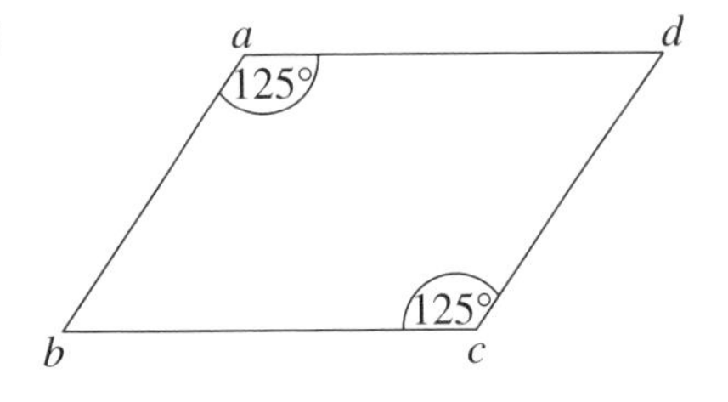

$|\angle bcd| = |\angle bad| = 125°$

opposite angles of the parallelogram

(ii)

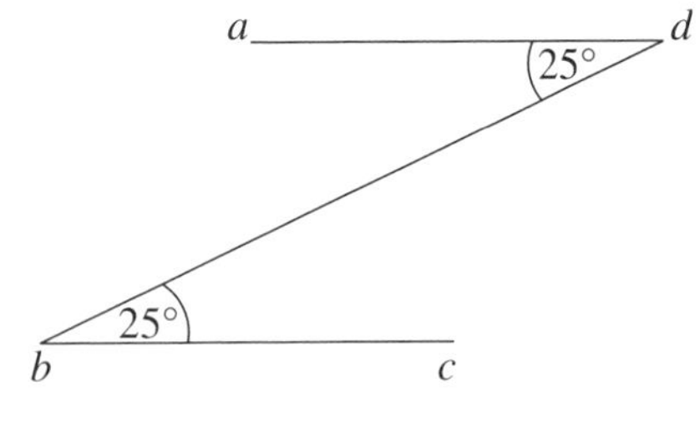

$|\angle adb| = |\angle cbd| = 25°$

alternate angles

(iii)

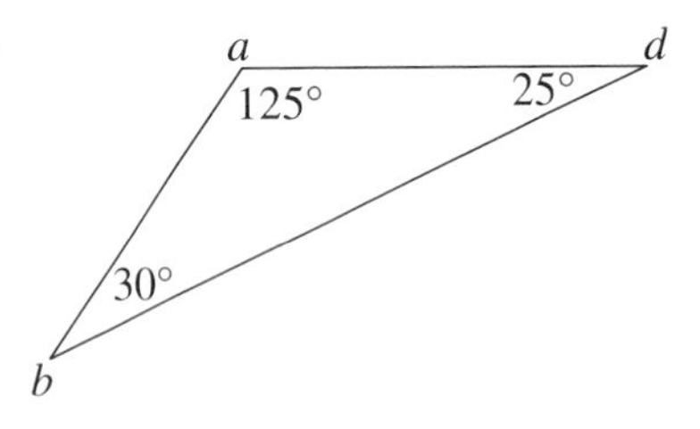

$|\angle abd| + |\angle bad| + |\angle adb| = 180°$

Three angles in a triangle add to 180°.

$|\angle abd| + 125° + 25° = 180°$

$|\angle abd| + 150° = 180°$

$|\angle abd| = 30°$

(iv)

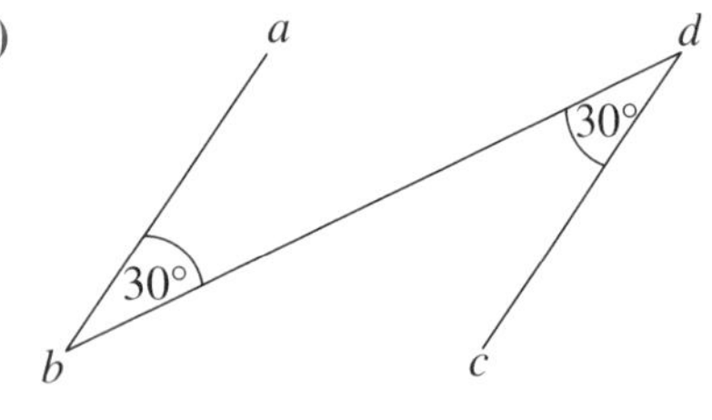

$|\angle cdb| = |\angle abd| = 30°$

alternate angles

Sometimes we have to prove that angles are equal.

Example 6

abcd is a rectangle.
aefd is a parallelogram.

Prove that: $|\angle bfd| = |\angle eba| + |\angle eab|$

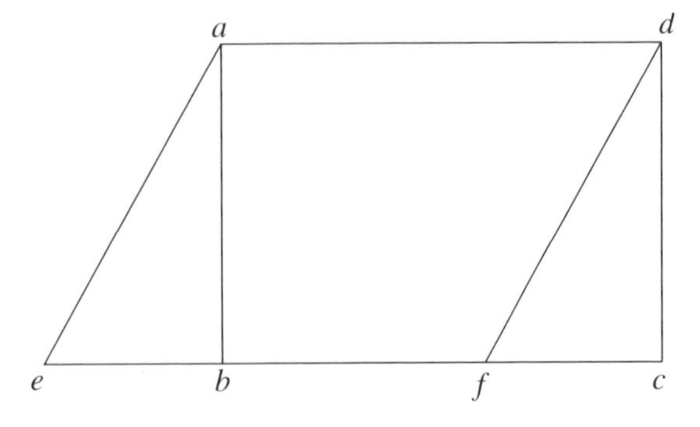

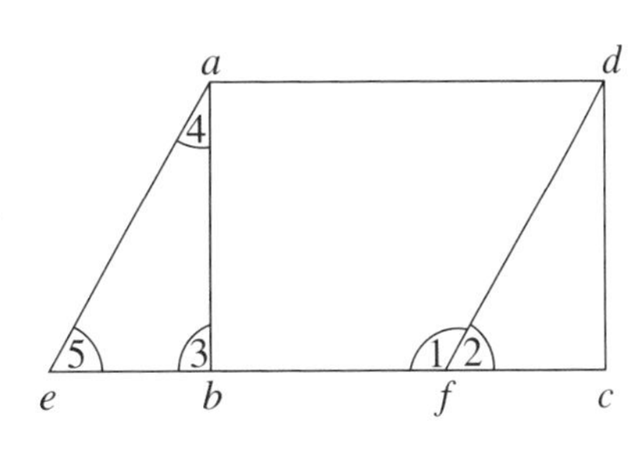

Solution:

Label angles 1, 2, 3, 4 and 5 as shown.

$$|\angle 2| = |\angle 5| \quad \textit{corresponding angles}$$

$$|\angle 1| + |\angle 2| = 180^\circ \quad \textit{straight angle}$$

$$|\angle 3| + |\angle 4| + |\angle 5| = 180^\circ \quad \textit{3 angles in a triangle}$$

$$\therefore \quad |\angle 1| + |\angle 2| = |\angle 3| + |\angle 4| + |\angle 5|$$

$$\therefore \quad |\angle 1| = |\angle 3| + |\angle 4| \qquad (\text{as } |\angle 2| = |\angle 5|)$$

i.e. $|\angle bfd| = |\angle eba| + |\angle eab|$

Circles

Example 1

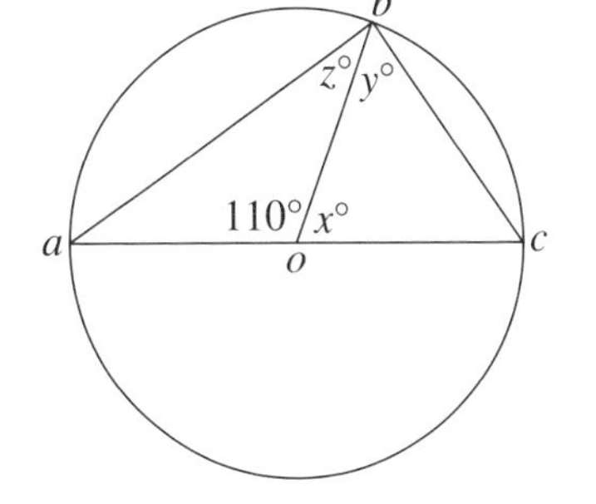

In the diagram,
o is the centre of the circle.
Calculate the value of:

(i) x **(ii)** y **(iii)** z,

giving a reason for each answer.

Solution:

(i) $x^\circ + 110^\circ = 180^\circ$ *straight angle*

$x + 110 = 180$

$x = 70$ (subtract 70 from both sides)

110° x°

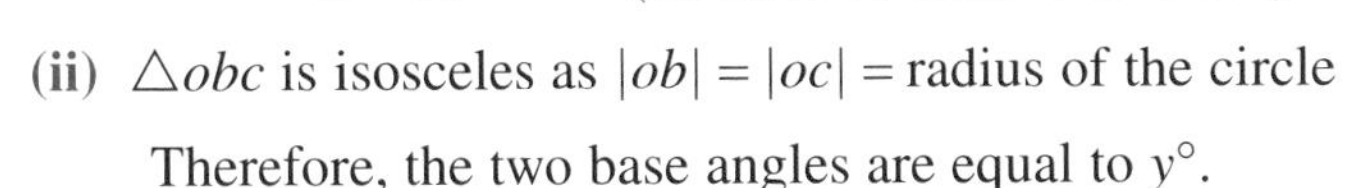

(ii) $\triangle obc$ is isosceles as $|ob| = |oc| =$ radius of the circle

Therefore, the two base angles are equal to y°.

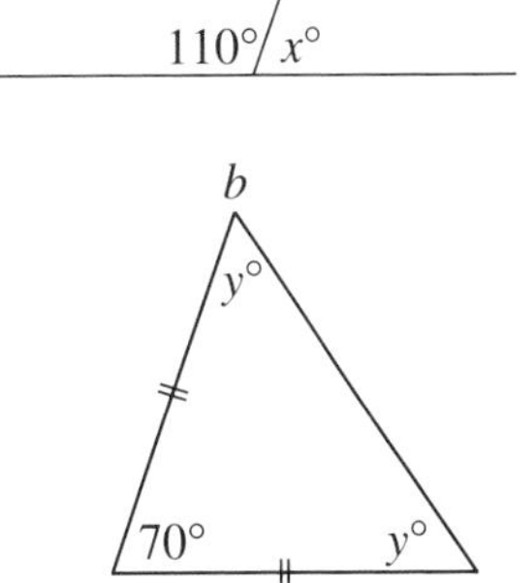

$y^\circ + y^\circ + 70^\circ = 180^\circ$ *three angles in a triangle*

$y + y + 70 = 180$

$2y + 70 = 180$

$2y = 110$ (subtract 70 from both sides)

$y = 55$ (divide both sides by 2)

(iii) $z^\circ + y^\circ = 90^\circ$ *angle in a semi-circle*

$z + y = 90$

$z + 55 = 90$ (put in $y = 55$)

$z = 35$ (subtract 55 from both sides)

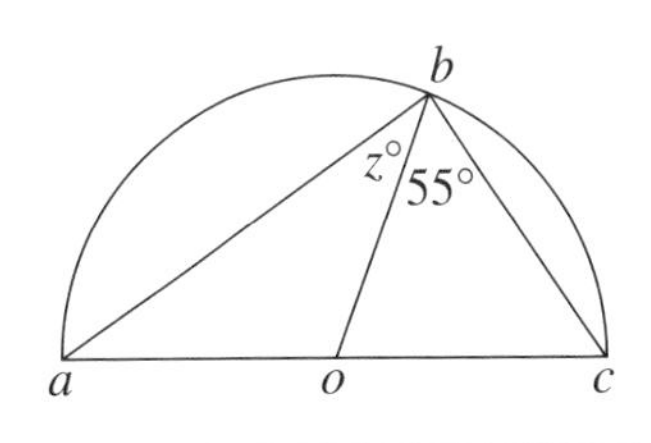

Example 2

In the diagram, o is the centre of the circle, ps is a tangent to the circle at p and $|\angle qpr| = 55°$.

Find, giving a reason in each case,

(i) $|\angle spr|$ **(ii)** $|\angle prq|$ **(iii)** $|\angle pqr|$.

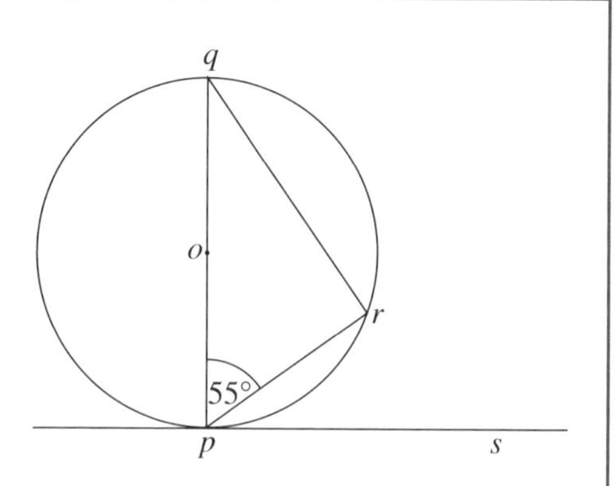

Solution:

(i) $|\angle spr| + |\angle qpr| = 90°$

tangent is perpendicular to a radius at the point of contact

$$|\angle spr| + 55° = 90°$$

$$|\angle spr| = 35°$$

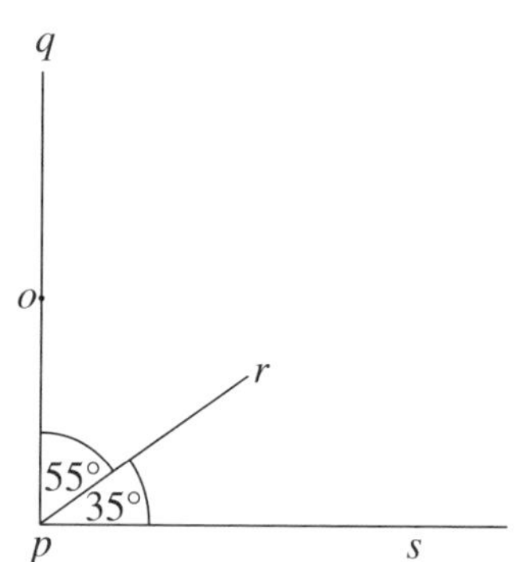

(ii) $|\angle prq| = 90°$

angle in a semi-circle is always 90°

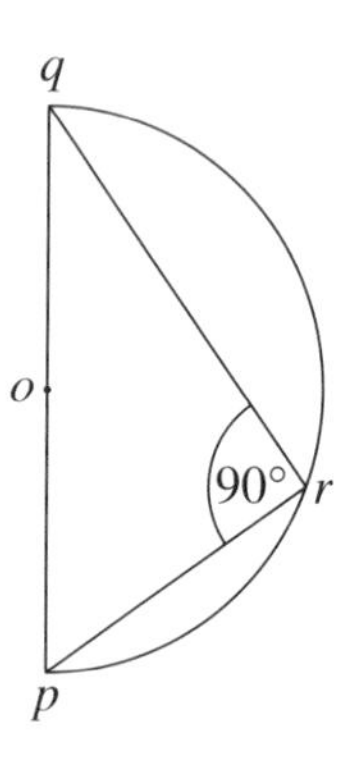

(iii) $|\angle pqr| + |\angle prq| + |\angle qpr| = 180°$

three angles in a triangle

$$|\angle pqr| + 90° + 55° = 180°$$

$$|\angle pqr| + 145° = 180°$$

$$|\angle pqr| = 35°$$

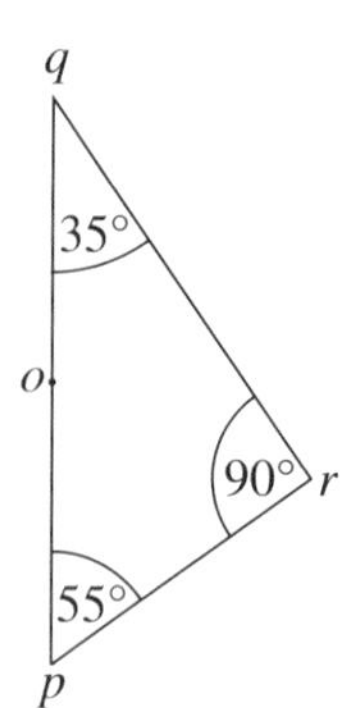

Example 3

p, q, r and s are four points on the circumference of a circle of centre k.

If $|\angle qrs| = 110°$ and $|\angle rqp| = 75°$,

calculate **(i)** $|\angle qps|$ **(ii)** $|\angle rsp|$.

Give a reason for your answers.

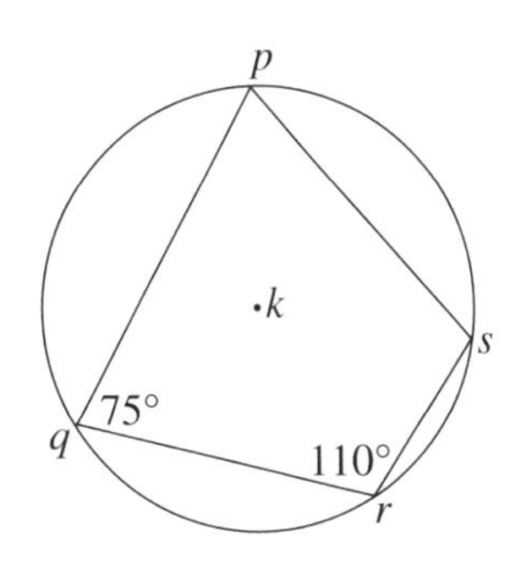

Solution:

(i) $|\angle qps| + |\angle qrs| = 180°$

opposite angles in a cyclic quadrilateral

$|\angle qps| + 110° = 180°$

$|\angle qps| = 70°$

(ii) $|\angle rsp| + |\angle rqp| = 180°$

opposite angles in a cyclic quadrilateral

$|\angle rsp| + 75° = 180°$

$|\angle rsp| = 105°$

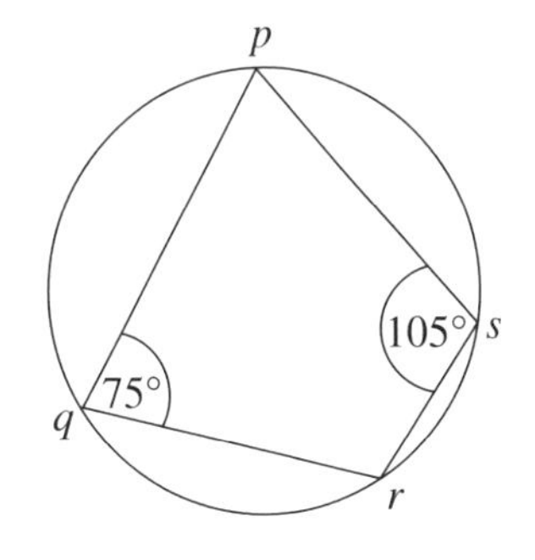

Chapter 20. TRANSFORMATIONS OF THE PLANE

Transformations

The movement of a figure, or point, from one position to another position is called **a transformation**.

The three transformations:

1. **Translation** A translation is a 'movement in a straight line'. Image does not flip over.	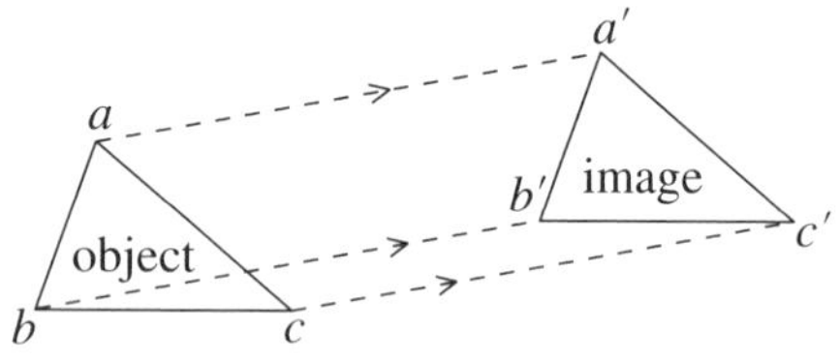
2. **Axial symmetry** Axial symmetry is a 'reflection in a line'. Image flips over.	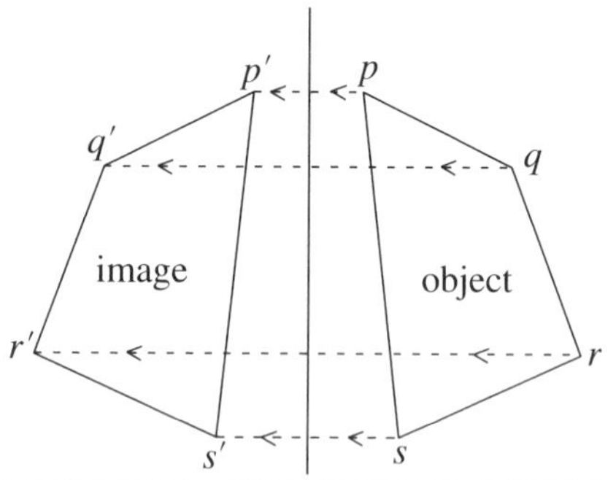
3. **Central symmetry** Central symmetry is a 'reflection in a point'.	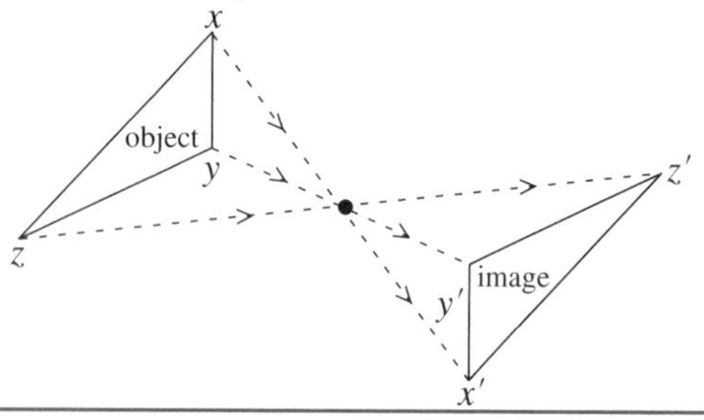

The **image** of a point is where the point moves to after the transformation.

Example 1

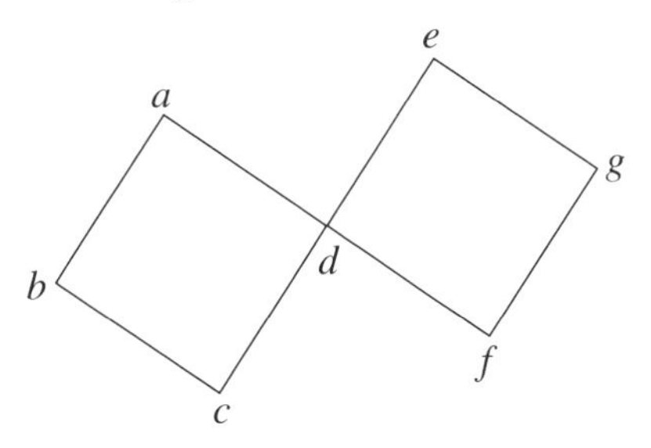

abcd and *dfge* are two squares of the same size.

Name:

(i) the image of a under the translation $\vec{ef}$

(ii) the image of $[df]$ under the axial symmetry in dg

(iii) the image of $\triangle abc$ under the central symmetry in d.

Solution:

(i) Under the translation $\vec{ef}$:

$a \longrightarrow c$ (a moves to c)

Therefore the image of a is c.

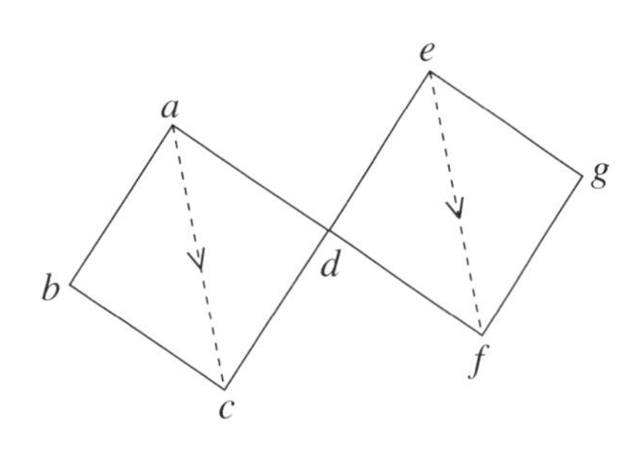

(ii) Under the axial symmetry in dg:

$d \longrightarrow d$ (own image)

$f \longrightarrow e$ (f moves to e)

Therefore the image of $[df]$ is $[de]$.

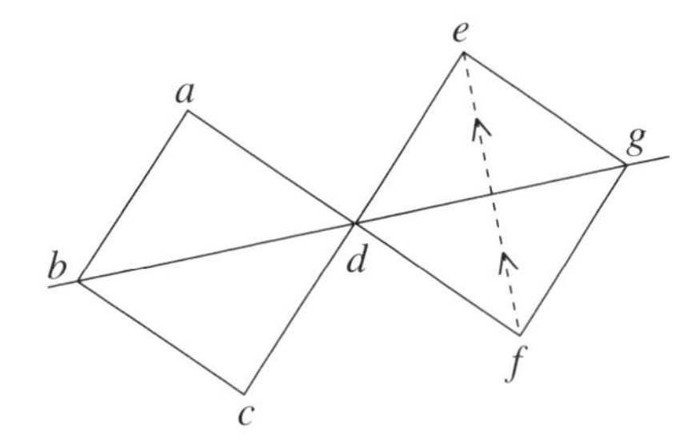

(iii) Under the central symmetry in d:

$a \longrightarrow f$ (a moves to f)

$b \longrightarrow g$ (b moves to g)

$c \longrightarrow e$ (c moves to e)

Therefore the image of $\triangle abc$ is $\triangle fge$.

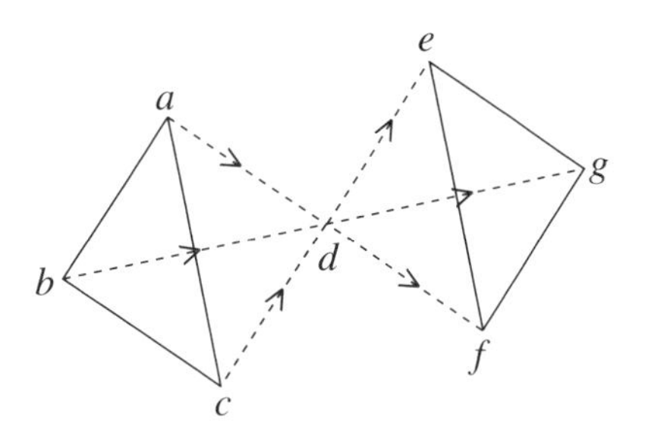

Example 2

abcd is a rectangle having diagonals intersecting at *k*.

p is the midpoint of [*ab*].

sacd and *btcd* are parallelograms.

$|bt| = 8$ and $|bc| = 6$.

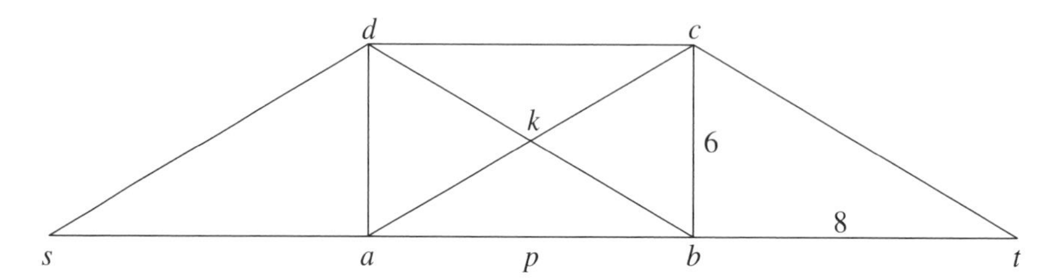

(i) Name the image of $\angle adb$ under the central symmetry in *k*.

(ii) Name the image of $\triangle sdb$ under the translation $\vec{ab}$.

(iii) Name the image of $\triangle akd$ under the axial symmetry in *pk*.

(iv) Say why triangles *sad* and *tbc* are congruent.

(v) Calculate the area of the figure *stcd*.

(vi) Calculate $|tc|$.

Solution:

(i) Under the central symmetry in *k*:

$a \longrightarrow c$ (*a* moves to *c*)

$d \longrightarrow b$ (*d* moves to *b*)

$b \longrightarrow d$ (*b* moves to *d*)

Therefore the image of $\angle adb$ is $\angle cbd$.

(ii) Under the translation $\vec{ab}$:

$s \longrightarrow a$ (*s* moves to *a*)

$d \longrightarrow c$ (*d* moves to *c*)

$b \longrightarrow t$ (*b* moves to *t*)

Therefore the image of $\triangle sdb$ is $\triangle act$.

(iii) Under the axial symmetry in *pk*:

$a \longrightarrow b$ (*a* moves to *b*)

$k \longrightarrow k$ (own image)

$d \longrightarrow c$ (*d* moves to *c*)

Therefore the image of $\triangle akd$ is $\triangle bkc$.

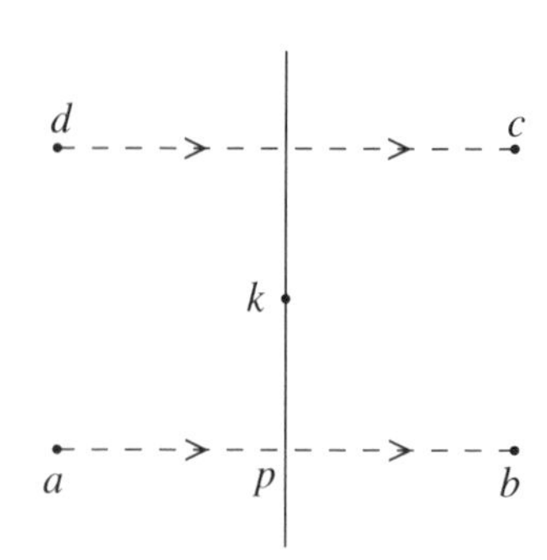

(iv) $|sa| = |dc|$ (opposite sides)

$|bt| = |dc|$ (opposite sides)

$\therefore\ |sa| = |bt|$ (both equal to $|dc|$)

$|\angle sad| = |\angle tbc| = 90^\circ$ (given)

$|ad| = |bc|$ (opposite sides)

$\therefore\ \triangle sad \equiv \triangle tbc$ (SAS)

(v) Area of *stcd*

$= \text{Area of rectangle } abcd + \triangle sad + \triangle tbc$

$= 6 \times 8 + \frac{1}{2} \times 8 \times 6 + \frac{1}{2} \times 8 \times 6$ ($\triangle sad$ and $\triangle tbc$ are congruent)

$= 48 + 24 + 24$

$= 96$

(vi) Using Pythagoras's theorem :

$|tc|^2 = |tb|^2 + |bc|^2$

$|tc|^2 = 8^2 + 6^2$

$|tc|^2 = 64 + 36$

$|tc|^2 = 100$

$|tc| = \sqrt{100}$

$|tc| = 10$

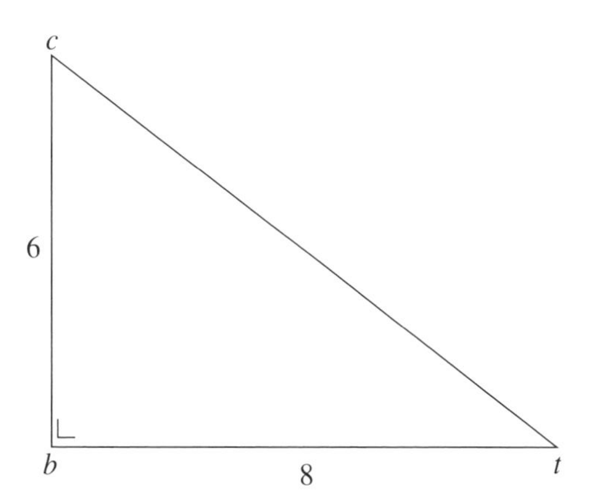

Example 3

Consider the capital letter H, shown on the right.

(i) State the number of axes (lines) of symmetry it possesses and indicate them with a broken line.

(ii) Show how to find its centre of symmetry.

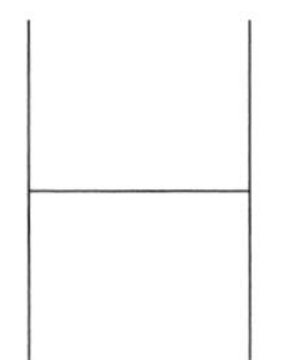

Solution:

(i) The capital letter H has 2 axes of symmetry, indicated by the broken lines.

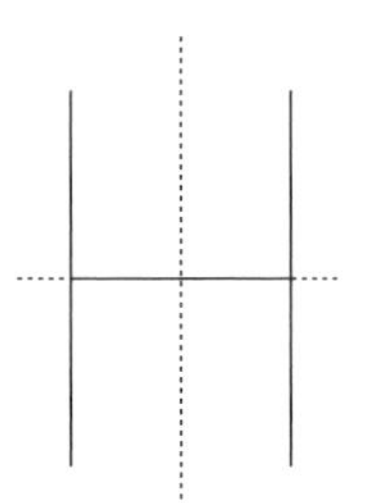

(ii) By drawing a line from the top of one side of the H to the bottom of the other side twice, as shown; the centre of symmetry, c, is the point of intersection of these lines.

Alternatively, the centre of symmetry can be found at the point of intersection of the axes of symmetry.

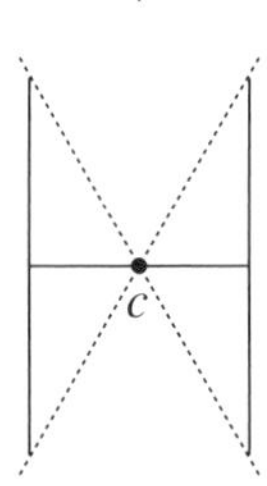

Chapter 21. PYTHAGORAS'S THEOREM

Pythagoras's Theorem

In a right-angled triangle, the square on the hypotenuse is equal to the sum of the squares on the other two sides.

$$c^2 = a^2 + b^2$$

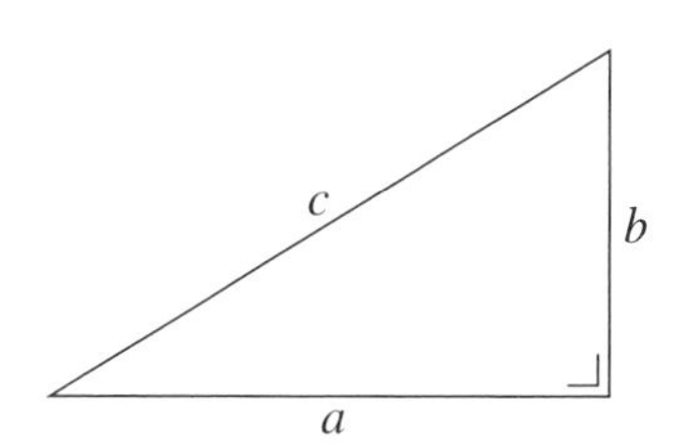

The converse (opposite) also applies.
If $c^2 = a^2 + b^2$, then the triangle must be right-angled.

Note: Pythagoras's theorem applies only to right-angled triangles.
We can use Pythagoras's theorem to find the missing length of a side in a right-angled triangle if we know the lengths of the other two sides.

Example 1

Find the value of

(i) x **(ii)** y.

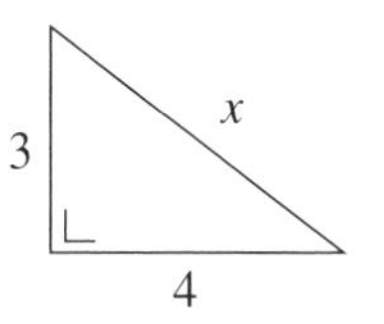

29
x
21

Solution:

(i)

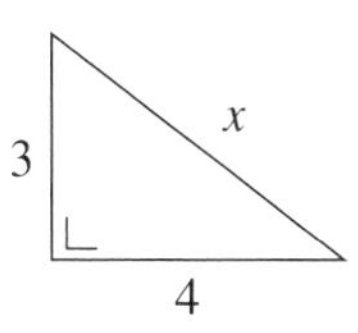

Using Pythagoras's theorem:

$$x^2 = 3^2 + 4^2$$
$$x^2 = 9 + 16$$
$$x^2 = 25$$
$$x = \sqrt{25}$$
$$x = 5$$

(ii)

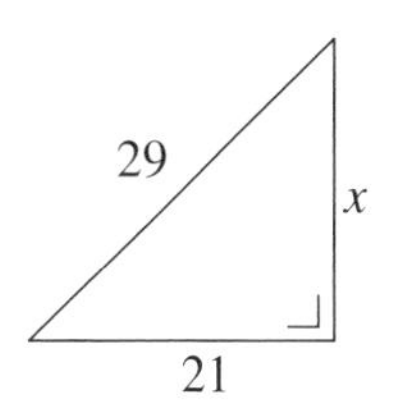

Using Pythagoras's theorem:

$$x^2 + 21^2 = 29^2$$
$$x^2 + 441 = 841$$
$$x^2 = 400$$
$$x = \sqrt{400}$$
$$x = 20$$

Example 2

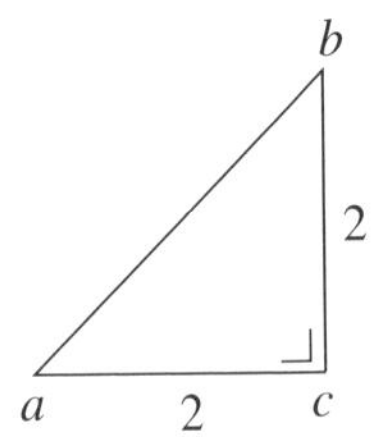

In the diagram,

$|ac| = |cd| = 2.$

Show that $|ab| = \sqrt{8}.$

Solution:

Using Pythagoras's theorem:

$|ab|^2 = |ac|^2 + |cb|^2$

$|ab|^2 = 2^2 + 2^2$

$|ab|^2 = 4 + 4$

$|ab|^2 = 8$

$|ab| = \sqrt{8}$

Example 3

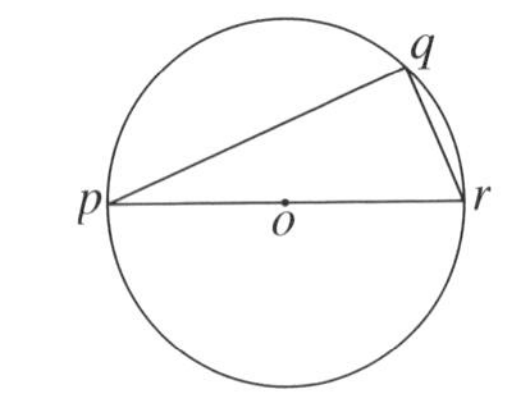

p, q and r are three points on the circumference of the circle of centre o.

If the radius of the circle is 8.5 cm and $|pq| = 15$ cm, calculate $|qr|$.

Solution:

$|\angle pqr| = 90°$ (angle in a semi-circle)

$\therefore$ $\triangle pqr$ is a right-angled triangle.

$|pr| = 2(\text{radius}) = 2(8.5) = 17$ cm

Using Pythagoras's theorem:

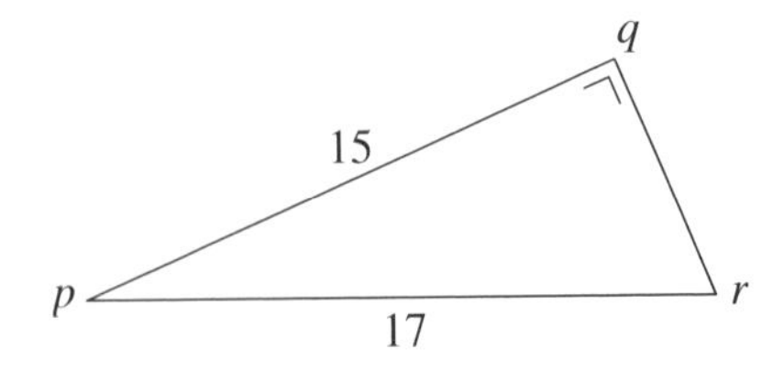

$|pq|^2 + |qr|^2 = |pr|^2$

$15^2 + |qr|^2 = 17^2$

$225 + |qr|^2 = 289$

$|qr|^2 = 64$

$|qr| = \sqrt{64}$

$|qr| = 8$

Therefore, $|qr| = 8$ cm

Example 4

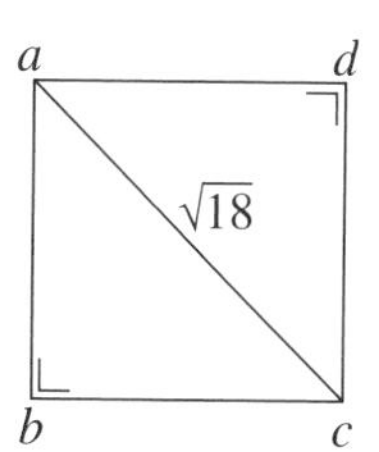

$abcd$ is a square and $|ac| = \sqrt{18}$.

Calculate the length of a side of the square.

Solution:

The diagonal bisects the square to create two right-angled triangles.

Therefore, we can apply Pythagoras's theorem.

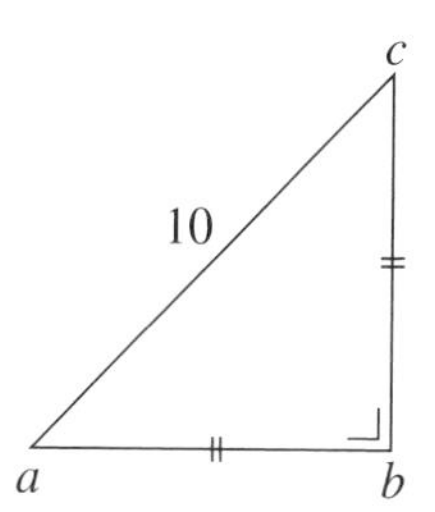

Let $x =$ the length of a side.

$$|ab|^2 + |bc|^2 = |ac|^2 \quad \text{(Pythagoras's theorem)}$$
$$x^2 + x^2 = (\sqrt{18})^2$$
$$2x^2 = 18$$
$$x^2 = 9 \quad \text{(divide both sides by 2)}$$
$$x = \sqrt{9} \quad \text{(take the square root of both sides)}$$
$$x = 3$$

Therefore the length of a side of the square is 3.

Note: $\left(\sqrt{a}\right)^2 = a$. For example, $\left(\sqrt{32}\right)^2 = 32$, $\left(\sqrt{50}\right)^2 = 50$.

Example 5

In the triangle abc, $|ab| = |bc|$,

$|ac| = 10$ and $|\angle abc| = 90°$.

Find $|ab|$, correct to two decimal places.

Solution:

Let $x = |ab| = |bc|$.

Using Pythagoras's theorem:

$$|ab|^2 + |bc|^2 = |ac|^2$$
$$x^2 + x^2 = 10^2$$
$$2x^2 = 100$$
$$x^2 = 50 \quad \text{(divide both sides by 2)}$$
$$x = \sqrt{50} \quad \text{(take the square root of both sides)}$$
$$x = 7.071067812$$

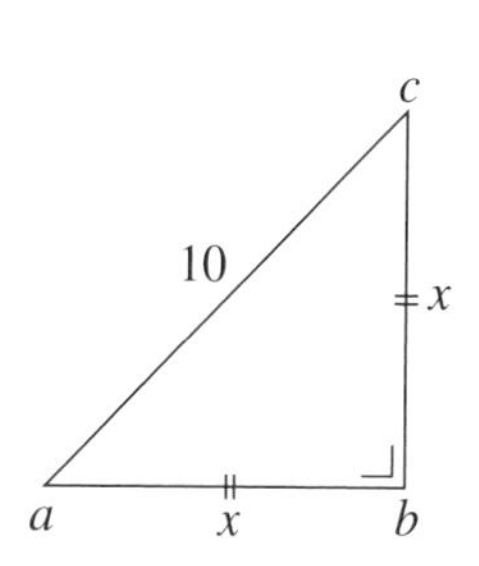

Therefore, $|ab| = 7.07$, correct to two decimal places.

Example 6

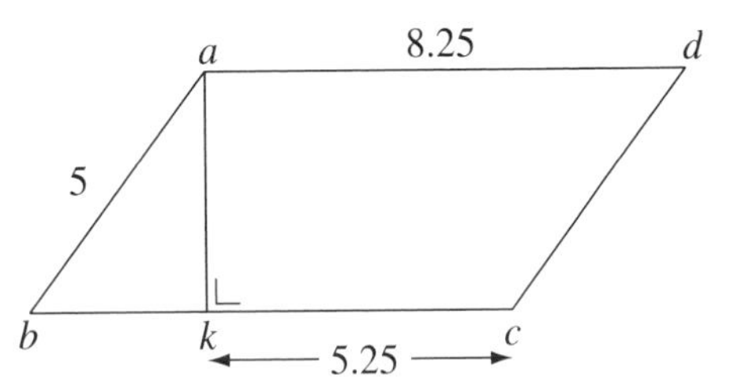

abcd is a parallelogram and $ak \perp bc$.

$|ab| = 5, \quad |ad| = 8.25, \quad |kc| = 5.25.$

Calculate:

(i) $|bk|$ **(ii)** $|ak|$ **(iii)** the area of the parallelogram *abcd*

(iv) the length of the perpendicular from *c* to *ab*.

Solution:

(i)

$$|bc| = 8.25 \qquad (|bc| = |ad|)$$

$$|bk| + |kc| = 8.25 \qquad (|bc| = |bk| + |kc|)$$

$$|bk| + 5.25 = 8.25 \qquad (|kc| = 5.25)$$

$$|bk| = 3 \qquad \text{(subtract 5.25 from both sides)}$$

8.25
b k c
3 5.25

(ii) $\triangle abk$ is a right-angled triangle.

Using Pythagoras's theorem:

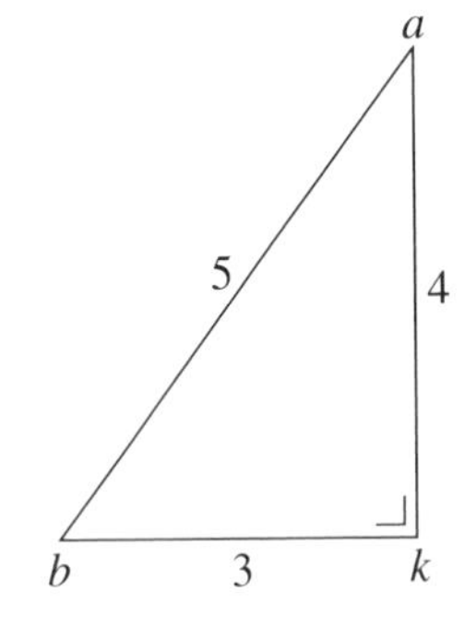

$$|ak|^2 + |bk|^2 = |ab|^2$$

$$|ak|^2 + 3^2 = 5^2$$

$$|ak|^2 + 9 = 25$$

$$|ak|^2 = 16$$

$$|ak| = \sqrt{16}$$

$$|ak| = 4$$

(iii) Area of parallelogram

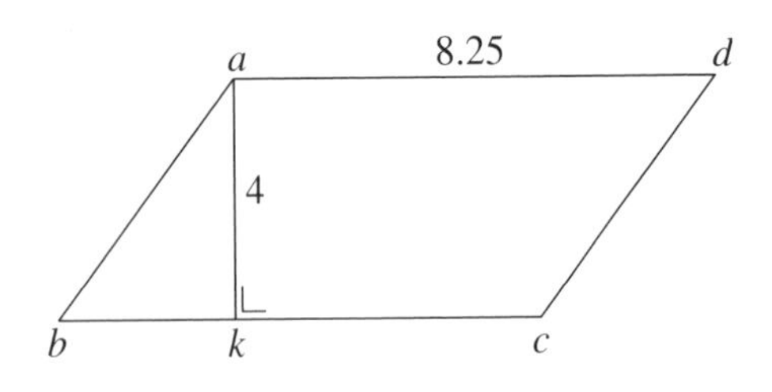

$= \text{base} \times \text{height}$

$= |ad| \times |ak|$

$= 8.25 \times 4$

$= 33$

(iv) Let the length of the perpendicular from c to $ab = h$.

Equation given in disguise:

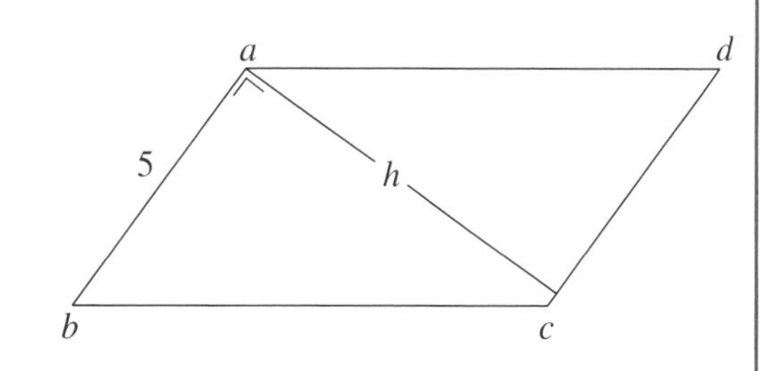

area of parallelogram $= 33$

$$\text{base} \times \text{height} = 33$$

$$|ab| \times h = 33$$

$$5h = 33$$

$$h = 6.6$$

Therefore the length of the perpendicular from c to ab is 6.6.

(Notice that $8.25 \times 4 = 5 \times 6.6$. Both equal 33.)

Chapter 22. CONSTRUCTIONS

The Four Constructions

There are four constructions on our course:

1. Perpendicular bisector of a line segment.
2. Bisector of an angle.
3. Divide a line segment into a given number of parts.
4. Construct a triangle given sufficient information.

Any work involving accurate constructions requires a good pencil, a compass, a ruler, and a protractor. It is very important not to rub out any construction lines or marks you make at any stage during a construction. All construction lines or marks should **always** be left on the diagram.

1. Perpendicular bisector of a line segment

The perpendicular bisector of a line segment, $[xy]$, is constructed with the following steps:

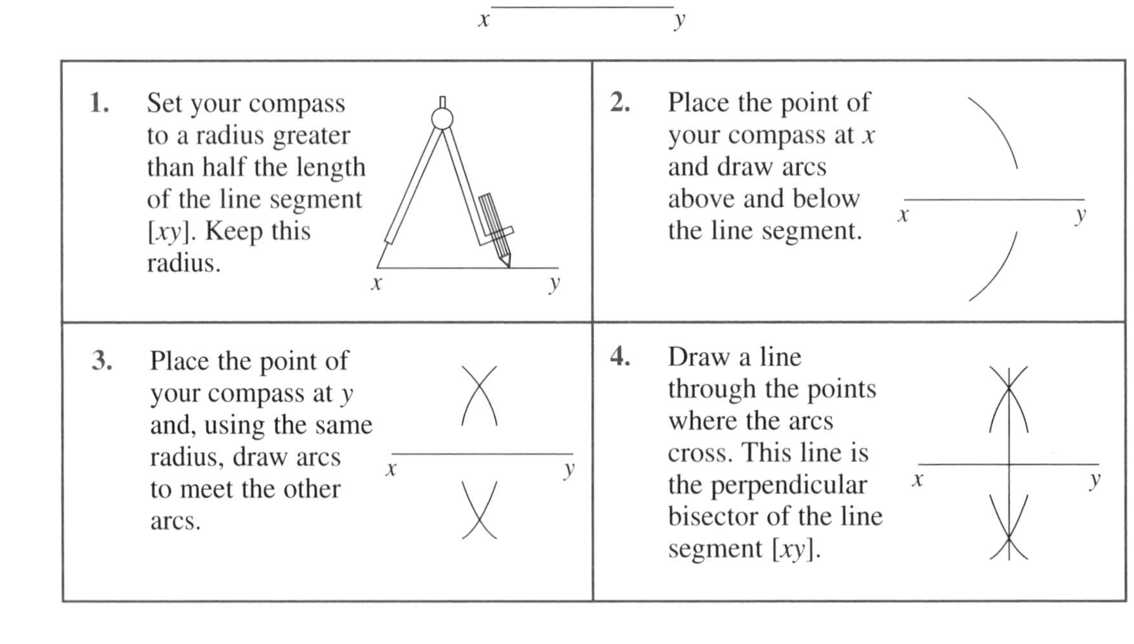

2. Bisector of an angle

The bisector of an angle is constructed with the following steps:

1. Place the point of your compass on the vertex, o, of the angle. Using the same radius, draw two arcs to meet the arms of the angle at x and y.

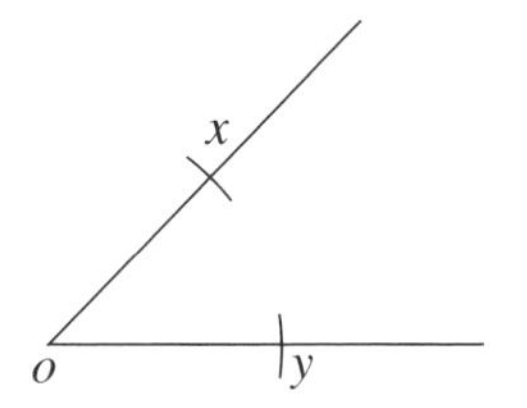

2. Place the point of your compass at x and draw an arc.

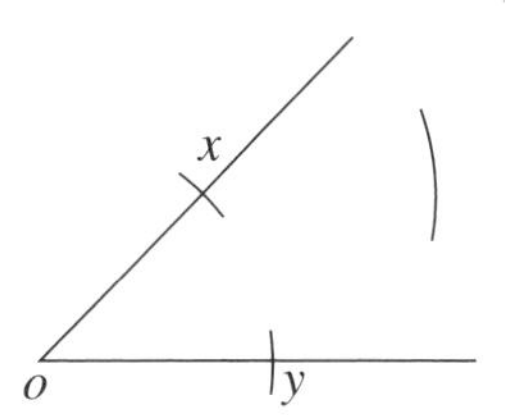

3. Place the point of your compass at y and, using the same radius, draw an arc to meet the other arc.

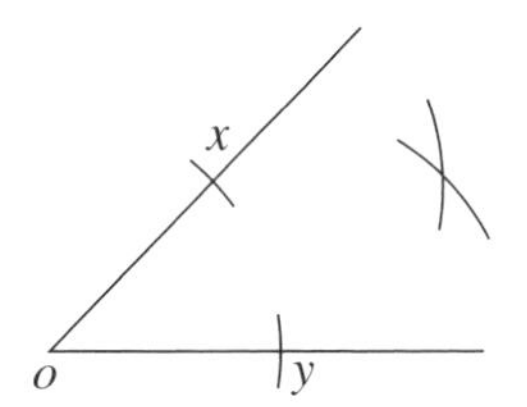

4. Draw a line through o and the point where the arcs cross. This line is the bisector of the angle.

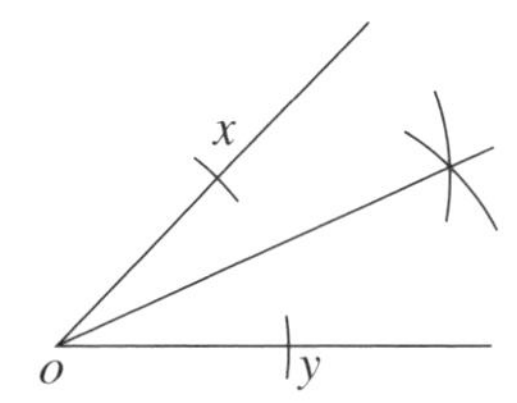

3. Divide a line segment into a given number of parts

A line segment, $[xy]$, is divided into three equal parts with the following steps:

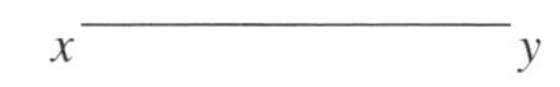

1. Draw a line through x at an acute angle to xy.

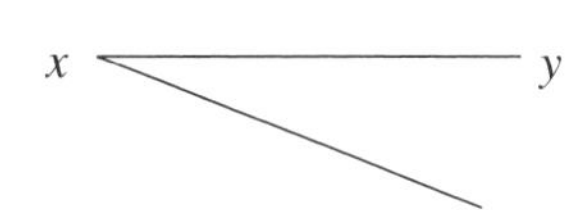

2. Using a compass, mark off three points a, b and c on this line so that $|xa| = |ab| = |bc|$.

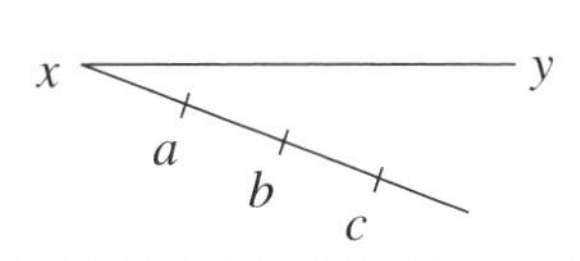

3. Join c to y.
Using a ruler and a set square, draw lines through a and b parallel to cy to meet the line segment at w and z.
z and w divide the line segment $[xy]$ into three equal parts.

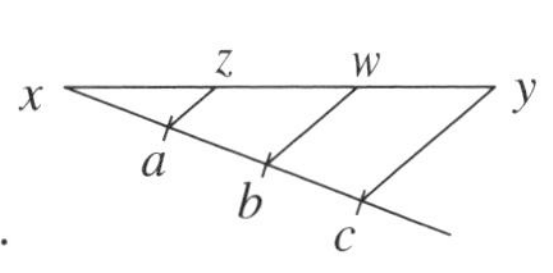

Note: This method can also be used to bisect a line segment or to divide a line segment into any number of equal parts.

4. Constructing triangles given sufficient information

The following hints are helpful when constructing triangles:

1. Draw a rough sketch first (usually freehand). Label it with the information given.
2. Use a pencil (it's easy to rub out if you make a mistake).
3. Leave all your construction lines on your final drawing (do not rub them out).
4. Draw your final diagram as accurately as possible.
5. Label your final drawing clearly.

The method used for drawing a triangle depends on the information you are given.
We will look at four cases. A triangle can be drawn if you are given:

1. The length of the three sides (SSS).
2. The length of two sides and the angle between them (SAS).
3. The length of one side and two angles (ASA).
4. A right angle, the length of the hypotenuse, and one other side (RHS).

Note: If you know two angles in a triangle it is possible to calculate the third angle. The four cases above are related to the **four cases of congruence**.

1. Given the length of three sides (SSS)

Example 1

Construct the triangle pqr so that $|pq| = 7$ cm, $|pr| = 5$ cm and $|qr| = 6$ cm.

Solution:

A rough diagram,
with the given information,
is shown on the right.

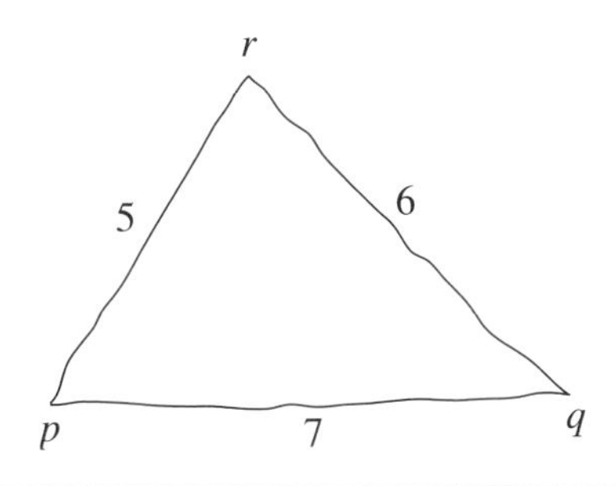

1. Using your ruler, draw a horizontal line segment 7 cm in length. Label the end points p and q.

p 7 cm q

2. Set your compass to a radius of 5 cm. Place the compass on p. Draw an arc above the line.

5 cm
p 7 cm q

3. Set your compass to a radius of 6 cm. Place the compass on q. Draw an arc above the line to meet the other arc. Label this point r.

r
6 cm
p 7 cm q

4. Using your ruler, join p to r and q to r. The triangle pqr is now drawn as required.

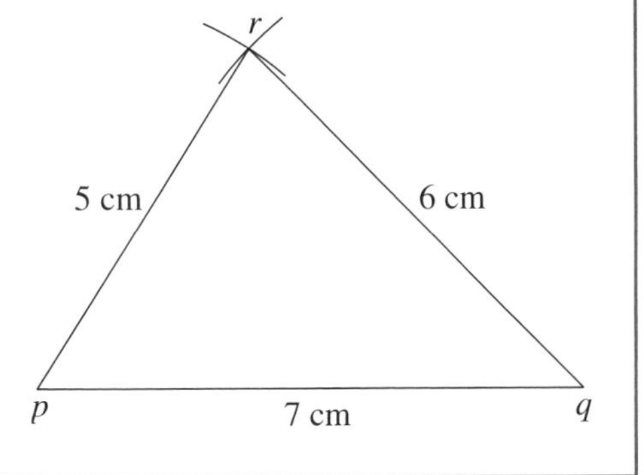

2. Given the length of two sides and the angle between them (SAS)

Example 2

Construct the triangle abc so that $|ab| = 6$ cm, $|\angle bac| = 65°$ and $|ac| = 4$ cm.

Solution:

A rough sketch,
with the given information,
is shown on the right.

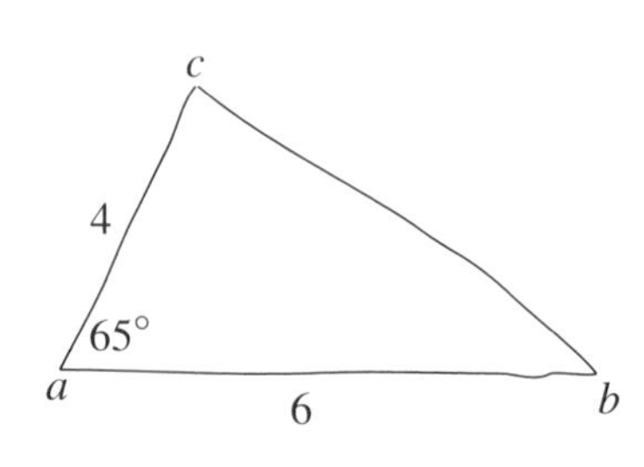

1. Using your ruler, draw a horizontal line segment 6 cm in length. Label the end points a and b.

a 6 cm b

2. Use your protractor to draw an angle of 65° at a.

65°
a b

3. Use your ruler, or compass, to mark the point c, so that $|ac| = 4$ cm.

c
4 cm
65°
a 6 cm b

4. Using your ruler join b to c. The triangle abc is now drawn as required.

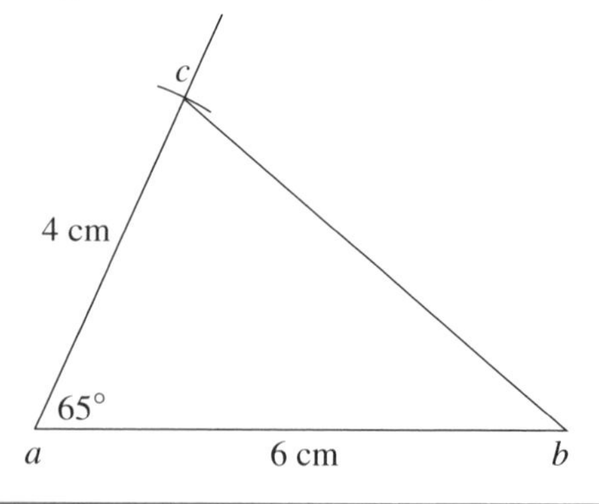

3. Given the length of one side and two angles (ASA)

Example 3

Construct a triangle xyz so that $|xy| = 6$ cm, $|\angle yxz| = 35°$ and $|\angle xyz| = 70°$.

Solution:

A rough sketch,
with the given information,
is shown on the right.

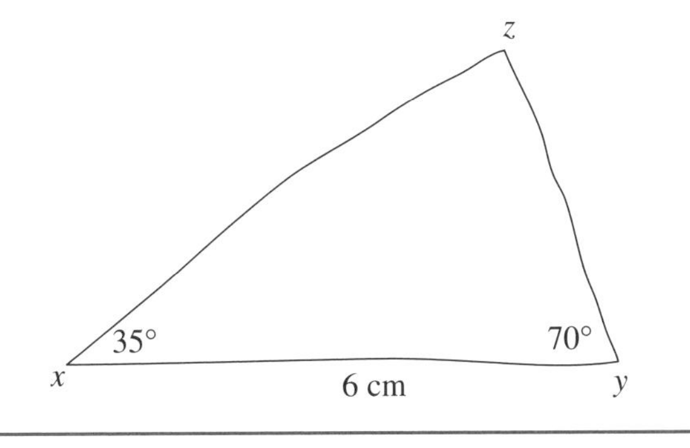

1. Using your ruler, draw a horizontal line segment 6 cm in length. Label the end points x and y.

x 6 cm y

2. Use your protractor to draw an angle of 35° at x.

35°
x 6 cm y

3. Use your protractor to draw an angle of 70° at y.

35° 70°
x 6 cm y

4. Where these two lines meet, label the point z. The triangle xyz is now drawn as required.

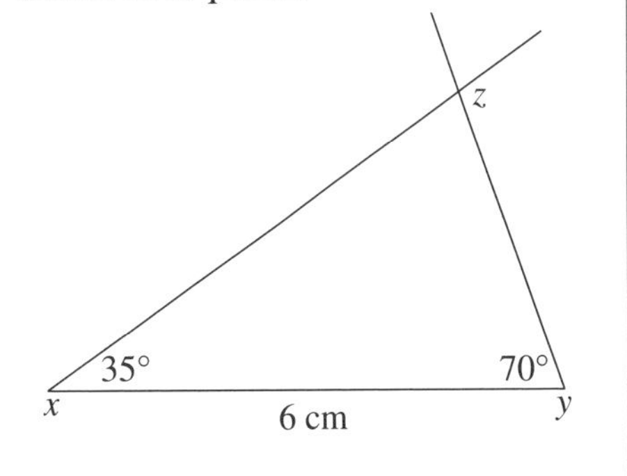

4. Given a right angle, the hypotenuse, and another side (RHS)

Example 4

Construct the triangle *abc* so that $|\angle bac| = 90°$, $|ab| = 6$ cm and $|bc| = 7$ cm.

Solution:

A rough sketch,
with the given information,
is shown on the right.

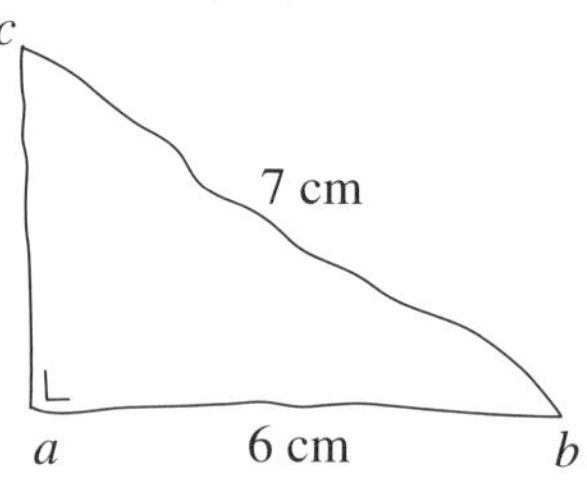

1. Using your ruler, draw a horizontal line segment 6 cm in length. Label the end points *a* and *b*.

a 6 cm *b*

2. Using your protractor or set square, draw an angle of 90° at *a*.

a 6 cm *b*

3. Set your compass to a radius of 7 cm. Place the compass point on *b*. Draw an arc to meet the vertical line. Label this point *c*.

c 7 cm *a* 6 cm *b*

4. Using your ruler, join *b* to *c*. The triangle *abc* is now drawn as required.

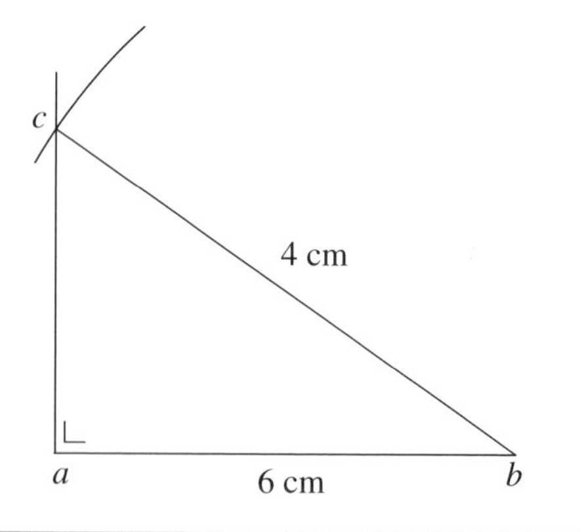

Chapter 23. CONGRUENT TRIANGLES

Congruent Triangles

Congruent means **identical**. Two triangles are said to be congruent if they are identical in every respect, i.e. they have **equal lengths of sides, equal angles, and equal areas**. In other words, they have the exact same sizes and shapes. One could be placed on top of the other so as to cover it exactly.

Conditions for congruent triangles

There are four ways to show that a pair of triangles are congruent:

1. Three sides SSS (Side-Side-Side) 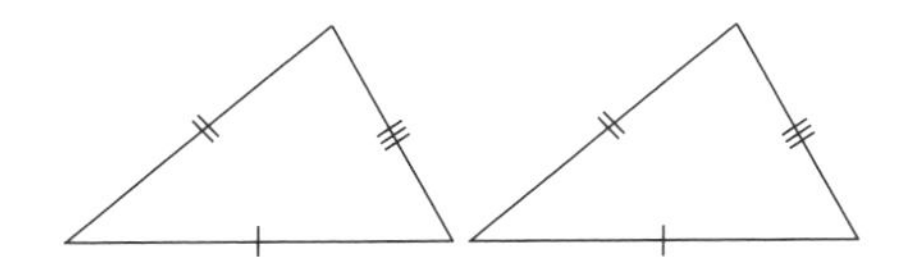	**2. Two sides and the included angle** SAS (Side-Angle-Side) 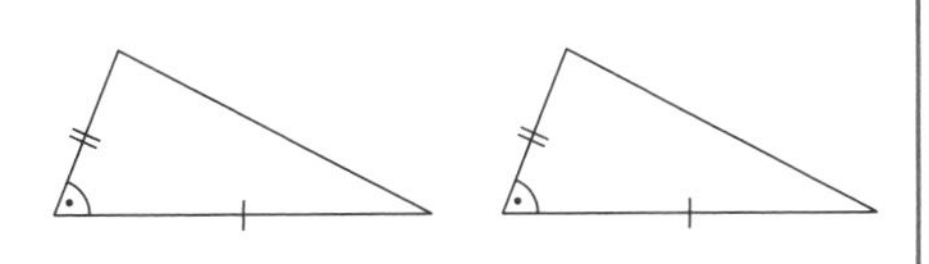
3. Two angles and a corresponding side ASA (Angle-Side-Angle) 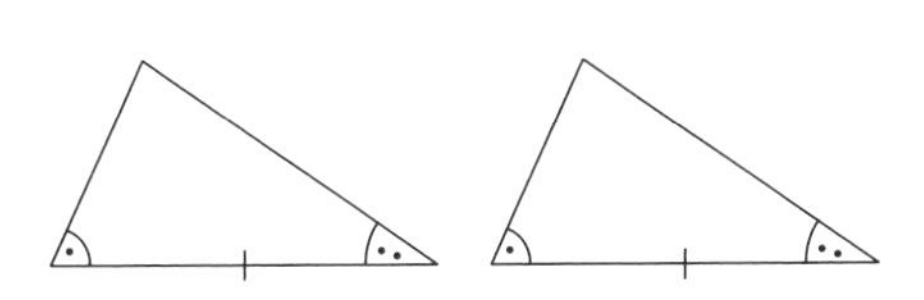	**4. Right angle, hypotenuse and one other side** RHS (Right-angle, Hypotenuse-Side) 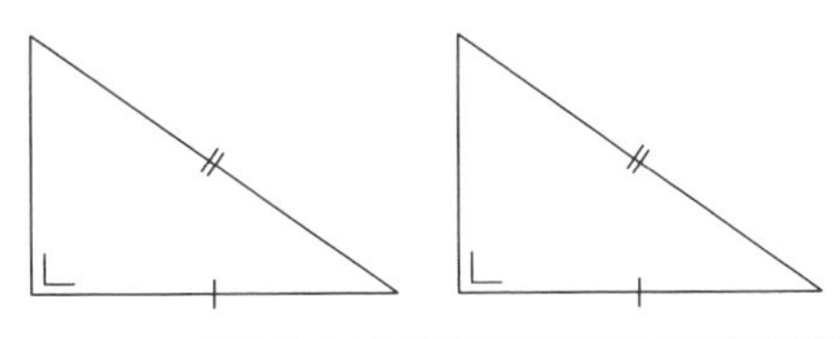

Note: Sides of equal length are indicated with the same number of dashes.
Angles of equal size are indicated with the same number of dots.

Example 1

In the diagram, $|ab| = |ac|$.

d is a point on $[bc]$,

such that $|\angle bad| = |\angle cad|$, as shown.

Prove that $\triangle bad$ and $\triangle cad$ are congruent.

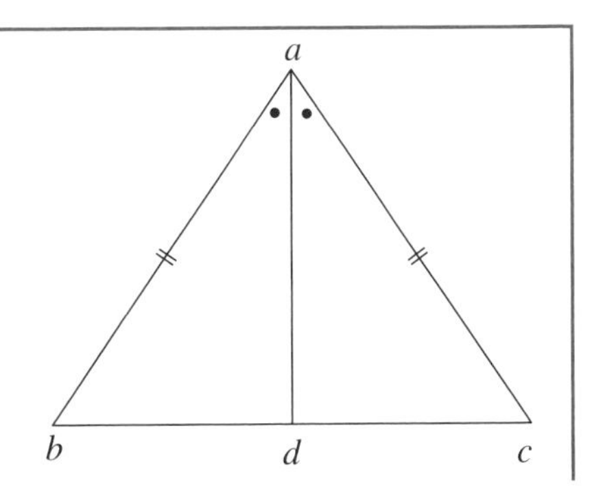

Solution:

Construction:

Redraw $\triangle bad$ and $\triangle cad$ separately.

Label angles 1 and 2.

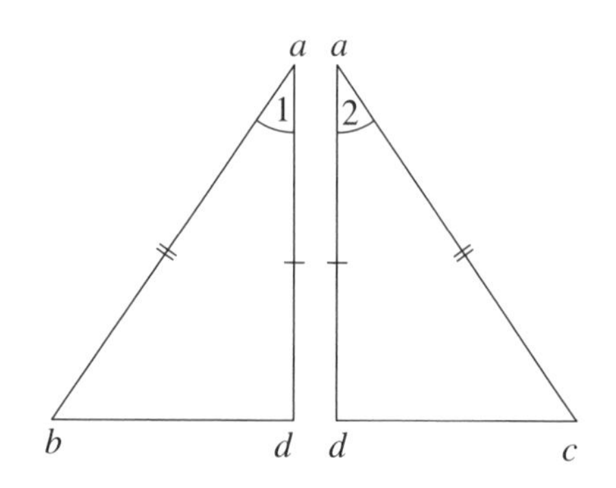

Proof:

	$\lvert ab\rvert = \lvert ac\rvert$	(given)
	$\lvert\angle 1\rvert = \lvert\angle 2\rvert$	(given)
	$\lvert ad\rvert = \lvert ad\rvert$	(common)
$\therefore$	$\triangle bad \equiv \triangle cad$	(SAS)

Note: Drawing $\triangle bad$ and $\triangle cad$ separately helps in the proof, but this is not necessary.

Example 2

pqrs is a parallelogram, with diagonals intersecting at *m*.

Prove that:

(i) $\triangle pqr$ is congruent to $\triangle rsp$

(ii) $\triangle pms$ is congruent to $\triangle rmq$.

Solution:

(i) Construction:

Redraw $\triangle pqr$ and $\triangle rsp$ separately.

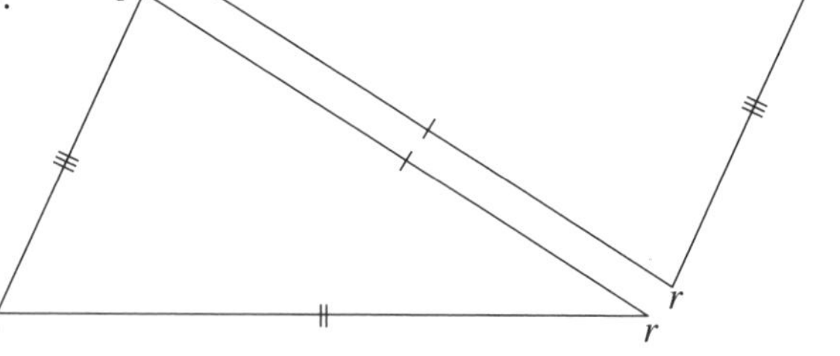

Proof:

	$\lvert pq\rvert = \lvert rs\rvert$	(opp. sides)
	$\lvert qr\rvert = \lvert sp\rvert$	(opp. sides)
	$\lvert pr\rvert = \lvert pr\rvert$	(common)
$\therefore$	$\triangle pqr \equiv \triangle rsp$	(SSS)

(ii) Construction:

Redraw $\triangle pms$ and $\triangle rmq$ separately.

Label angles 1, 2, 3 and 4.

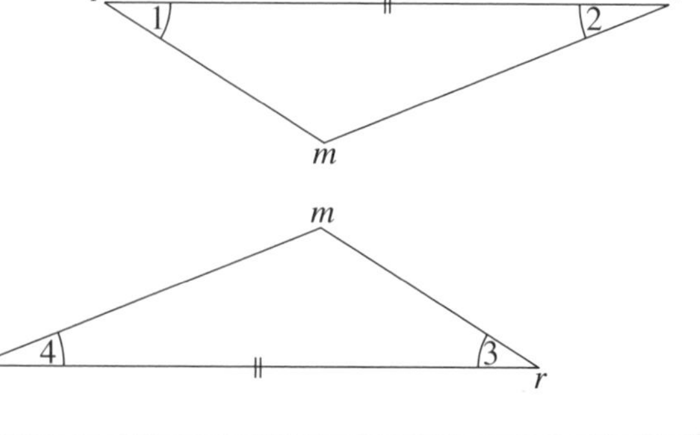

Proof:

	$\lvert\angle 1\rvert = \lvert\angle 3\rvert$	(alternate angles)
	$\lvert ps\rvert = \lvert rq\rvert$	(opp. sides)
	$\lvert\angle 2\rvert = \lvert\angle 4\rvert$	(alternate angles)
$\therefore$	$\triangle pms \equiv \triangle rmq$	(ASA)

Example 3

From a point p outside a circle, centre o, two tangents are drawn to touch the circle at q and r, as shown.

Prove that $|pq| = |pr|$.

Solution:

Construction:

Join p to o, q to o and r to o. Label angles 1 and 2.

Proof:

Consider $\triangle opq$ and $\triangle opr$.

$|\angle 1| = |\angle 2| = 90°$ as pq and pr are tangents

$|op| = |op|$ (common)

$|oq| = |or|$ (both radii)

$\therefore \triangle opq \equiv \triangle opr$ (RHS)

$\therefore |pq| = |pr|$ (corresponding sides)

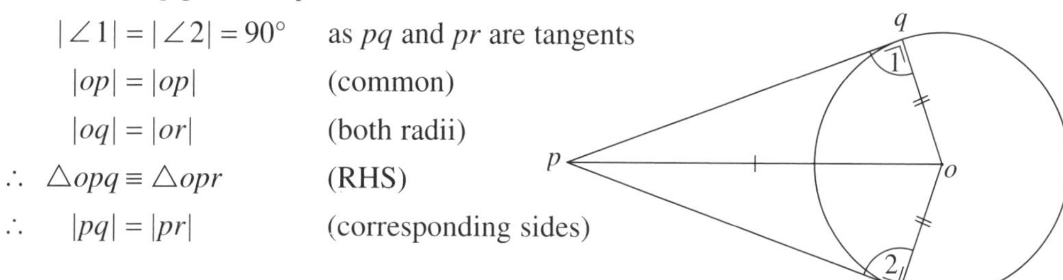

Chapter 24. COORDINATE GEOMETRY

Formulas

In all cases (x_1, y_1) and (x_2, y_2) represent points.

1. **Distance between two points**

$$\sqrt{(x_2 - x_1)^2 + (y_2 - y_1)^2}$$

2. **Midpoint of a line segment**

$$\left(\frac{x_1 + x_2}{2}, \frac{y_1 + y_2}{2}\right)$$

3. **Slope of a line, *m*, given two points**

$$m = \frac{y_2 - y_1}{x_2 - x_1}$$

4. **Equation of a line**

To find the equation of a line we need:

(i) The slope of the line, m

(ii) A point on the line (x_1, y_1)

Then use the formula:

$$(y - y_1) = m(x - x_1)$$

In short: we need the **slope** and a **point** on the line.

Note: Formulas 1 to 4 will be printed on the examination paper.

5. **Verify that a point belongs to a line**

   Substitute the coordinates of the point into the equation of the line. If the coordinates satisfy the equation, then the point is on the line. Otherwise, the point is not on the line.

6. **Point of intersection of two lines**

   Use the method of solving simultaneous equations to find the point of intersection of two lines.

7. **Graphing lines**

   To draw a line only two points are needed. The easiest points to find are where lines cut the x- and y-axes. This is known as the **intercept method**.

Note: On the x-axis, $y = 0$. On the y-axis, $x = 0$.

To draw a line, do the following:

1. Let $y = 0$ and find x.
2. Let $x = 0$ and find y.
3. Plot these two points.
4. Draw the line through these points.

8. Transformations of the plane

(i) Translation

A translation moves a point in a straight line.

(ii) Axial symmetry in the axes or central symmetry in the origin

The following three patterns emerge and it is worth memorising them:

1. Axial symmetry in the x-axis $\rightarrow$ **change the sign of y.**
2. Axial symmetry in the y-axis $\rightarrow$ **change the sign of x.**
3. Central symmetry in the origin, (0, 0) $\rightarrow$ **change the sign of both x and y.**

Alternatively, plot the point on the coordinated plane and use your knowledge of axial symmetry and central symmetry to find the image.

Example 1

Write down the coordinates of the points:

a, b, c, d, e, f.

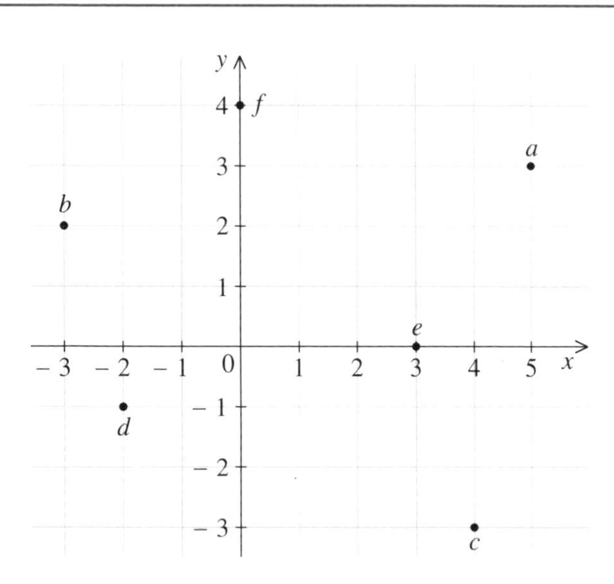

Solution:

$a(5, 3)$ $\quad$ $b(-3, 2)$ $\quad$ $c(4, -3)$ $\quad$ $d(-2, -1)$ $\quad$ $e(3, 0)$ $\quad$ $f(0, 4)$

Example 2

Plot the points $a(1, 2)$, $b(-3, -2)$, $c(4, -1)$, $d(-2, 4)$, $e(-1, 0)$, $f(0, -3)$.

Solution:

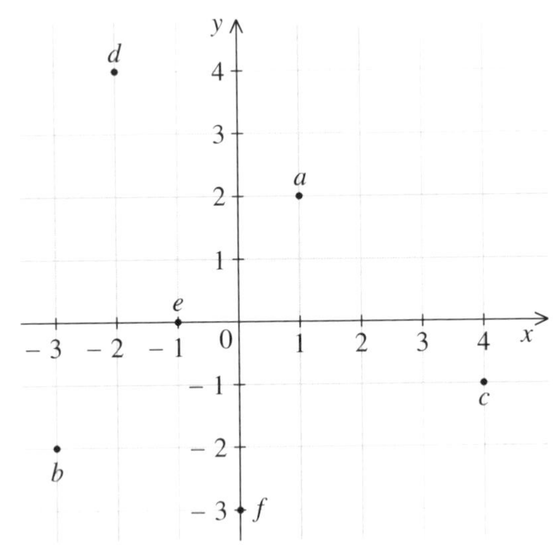

Example 3

(i) The line L has a slope of 4 and contains the point $(1, -3)$. Find the equation of L.

(ii) The line M has slope $-\frac{2}{3}$ and contains the point $(-4, 2)$. Find the equation of M.

(i) Line L: Slope $= 4$ and contains the point $(1, -3)$:

$m = 4, \quad x_1 = 1, \quad y_1 = -3$

$$(y - y_1) = m(x - x_1)$$
$$(y + 3) = 4(x - 1)$$
$$y + 3 = 4x - 4$$
$$-4x + y + 3 + 4 = 0$$
$$-4x + y + 7 = 0$$
$$4x - y - 7 = 0$$

(ii) Line M: Slope $= -\frac{2}{3}$ and contains the point $(-4, 2)$:

$m = -\frac{2}{3}, \quad x_1 = -4, \quad y_1 = 2$

$$(y - y_1) = m(x - x_1)$$
$$(y - 2) = -\frac{2}{3}(x + 4)$$
$$3(y - 2) = -2(x + 4)$$

(multiply both sides by 3)

$$3y - 6 = -2x - 8$$
$$2x + 3y - 6 + 8 = 0$$
$$2x + 3y + 2 = 0$$

Example 4

$a(3, 7)$ and $b(5, 1)$ are two points.

Find:

(i) the midpoint of $[ab]$

(ii) $|ab|$

(iii) the slope of ab

(iv) the equation of ab.

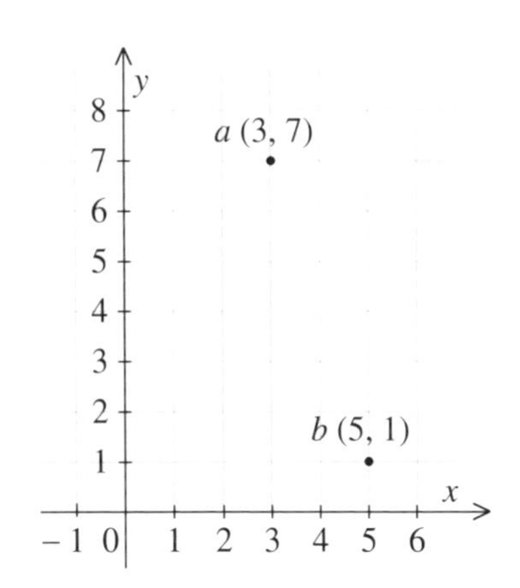

Solution:

(i) midpoint of [*ab*]

$a(3, 7) \qquad b(5, 1)$

$(x_1, y_1) \qquad (x_2, y_2)$

$$\text{midpoint} = \left(\frac{x_1 + x_2}{2}, \frac{y_1 + y_2}{2}\right)$$

$$= \left(\frac{3+5}{2}, \frac{7+1}{2}\right)$$

$$= \left(\frac{8}{2}, \frac{8}{2}\right)$$

$$= (4, 4)$$

(ii) |*ab*|

$a(3, 7) \qquad b(5, 1)$

$(x_1, y_1) \qquad (x_2, y_2)$

$$|ab| = \sqrt{(x_2 - x_1)^2 + (y_2 - y_1)^2}$$

$$= \sqrt{(5-3)^2 + (1-7)^2}$$

$$= \sqrt{(2)^2 + (-6)^2}$$

$$= \sqrt{4 + 36}$$

$$= \sqrt{40}$$

(iii) slope of *ab*

$a(3, 7) \qquad b(5, 1)$

$(x_1, y_1) \qquad (x_2, y_2)$

$$\text{slope} = m = \frac{y_2 - y_1}{x_2 - x_1}$$

$$= \frac{1-7}{5-3}$$

$$= \frac{-6}{2}$$

$$= -3$$

(iv) equation of *ab*

containing $a(3, 7)$ with slope -3

$x_1 = 3, \quad y_1 = 7, \quad m = -3$

$$(y - y_1) = m(x - x_1)$$

$$(y - 7) = -3(x - 3)$$

$$y - 7 = -3x + 9$$

$$3x + y - 7 - 9 = 0$$

$$3x + y - 16 = 0$$

Example 5

$a(-2, 1)$ and $c(6, 5)$ are two points.

(i) Find the coordinates of b, the midpoint of the line segment $[ac]$.

(ii) Verify that $|ab| = |bc|$.

(iii) Find the equation of the line ac.

Solution:

(i) **Midpoint of the line segment [*ac*]**

$a(-2, 1)$ $\quad$ $c(6, 5)$

(x_1, y_1) $\quad$ (x_2, y_2)

$$\text{Midpoint} = \left(\frac{x_1 + x_2}{2}, \frac{y_1 + y_2}{2}\right)$$

$$= \left(\frac{-2 + 6}{2}, \frac{1 + 5}{2}\right)$$

$$= \left(\frac{4}{2}, \frac{6}{2}\right)$$

$$= (2, 3)$$

Thus, the coordinates of b are $(2, 3)$.

$c(6, 5)$

$b(2, 3)$

$a(-2, 1)$

(ii) $|\boldsymbol{ab}|$

$a(-2, 1)$ $\quad$ $b(2, 3)$

(x_1, y_1) $\quad$ (x_2, y_2)

$$|ab| = \sqrt{(x_2 - x_1)^2 + (y_2 - y_1)^2}$$

$$= \sqrt{(2 + 2)^2 + (3 - 1)^2}$$

$$= \sqrt{(4)^2 + (2)^2}$$

$$= \sqrt{16 + 4}$$

$$= \sqrt{20}$$

$|\boldsymbol{bc}|$

$b(2, 3)$ $\quad$ $c(6, 5)$

(x_1, y_1) $\quad$ (x_2, y_2)

$$|bc| = \sqrt{(x_2 - x_1)^2 + (y_2 - y_1)^2}$$

$$= \sqrt{(6 - 2)^2 + (5 - 3)^2}$$

$$= \sqrt{(4)^2 + (2)^2}$$

$$= \sqrt{16 + 4}$$

$$= \sqrt{20}$$

Therefore, $|ab| = |bc|$, as both are equal to $\sqrt{20}$.

(iii) Equation of the line *ac*

The slope is missing.

We first find the slope and use **either** point to find the equation.

$a(-2, 1)$ $\quad$ $c(6, 5)$

(x_1, y_1) $\quad$ (x_2, y_2)

$$\text{Slope} = m = \frac{y_2 - y_1}{x_2 - x_1}$$

$$= \frac{5-1}{6+2}$$

$$= \frac{4}{8}$$

$$= \frac{1}{2}$$

Therefore, the slope of ac is $\frac{1}{2}$.

Equation of *ac*

Slope $= \frac{1}{2}$ containing the point $a(-2, 1)$

$m = \frac{1}{2}$, $\quad x_1 = -2$, $\quad y_1 = -1$

$$(y - y_1) = m(x - x_1)$$

$$(y - 1) = \tfrac{1}{2}(x + 2)$$

$$2(y - 1) = 1(x + 2)$$

(multiply both sides by 2)

$$2y - 2 = x + 2$$

$$-x + 2y - 2 - 2 = 0$$

$$-x + 2y - 4 = 0$$

$$x - 2y + 4 = 0$$

Example 6

L is the line $2x + 3y - 10 = 0$.

(i) Show that the point $(8, -2)$ is on the line L.

(ii) L cuts the x-axis at the point c. Find the coordinates of the point c.

Solution:

(i) $(8, -2)$

$2x + 3y - 10 = 0$

Substitute $x = 8$ and $y = -2$

$2(8) + 3(-2) - 10$

$= 16 - 6 - 10$

$= 16 - 16$

$= 0$

Satisfies the equation;

therefore, $(8, -2)$ is on the line L.

(ii) On the x-axis, $y = 0$

Therefore, let $y = 0$

$$2x + 3y - 10 = 0$$

$$2x + 3(0) - 10 = 0$$

$$2x + 0 - 10 = 0$$

$$2x - 10 = 0$$

$$2x = 10$$

$$x = 5$$

When $y = 0$, $\quad x = 5$;

therefore, the line L cuts the x-axis at the point $c(5, 0)$.

Example 7

(i) The point $(k, 1)$ is on the line $5x + 3y - 13 = 0$. Calculate the value of k.

(ii) The point $(3, h)$ is on the line $2x - 3y + 6 = 0$. Find the value of h.

Solution:

(i) $(k, 1)$

$$5x + 3y - 13 = 0$$

$$5(k) + 3(1) - 13 = 0$$

(put in $x = k$ and $y = 1$)

$$5k + 3 - 13 = 0$$

$$5k - 10 = 0$$

$$5k = 10$$

$$k = 2$$

(ii) $(3, h)$

$$2x - 3y + 6 = 0$$

$$2(3) - 3(h) + 6 = 0$$

(put in $x = 3$ and $y = h$)

$$6 - 3h + 6 = 0$$

$$-3h + 12 = 0$$

$$-3h = -12$$

$$3h = 12$$

$$h = 4$$

Example 8

The line $3x + 2y + a = 0$ contains the point $(-1, -3)$. Find the value of a.

Solution:

$(-1, -3)$

$$3x + 2y + a = 0$$

$$3(-1) + 2(-3) + a = 0$$

(put in $x = -1$ and $y = -3$)

$$-3 - 6 + a = 0$$

$$a - 9 = 0$$

$$a = 9$$

Example 9

L is the line $3x - 4y + 12 = 0$.

L cuts the x-axis at p and the y-axis at q.

(i) Find the coordinates of p and the coordinates of q.

(ii) Draw the graph of L.

(iii) Find the area of the triangle opq, where o is the origin.

Solution:

(i) On the x-axis, $y = 0$.

On the y-axis, $x = 0$.

$3x - 4y = -12$

$y = 0$	$x = 0$
$3x = -12$	$-4y = -12$
$x = -4$	$4y = 12$
$p(-4, 0)$	$y = 3$
	$q(0, 3)$

The coordinates of p are $(-4, 0)$.

The coordinates of q are $(0, 3)$.

(ii) Plot the points $p(-4, 0)$ and $q(0, 3)$ and draw a line through these points.

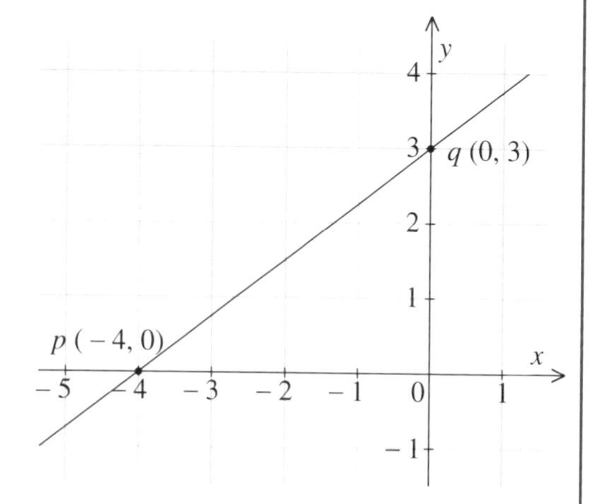

(iii) Area of triangle opq

$= \frac{1}{2}$ (base)(perpendicular height)

$= \frac{1}{2} \times |op| \times |oq|$

$= \frac{1}{2} \times 4 \times 3$

$= 6$

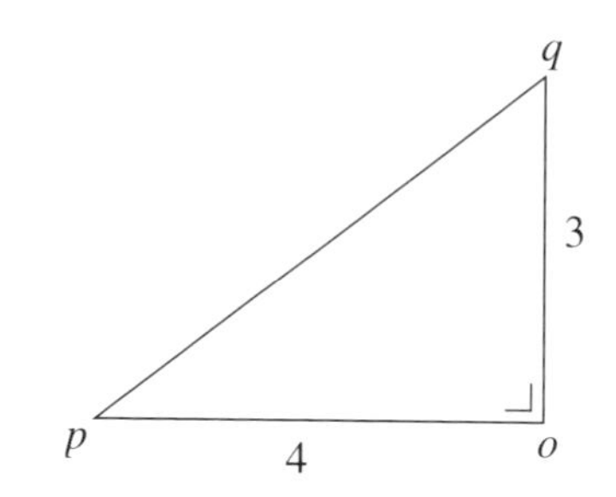

Example 10

$a(-1, 1)$ and $b(4, -2)$ are two points.

Find the image of the point $(-2, 4)$ under the translation $\overrightarrow{ab}$.

Solution:

Under the translation $\overrightarrow{ab}$: $(-1, 1) \rightarrow (4, -2)$

Rule: 'add 5 to x, subtract 3 from y'

1. **Mathematical Method:** (apply the rule directly)

   $(-2, 4) \rightarrow (-2+5, 4-3) = (3, 1)$

   Therefore the image of $(-2, 4)$ is $(3, 1)$.

2. **Graphical Method:**

   Plot the point $(-2, 4)$ on the coordinated plane.

   Split the move into two parts:

   - horizontal move: five steps to the right (add 5 to x)
   - vertical move: three steps down (subtract 3 from y).

   Therefore the image of $(-2, 4)$ is $(3, 1)$.

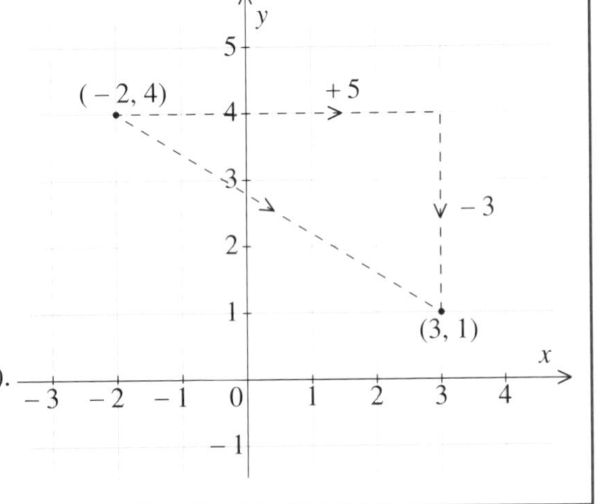

Example 11

Find the image of (3, 4) under:

(i) S_x, axial symmetry in the x-axis

(ii) S_y, axial symmetry in the y-axis

(iii) S_o, central symmetry in the origin, (0, 0).

Solution:

1. Mathematical Method:

(i) $S_x(3, 4) = (3, -4)$ (change the sign of y)

(ii) $S_y(3, 4) = (-3, 4)$ (change the sign of x)

(iii) $S_o(3, 4) = (-3, -4)$ (change the sign of both x and y)

2. Graphical Method:

From the graph it can be seen that:

(i) $S_x(3, 4) = (3, -4)$

(ii) $S_y(3, 4) = (-3, 4)$

(iii) $S_o(3, 4) = (-3, -4)$

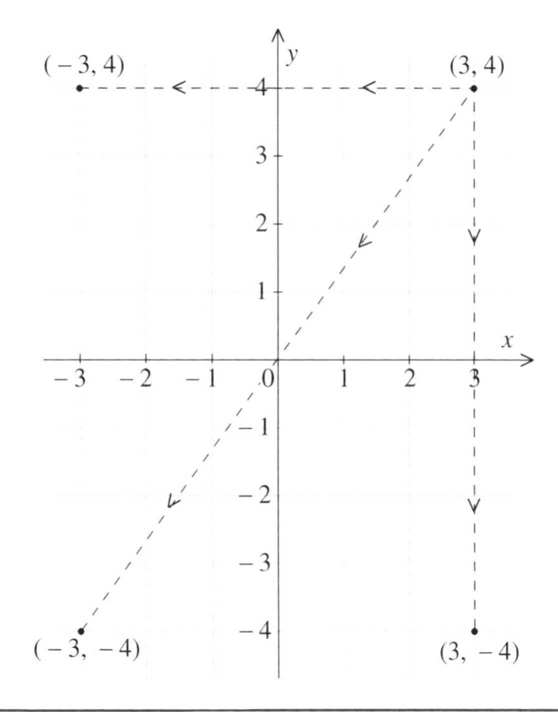

Example 12

L: $x + 2y = 4$ and K: $x + y = 3$ are the equations of two lines.

(i) Draw the graph of L and K on the one diagram.

(ii) From the graph write down the point of intersection of L and K.

(iii) Solve algebraically the simultaneous equations:

$$x + 2y = 4$$
$$x + y = 3$$

and verify your answer to part **(ii)**.

Solution:

(i) $x + 2y = 4$

$y = 0$	$x = 0$
$x = 4$	$2y = 4$
(4, 0)	$y = 2$
	(0, 2)

Draw a line through these points.

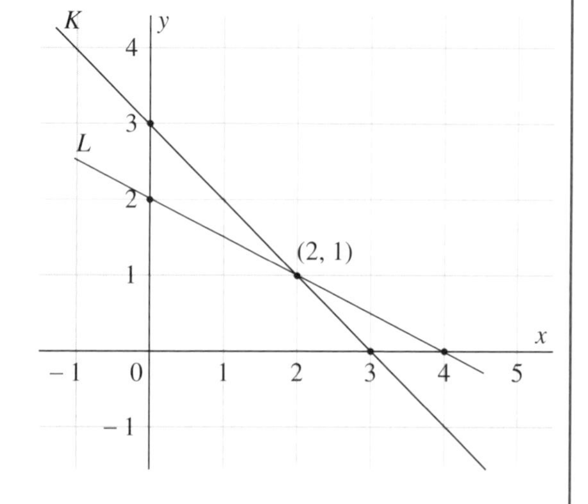

$x + y = 3$

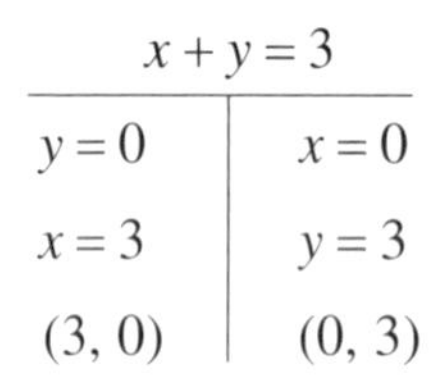

$y = 0$	$x = 0$
$x = 3$	$y = 3$
(3, 0)	(0, 3)

Draw a line through these points.

(ii) From the graph, the point of intersection is (2, 1).

(iii) Label the equations ① and ②.

$$x + 2y = 4 \quad ①$$
$$x + y = 3 \quad ②$$

Make the coefficients of y the same, but of opposite sign.

$$x + 2y = 4 \quad ①$$

Leave ① unchanged, multiply ② by – 1.

$$-x - y = -3 \quad ② \times -1$$

Add these new equations.

$$y = 1$$

Put $y = 1$ into ① or ②

$$x + y = 3 \quad ②$$
$$\downarrow$$
$$x + 1 = 3$$
$$x = 2$$

Therefore the point of intersection of L and K is (2, 1), the same answer as in part **(ii)**.

Chapter 25. TRIGONOMETRY

Trigonometry

1. Trigonometry ratios

Consider the right-angled triangle below with the acute angle P:

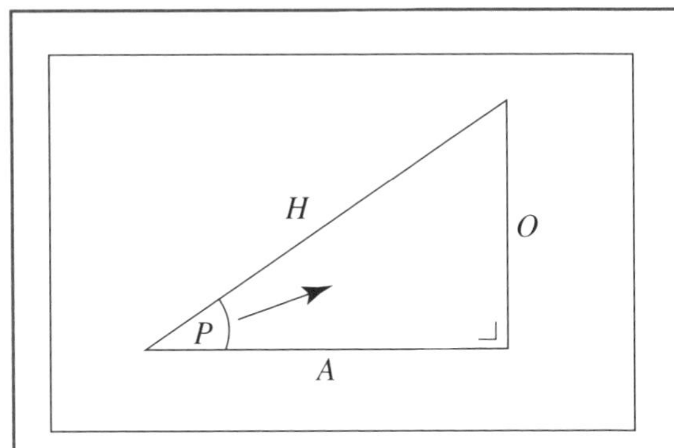

Ratios

$$\sin P = \frac{\text{opposite}}{\text{hypotenuse}} = \frac{O}{H}$$

$$\cos P = \frac{\text{adjacent}}{\text{hypotenuse}} = \frac{A}{H}$$

$$\tan P = \frac{\text{opposite}}{\text{adjacent}} = \frac{O}{A}$$

Memory Aid: Oh, hell, another hour of algebra, sin, cos, and tan.
Each trigonometric ratio links two sides and an angle in a right-angled triangle.

We can write trigonometric ratios for the two acute angles in a right-angled triangle. Make sure you know which angle you are using and which sides are the opposite and adjacent (the hypotenuse is always opposite the right angle). A good idea is to draw an arrow for the angle under consideration to indicate the opposite side to the angle.

2. Angles of elevation, depression

Angle of elevation
If the object is above the level of the observer, the angle between the horizontal and the observer's line of vision is called the **angle of elevation** (upwards from the horizontal).

object
line of vision
observer's eye
$A°$
horizontal

$A°$ = angle of elevation of object

Angle of depression
If the object is below the level of the observer, the angle between the horizontal and the observer's line of vision is called the **angle of depression** (downwards from the horizontal).

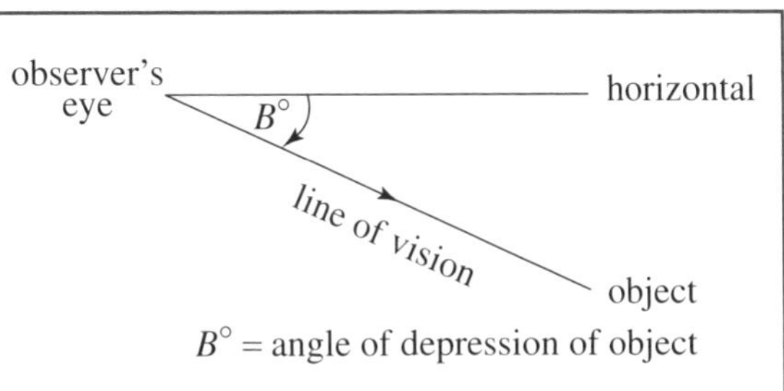

$B°$ = angle of depression of object

Calculating Angles and Lengths of Sides in Right-angled Triangles

Example 1

The right-angled triangle *abc* has measurements as shown.

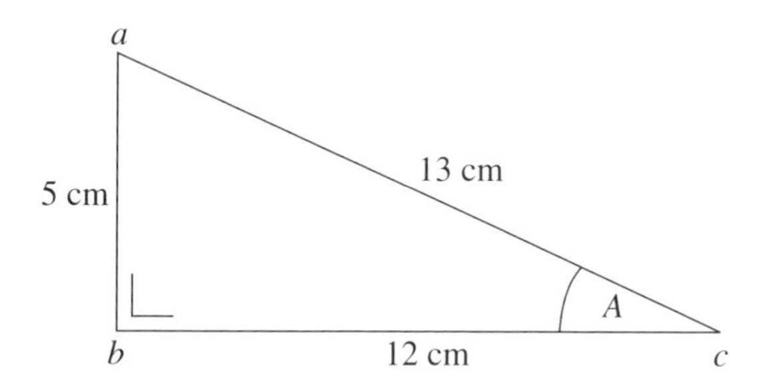

(i) Write down the length of the hypotenuse.

(ii) Write down the length of the side opposite the angle A.

(iii) Write down the length of the side adjacent to the angle A.

(iv) Write down, as fractions, the value of $\sin A$, $\cos A$ and $\tan A$.

(v) Calculate, correct to one decimal place, the angle A.

Solution:

(i) The hypotenuse $[ac]$ is the longest side. Therefore, the length of the hypotenuse $= |ac| = 13$ cm.

(ii) Draw an arrow from the angle A. The arrow points to the side, $[ab]$, which is opposite the angle A. Therefore, the length of the side opposite angle $A = |ab| = 5$ cm.

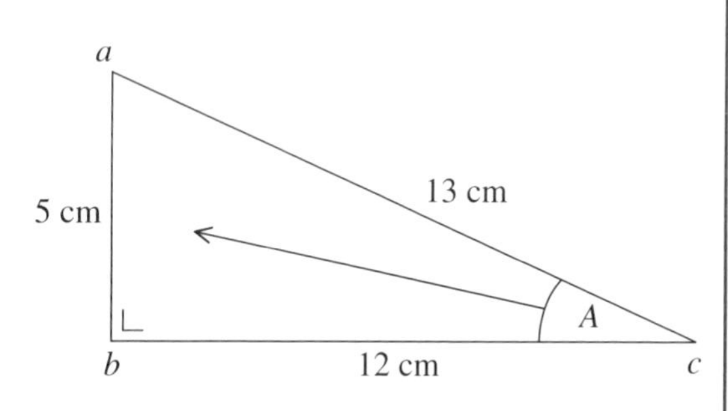

(iii) The remaining side, $[bc]$, is called the side adjacent to the angle A. Therefore, the length of the side adjacent to the angle $A = |bc| = 12$ cm.

(iv) $\sin A = \dfrac{\text{opposite}}{\text{hypotenuse}}$ $\qquad$ $\cos A = \dfrac{\text{adjacent}}{\text{hypotenuse}}$ $\qquad$ $\tan A = \dfrac{\text{opposite}}{\text{adjacent}}$

$\sin A = \dfrac{5}{13}$ $\qquad$ $\cos A = \dfrac{12}{13}$ $\qquad$ $\tan A = \dfrac{5}{12}$

(v) As we know the lengths of the three sides we can use the sin ratio, cos ratio or tan ratio to find the value of the angle A.

Using the tan ratio:

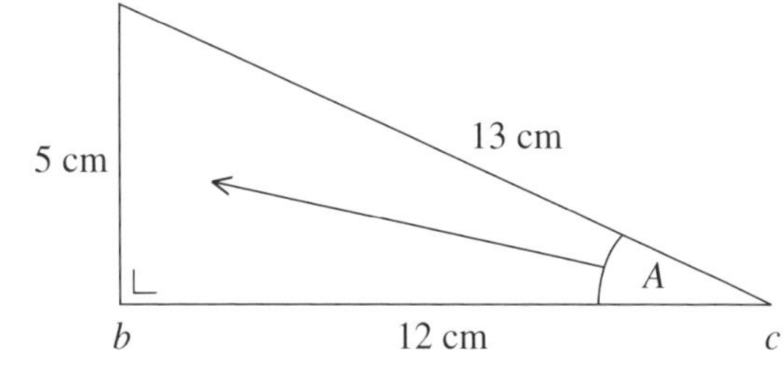

$$\tan A = \frac{5}{12}$$

$$A = \tan^{-1}\left(\frac{5}{12}\right)$$

$$A = 22.61986495^\circ$$ (2nd tan (5 ÷ 12) =)

$$A = 22.6^\circ$$ (correct to one decimal place)

Note: $\sin^{-1}\left(\frac{5}{13}\right)$ and $\cos^{-1}\left(\frac{12}{13}\right)$ would give the same value for angle A.

Example 2

In the triangle abc, $|ac| = 8$, $|bc| = 15$ and $ac \perp bc$.
Find the value of:

(i) $|ab|$ **(ii)** $\sin A$ **(iii)** $\cos A$ **(iv)** $\tan A$.

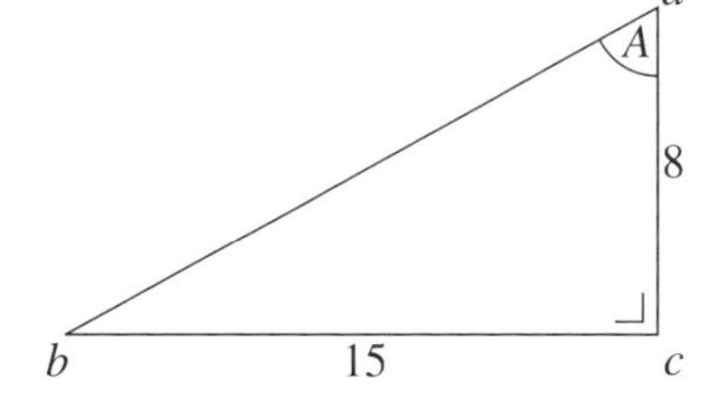

Solution:

(i) Using Pythagoras's theorem:

$$|ab|^2 = |ac|^2 + |bc|^2$$

$$|ab|^2 = 8^2 + 15^2$$

$$|ab|^2 = 64 + 225$$

$$|ab|^2 = 289$$

$$|ab| = \sqrt{289} = 17$$

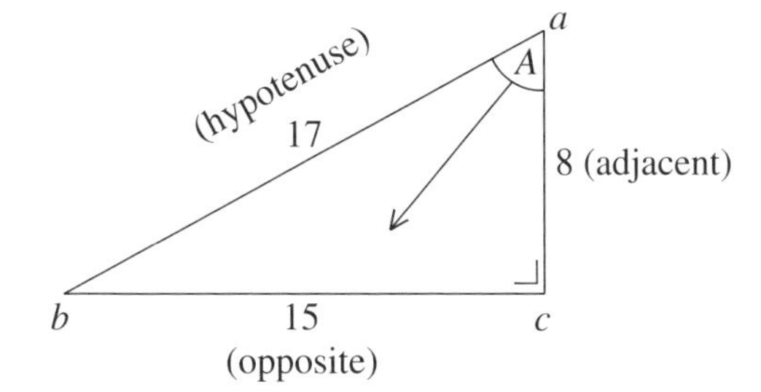

(ii) $\sin A = \frac{\text{opposite}}{\text{hypotenuse}}$

$\sin A = \frac{15}{17}$

(iii) $\cos A = \frac{\text{adjacent}}{\text{hypotenuse}}$

$\cos A = \frac{8}{17}$

(iv) $\tan A = \frac{\text{opposite}}{\text{adjacent}}$

$\tan A = \frac{15}{8}$

Example 3

In the right-angled triangle pqr,
$|pq| = 10$ and $|qr| = 3$.

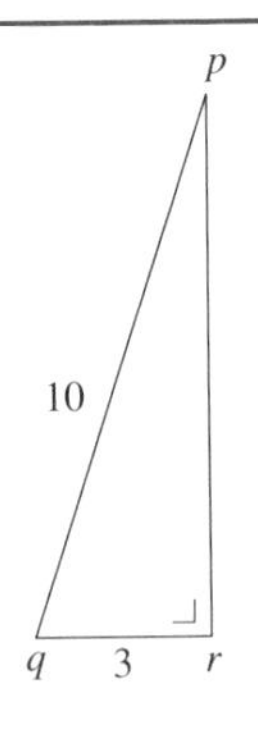

(i) Find the value of $\cos \angle pqr$.

(ii) Hence find the measure of $\angle pqr$, correct to the nearest degree.

Solution:

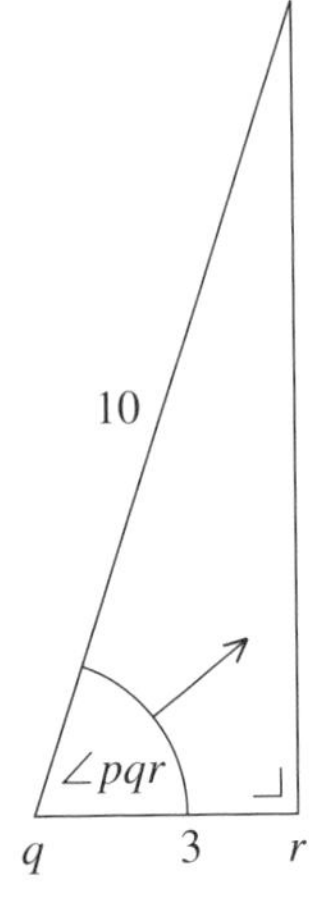

(i)

$$\cos \angle pqr = \frac{\text{adjacent}}{\text{hypotenuse}}$$

$$\cos \angle pqr = \frac{3}{10}$$

(ii)

$$|\angle pqr| = \cos^{-1}\left(\frac{3}{10}\right)$$

$$|\angle pqr| = 72.54239688$$

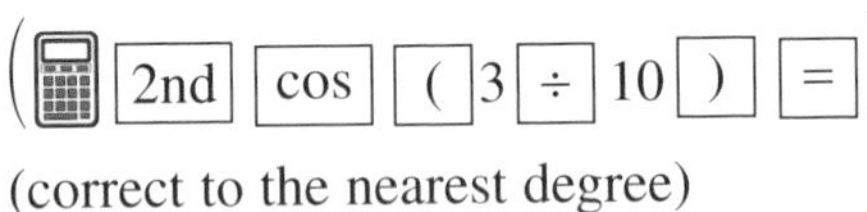

$$|\angle pqr| = 73^\circ$$

(correct to the nearest degree)

Example 4

In the right-angled triangle abc,
$|ab| = 23$ and $|bc| = 15$.
Calculate A, correct to the nearest degree.

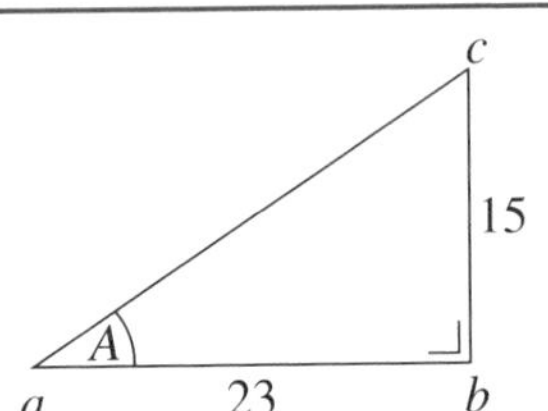

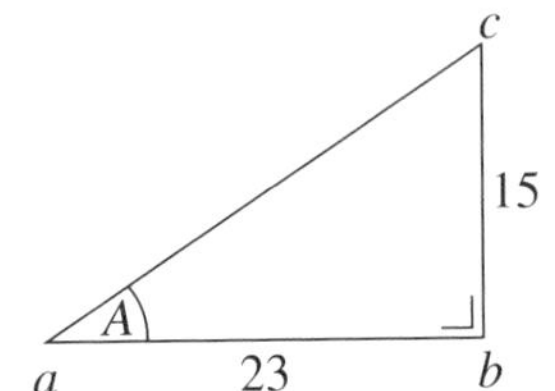

Solution:

For angle A,
we know the opposite and the adjacent,
therefore use the tan ratio:

$$\tan A = \frac{\text{opposite}}{\text{adjacent}}$$

$$\tan A = \frac{15}{23}$$

$$A = \tan^{-1}\left(\frac{15}{23}\right)$$

$$A = 33.11134196^\circ$$

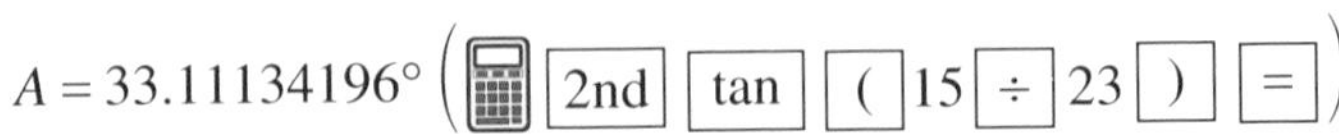

$$A = 33^\circ$$

(correct to the nearest degree)

Example 5

In the right-angled triangle pqr,

$|pq| = 7.8$ and $|\angle pqr| = 51°$.

Calculate $|qr|$, correct to one decimal place.

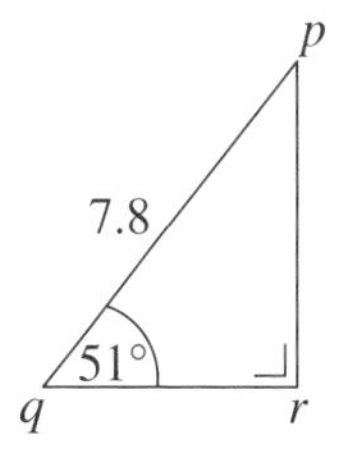

Solution:

We know the hypotenuse, and require the length of the side adjacent to the angle 51°.

Therefore use the cos ratio:

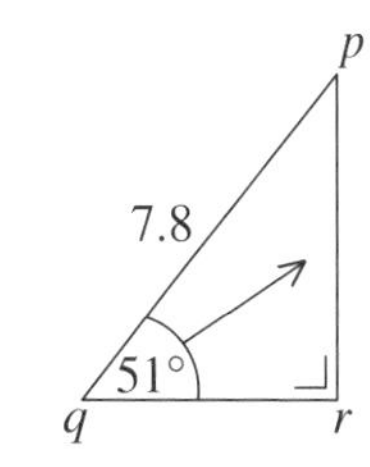

$$\cos \angle pqr = \frac{\text{adjacent}}{\text{hypotenuse}}$$

$$\cos 51° = \frac{|qr|}{7.8}$$

$7.8 \cos 51° = |qr|$ (multiply both sides by 7.8)

$4.90869905 = |qr|$

$4.9 = |qr|$ (correct to one decimal place)

Practical Applications

Example 1

A vertical building is 8 m high. It casts a shadow three times its height on horizontal ground.

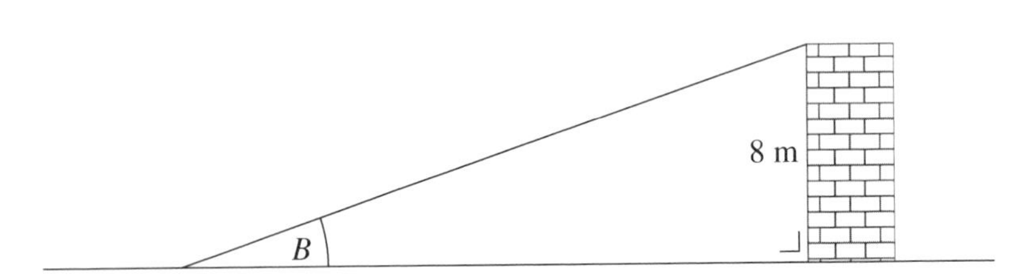

(i) Write down the length of the shadow.

(ii) Find B, the angle of elevation of the sun, correct to the nearest degree.

Solution:

(i) Length of the shadow = 3 times height of building

$$= 3 \times 8 \text{ m}$$

$$= 24 \text{ m}$$

(ii) Represent the situation with a right-angled triangle.

We know the opposite and the adjacent.

Therefore, use the tan ratio:

$$\tan B = \frac{\text{opposite}}{\text{adjacent}}$$

$$\tan B = \frac{8}{24}$$

$$\tan B = \frac{1}{3}$$

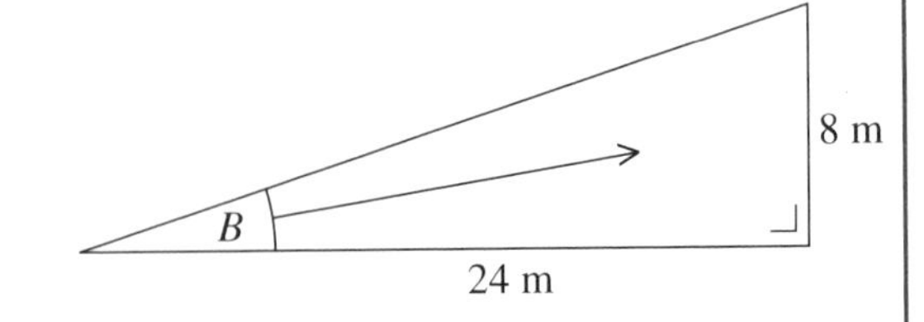

$$B = \tan^{-1}\left(\frac{1}{3}\right)$$

$B = 18.43494882°$

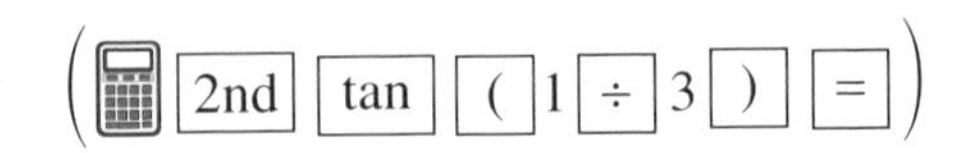

$B = 18°$ (correct to the nearest degree)

Example 2

Ciara wished to measure the width of a river.

She was at a on the riverbank, directly opposite b on the other bank.

Ciara walked from a to c, along the riverbank, at an average speed on 1.5m/s.

It took Ciara 30 seconds to reach c.

She then measured $\angle acb$ and found it to be 25°.

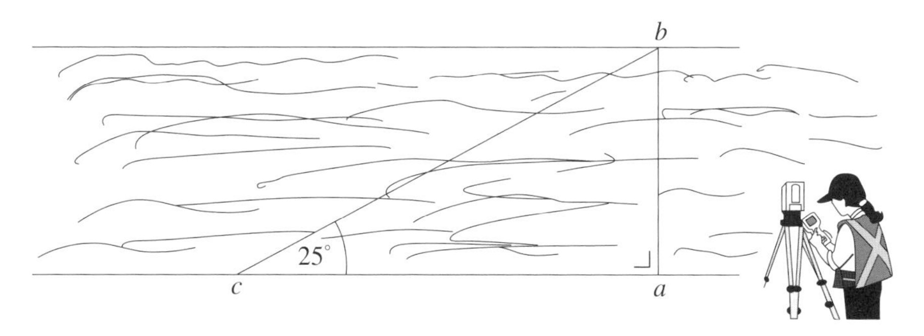

(i) Calculate $|ac|$, the distance walked by Ciara.

(ii) Hence, calculate $|ab|$, the width of the river.

Give your answer correct to the nearest metre.

Solution:

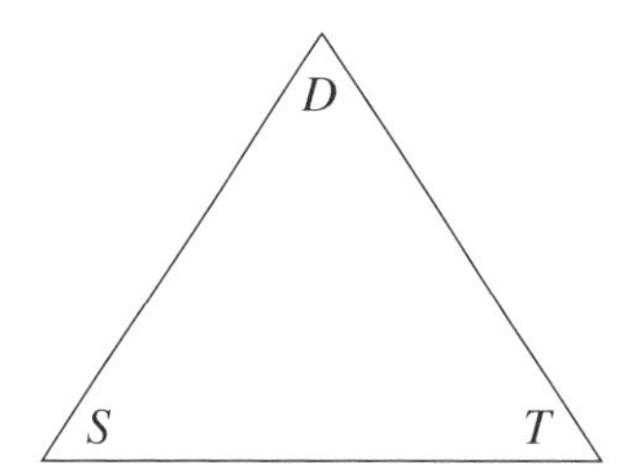

(i) $|ac|$

Speed = 1.5 m/s Time = 30 seconds

Distance = Speed × Time

$= 1.5 \times 30$

$= 45$

$\therefore \quad |ac| = 45$ m

(ii) Calculate $|ab|$, the width of the river.

Represent the situation with a right-angled triangle.

Let w m = the width of the river.

We know the adjacent and need to find the opposite.

Therefore, use the tan ratio:

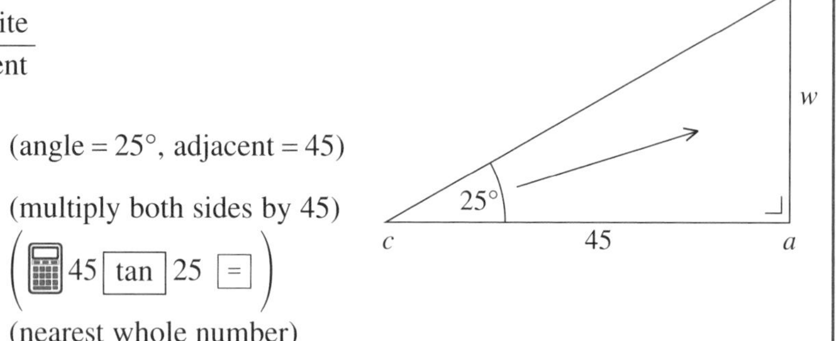

$$\tan A = \frac{\text{opposite}}{\text{adjacent}}$$

$\tan 25° = \dfrac{w}{45}$ (angle = 25°, adjacent = 45)

$45 \tan 25° = w$ (multiply both sides by 45)

$20.98384462 = w$

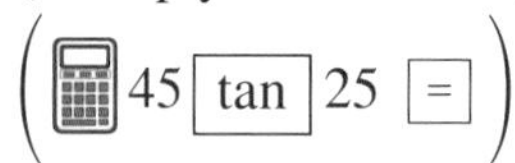

$21 = w$ (nearest whole number)

Thus, the width of the river = 21 m (correct to the nearest metre).

Example 3

$[ad]$ is a vertical mast standing on level ground. Wires join a to the ground at b and at c, as in the diagram.

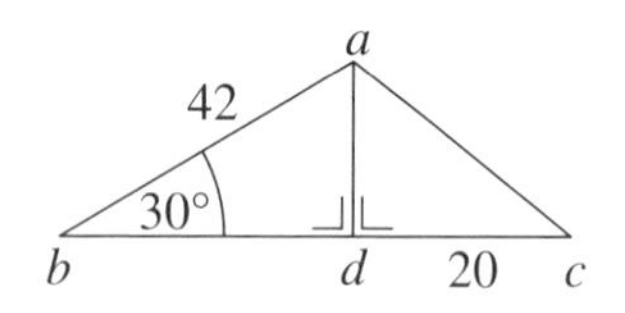

Given that $|ab| = 42$ m, $|dc| = 20$ m and $|\angle abd| = 30°$, calculate:

(i) $|ad|$ **(ii)** $|ac|$

(iii) $|\angle acd|$, correct to the nearest degree.

Solution:

It helps to redraw the right-angled triangles abd and acd separately.

(i) We know the hypotenuse and require the opposite to the angle 30°.

Therefore we use the sin ratio:

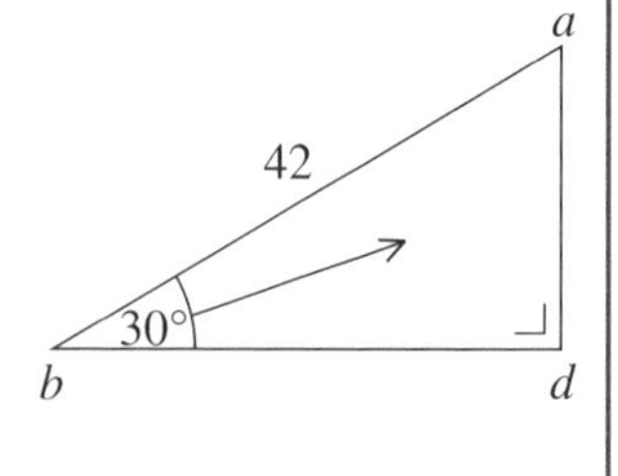

$$\sin A = \frac{\text{opposite}}{\text{hypotenuse}}$$

$\sin 30° = \dfrac{|ad|}{42}$ (angle = 30°, hypotenuse = 42)

$42 \sin 30° = |ad|$ (multiply both sides by 42)

$21 \text{ m} = |ad|$

(ii) Using Pythagoras's theorem on triangle *acd*:

$|ac|^2 = |ad|^2 + |dc|^2$

$|ac|^2 = 21^2 + 20^2$

$|ac|^2 = 441 + 400$

$|ac|^2 = 841$

$|ac| = \sqrt{841} = 29$

Therefore $|ac| = 29$ m.

(iii) $\tan\angle acd = \frac{21}{20} \quad \left(\frac{\text{opposite}}{\text{adjacent}}\right)$

$|\angle acd| = \tan^{-1}\left(\frac{21}{20}\right)$

$|\angle acd| = 46.39718103°$

$|\angle acd| = 46°$ (nearest degree)

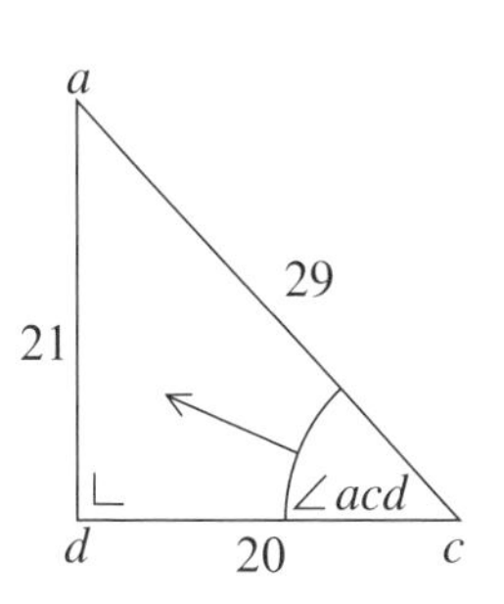

Example 4

An aeroplane leaves the ground at an angle of 18° to the runway. Its speed is 1.5 km/min.

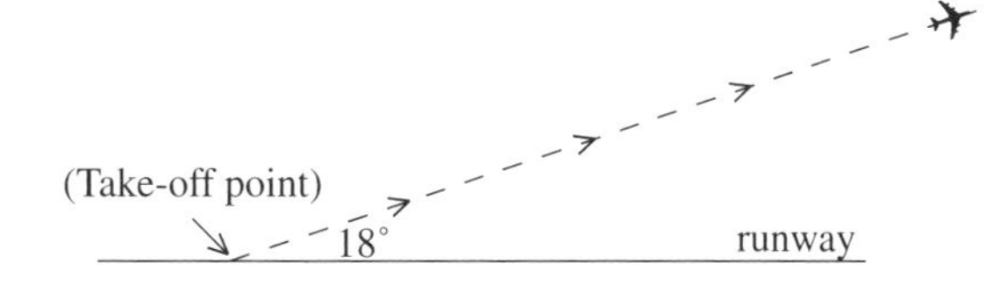

(i) How far does the aeroplane travel in the air in the first three minutes? Give your answer in metres.

(ii) What is its height above the ground after three minutes, correct to the nearest metre?

Solution:

(i) Distance = Speed × Time = 1.5 km × 3 = 4.5 km = 4,500 m

Therefore the plane would travel 4,500 m in the air in the first 3 minutes.

(ii) Represent the situation with a right-angled triangle.

Let the height of the plane above the ground after 3 minutes be *h* m.

We know the hypotenuse and require the opposite to the angle 18°.

Therefore we use the sin ratio:

$$\sin A = \frac{\text{opposite}}{\text{hypotenuse}}$$

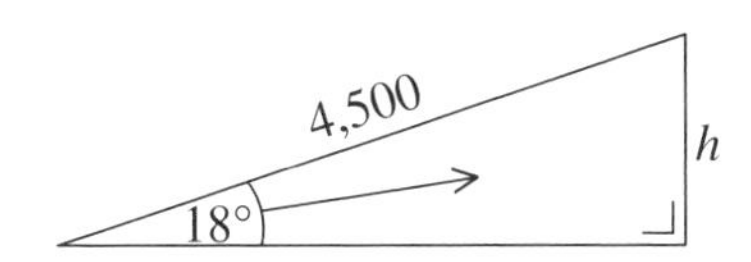

$\sin 18° = \frac{h}{4{,}500}$ (angle = 18°, hypotenuse = 4,500)

$4{,}500 \sin 18° = h$ (multiply both sides by 4,500)

$1390.576475 = h$ (4,500 [sin] 18 [=])

$1{,}391 \text{ m} = h$ (correct to the nearest metre)

Therefore, the height of the plane after 3 minutes was 1,391 m (correct to the nearest metre).

Example 5

A vertical flagpole $[pq]$, 12 m high, is supported by a cable $[qr]$ as shown in the diagram.

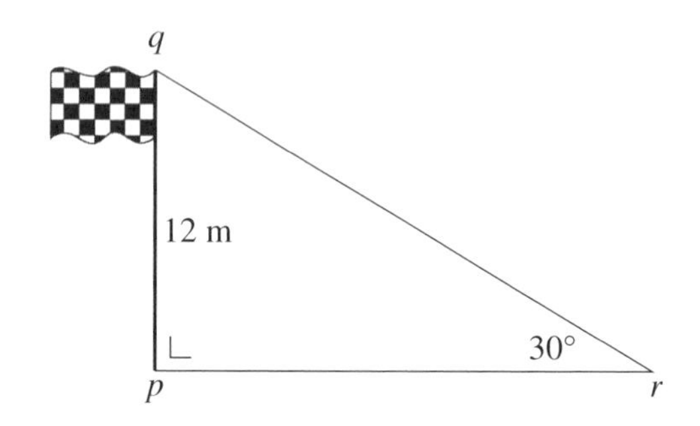

(i) Given that $|\angle qrp| = 30°$, find the length of the cable $[qr]$.

(ii) How far is r from p, the foot of the flagpole?

Give your answer correct to one decimal place.

Solution:

Represent the situation with a right-angled triangle.

We require the hypotenuse and know the opposite to the angle.

Therefore we use the sin ratio:

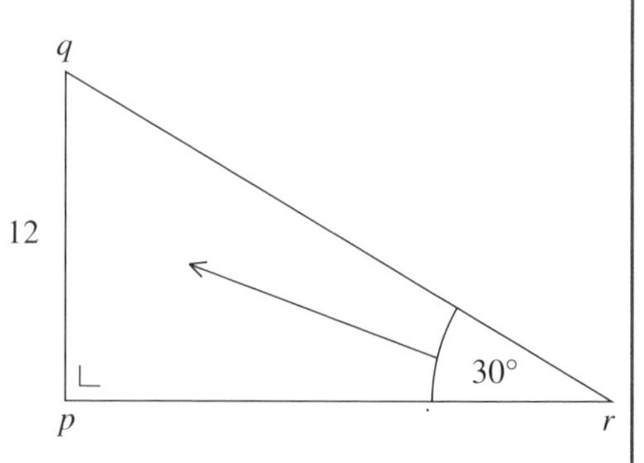

$$\sin A = \frac{\text{opposite}}{\text{hypotenuse}}$$

$$\sin A = \frac{|pr|}{|qr|}$$

$$\sin 30° = \frac{12}{|qr|}$$ (angle = 30°, $|pr| = 12$)

$|qr|\sin 30° = 12$ (multiply both sides by $|qr|$)

$|qr| = \dfrac{12}{\sin 30°}$ (divide both sides by sin 30°)

$|qr| = 24$ m (12 [÷] [sin] 30 [=])

(iii) As we know two sides we can use Pythagoras's theorem to calculate the third side.

Using Pythagoras's theorem:

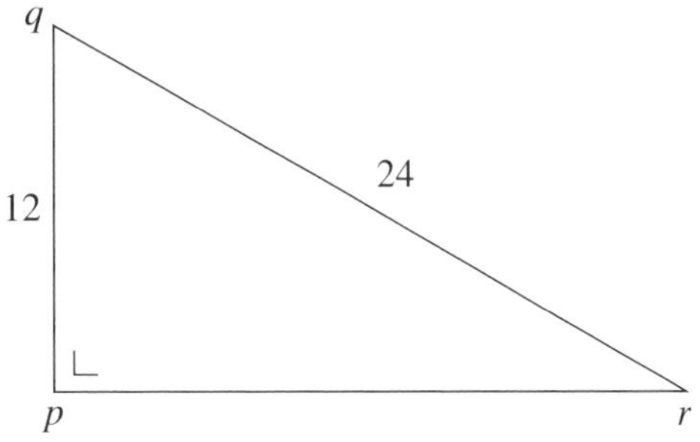

$|pr|^2 + |pq|^2 = |qr|^2$

$|pr|^2 + 12^2 = 24^2$

$|pr|^2 + 144 = 576$

$|pr|^2 = 432$ (subtract 144 from both sides)

$|pr| = \sqrt{432}$

$|pr| = 20.78460969$ ([√] 432 [=])

$|pr| = 20.8$ m (correct to one decimal place)

q
12
24
p
r

EXAM PAPERS

JUNIOR CERTIFICATE EXAMINATION, 2006

MATHEMATICS – ORDINARY LEVEL – PAPER 1 (300 marks)

THURSDAY, 8 JUNE – MORNING, 9:30 to 11:30

Time: 2 hours

Attempt **ALL** questions. Each question carries 50 marks.

The symbol ✍ indicates that supporting work <u>must</u> be shown to obtain full marks.

---

1. (a) $A = \{a, b, c, d, e\}$ $B = \{c, d, f, g\}$

Fill the elements of A and B into the following Venn diagram:

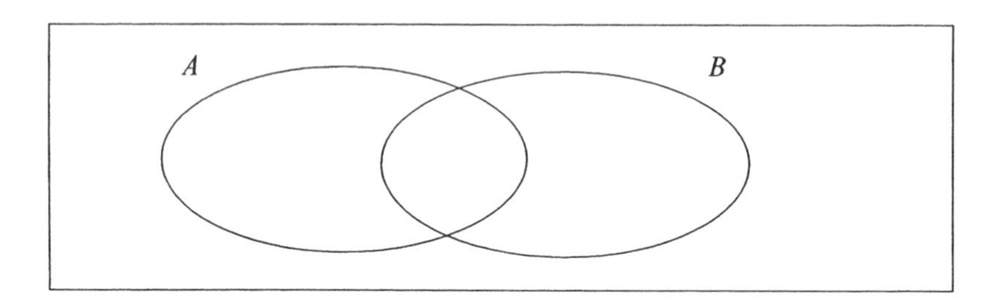

1. (b) U is the universal set.

$P = \{1, 4, 5, 7\}$

$Q = \{4, 6, 7, 9, 10\}$

$R = \{1, 7, 8, 10\}$

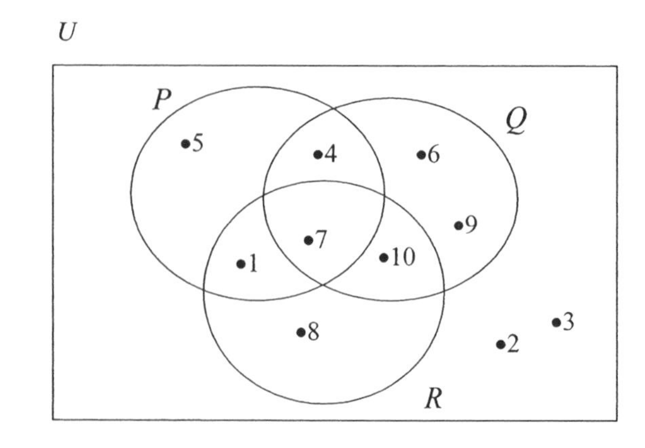

(i) List the elements of $Q \cup R$.

(ii) List the elements of $Q \setminus (P \cup R)$.

(iii) List the elements of P', the complement of the set P.

(iv) Write down # R.

1. (c) There are 30 students in a class.
21 own a mobile phone (M) and 12 own a computer (C).
7 own both a mobile phone and a computer.

(i) Represent this information in the Venn diagram below.

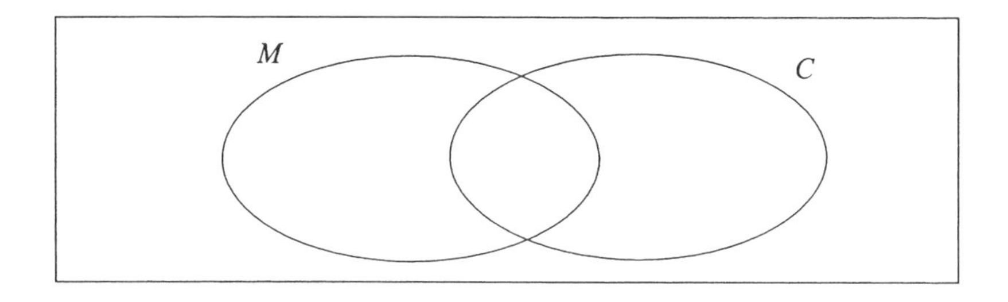

(ii) How many students own a mobile phone but not a computer?

(iii) How many students own neither a mobile phone nor a computer?

(iv) How many students do not own a mobile phone?

2. (a) ✍ In a school of 646 pupils the ratio of girls to boys is 9:8.
Find the number of girls and the number of boys in the school.

2. (b) ✍ (i) On a day when €1 = \$1.21, find the value in euro of \$6,655.

✍ (ii) By rounding each of these numbers to the nearest whole number,

estimate the value of $\frac{4.368 + 10.92}{3.12}$.

$\frac{4.368 + 10.92}{3.12}$ is approximately equal to:

$$\frac{\square + \square}{\square} = \frac{\square}{\square} = \square$$

(iii) Using a calculator, or otherwise, find the exact value of $\frac{4.368 + 10.92}{3.12}$.

2. (c) (i) Using a calculator, or otherwise, find the exact value of $(4^2)^3$.

✍ (ii) Using a calculator, or otherwise, multiply 65.5 by 40 and express your answer in the form $a \times 10^n$, where $1 \leq a < 10$ and $n \in \mathbf{Z}$.

✍ (iii) Using a calculator, or otherwise, evaluate

$$\frac{1}{0.0125} + \frac{\sqrt{86.49}}{15.5} \times 7.48.$$

Give your answer correct to two decimal places.

3. (a) ✍ Find the total cost of the following bill:

6 litres of milk at €1.05 a litre

3 loaves of bread at €1.20 a loaf

5 apples at 65c each.

3. (b) ✍ (i) Vat at 21% is added to a bill of €750.
Calculate the total bill.

✍ (ii) €7,450 is invested at 2.6 % per annum.
What is the amount of the investment at the end of one year?

3. (c) John's weekly wage is €730.
He pays income tax at the rate of 20% on the first €440 of his wage and income tax at the rate of 42% on the remainder of his wage. John has a weekly tax credit of €65.

✍ (i) Find the tax on the first €440 of his wage, calculated at the rate of 20%

✍ (ii) Find the tax on the remainder of his wage, calculated at the rate of 42%.

✍ (iii) Hence calculate John's gross tax.

✍ (iv) Calculate John's take-home pay.

4. (a) If $a = 2$ and $b = 5$, find the value of :

✍ (i) $3a + b$

✍ (ii) $ab - 3$.

4. (b) ✍ (i) Solve the equation $2(x - 3) = x + 1$.

✍ (ii) Multiply $(x - 5)$ by $(2x + 3)$.
Write your answer in its simplest form.

4. (c) The cost of 2 jumpers and 3 shirts is €84.
The cost of 4 jumpers and 1 shirt is €78.
Let €x be the cost of a jumper and let €y be the cost of a shirt.

(i) Write down two equations, each in x and y, to represent the above information.

(ii) Solve these equations to find the cost of a jumper and the cost of a shirt.

(iii) Verify your result.

5. (a) Write in its simplest form: $4(x+3)+2(5x+4)$.

5. (b) Factorise:

(i) $xy+wy$

(ii) $ax-ay+bx-by$

(iii) p^2-36

(iv) $4a^2+8a$.

5. (c) (i) Solve the equation $x^2-5x-14=0$.

(ii) Express $\frac{3x+2}{4}-\frac{x+4}{5}$ as a single fraction.

Give your answer in its simplest form.

(iii) Verify your answer to part **(ii)** by letting $x=6$.

6. (a) $f(x)=2x-1$. Find: **(i)** $f(4)$ **(ii)** $f(-5)$.

6. (b) Draw the graph of the function

$$f\colon x \to 1+4x-x^2$$

in the domain $-1 \le x \le 5$, where $x \in \mathbf{R}$.

6. (c) (i) Draw the axis of symmetry of the graph drawn in **6 (b)** above.
Work to be shown on the graph.

(ii) Use the graph drawn in **6 (b)** to estimate the value of $f(x)$ when $x=3.5$.
Work to be shown on the graph.

JUNIOR CERTIFICATE EXAMINATION, 2006

MATHEMATICS – ORDINARY LEVEL – PAPER 2 (300 marks)

THURSDAY, 12 JUNE – MORNING, 9:30 to 11:30

Time: 2 hours

Attempt **ALL** questions. Each question carries 50 marks.

The symbol ✍ indicates that supporting work <u>must</u> be shown to obtain full marks.

---

1. (a) ✍ Multiply 375 m by 4.
Give your answer in kilometres (km).

1. (b) The gable-end of a house has measurements as shown in the diagram

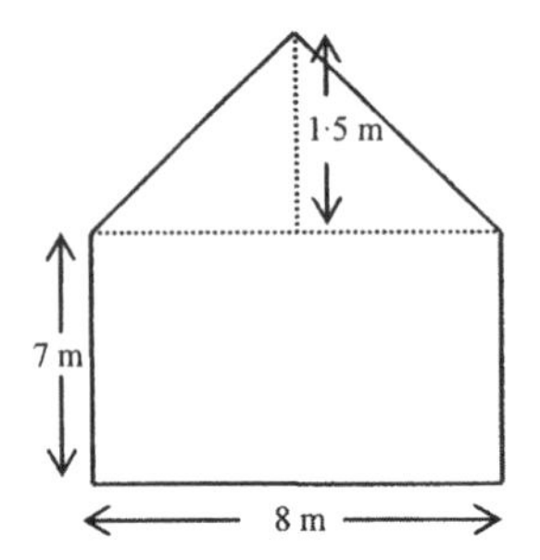

✍ (i) Find, in m^2, the area of the bottom rectangular section of the gable-end

✍ (ii) Find, in m^2, the area of the top triangular section of the gable-end

✍ (iii) The cost of 5 litres of paint is €23.
5 litres of this paint will cover an area of $31 m^2$.
Find the cost of painting the gable-end with this paint.

1. (c) Peter travelled 50 km to a football match and he returned home by the same route when the match was over.

✍ (i) Peter travelled to the match at an average speed of 60 km/h.
How many minutes did the journey to the match take?

✍ (ii) Peter arrived at the match at 17:35. At what time did he leave from home to travel to the match?

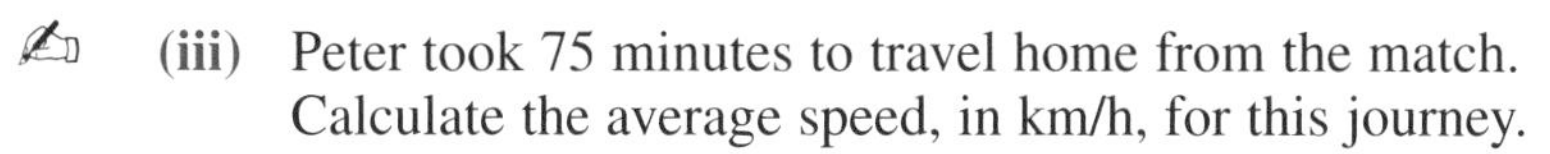

(iii) Peter took 75 minutes to travel home from the match.
Calculate the average speed, in km/h, for this journey.

2. (a) The length of each side of a square tile is 9 cm.
What area, in cm^2, will 12 of these tiles cover?

9 cm

2. (b) (i) A circular disc has a radius of 5 cm.
Taking π as 3.14, find, in cm^2, the area of the disc.

5cm

(ii) A rectangular piece of cardboard has measurements as shown.
Two circular pieces, each of radius length 5 cm, are cut out of this rectangular piece of cardboard as shown.

24 cm
12 cm

Find, in cm^2, the area of the remaining piece of cardboard.

2. (c) A solid metal cylinder has radius 10 cm and height 15 cm.

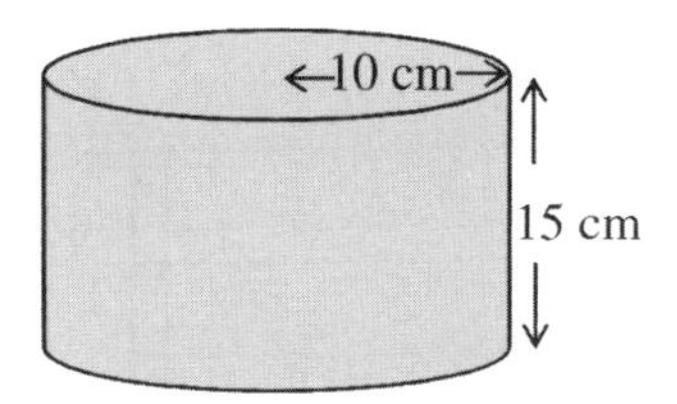

(i) Taking π as 3.14, find, in cm^3, the volume of the solid metal cylinder.

(ii) The cylinder was melted down and half of the metal was recast as a rectangular solid.
This rectangular solid has length 15 cm and width 14 cm. Calculate, in cm, its height, correct to one decimal place.

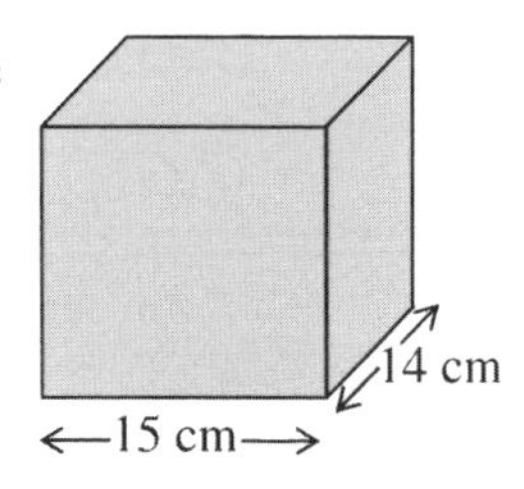

(iii) The other half of the metal was recast as a sphere. This sphere had a surface area of 272.57π cm^2. Find, in cm, the radius of the sphere, correct to two decimal places.

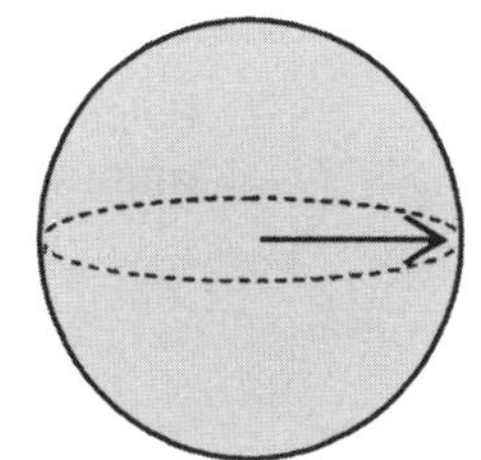

3. (a) Find the mean of the numbers: 3.2, 4.4, 4.6, and 7.8.

3. (b) A group of students were surveyed to find their favourite channel from four given TV channels. The pie chart represents the results of the survey.

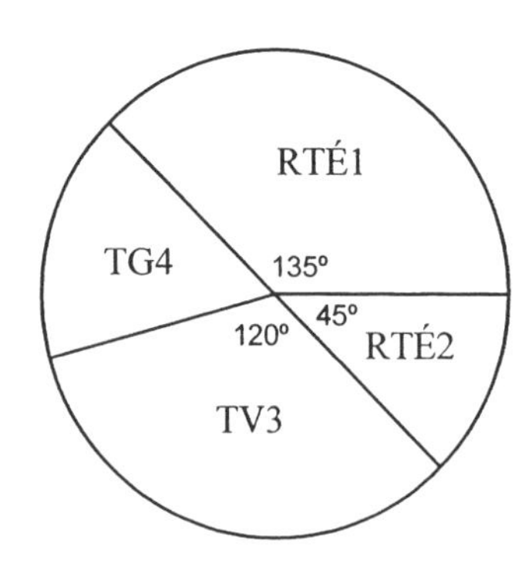

(i) What is the measure of the angle for TG4?

(ii) 12 students replied that RTÉ2 was their favourite channel. How many students were surveyed?

(iii) How many gave TV3 as their reply?

3. (c) The marks gained in a test by 20 students were

40	30	20	50	40
30	20	40	30	10
50	40	30	10	30
50	20	30	40	20

(i) Complete the following frequency table:

Marks	10	20	30	40	50
Number of students					

(ii) Draw a bar chart of the data.

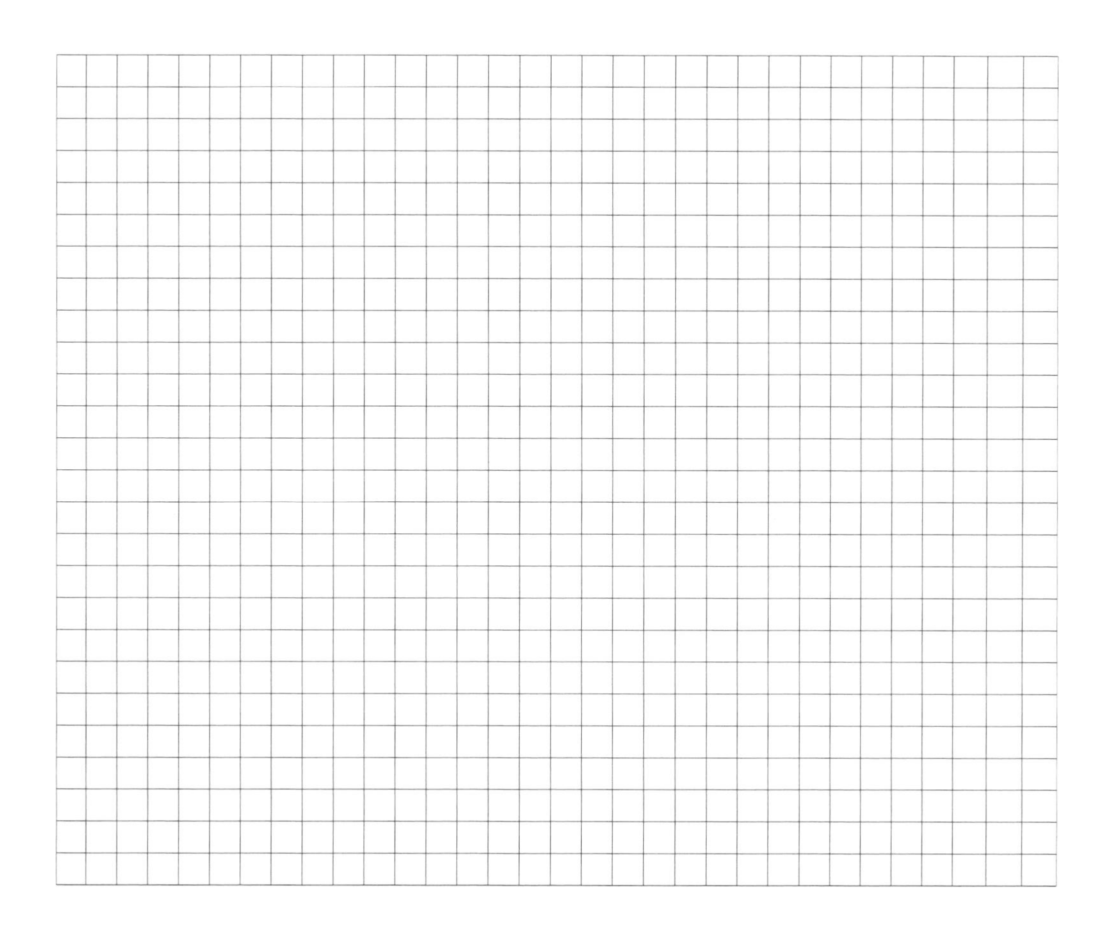

✍ **(iii)** Calculate the mean mark.

4. **(a)** Find the value of x and the value of y in the diagram.

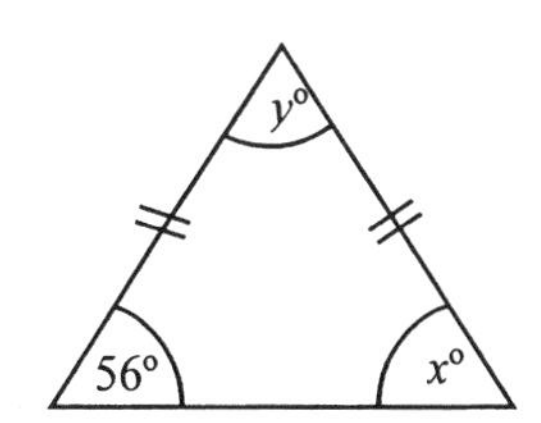

4. **(b)** *pqrs* is a parallelogram.
The diagonals $[sq]$ and $[pr]$ intersect at m.

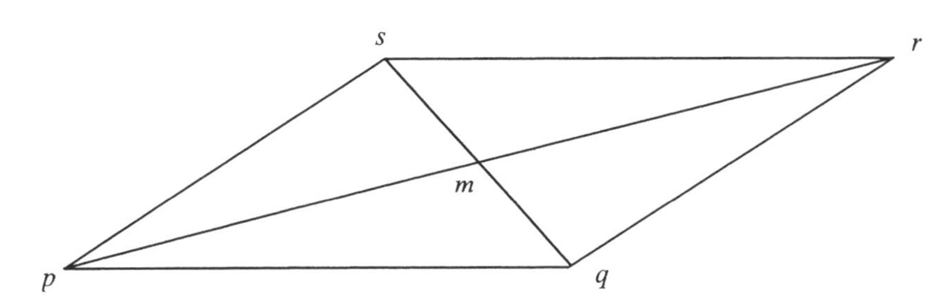

(i) The $\triangle psq$ has area 12 cm^2.
Write down the area of the parallelogram *pqrs* and give a reason for your answer.

(ii) Given that $|sq| = 4.1$ cm, find $|mq|$ and give a reason for your answer.

✍ **(iii)** Bisect the given angle $\angle bac$ without using a protractor.
Show all construction lines.

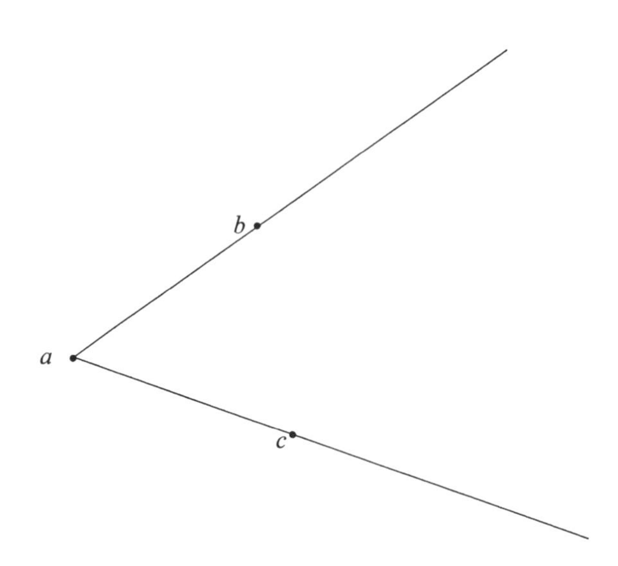

4. **(c)** $[ab]$ and $[de]$ are diameters of a circle with centre c.
$de \perp ab$.

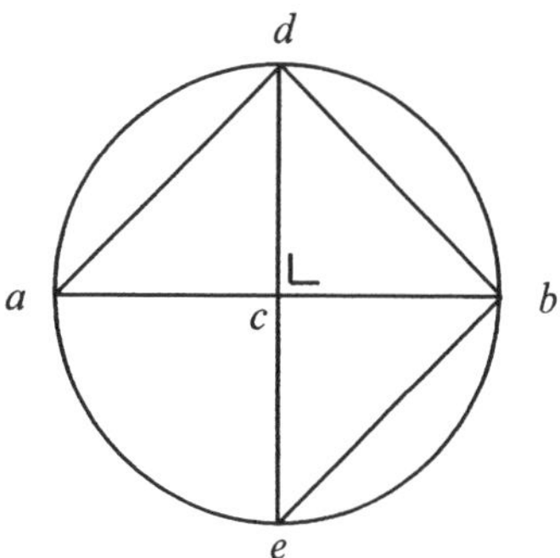

(i) Write down $|\angle cad|$.

(ii) Show that $\triangle acd$ and $\triangle bce$ are congruent.

✍ **(iii)** $[xw]$ is a diameter of a circle with centre o.
z is a point on the circle.

Given $|ow| = 5$ cm, $|wz| = 6$ cm, use the Theorem of Pythagoras to find $|xz|$.

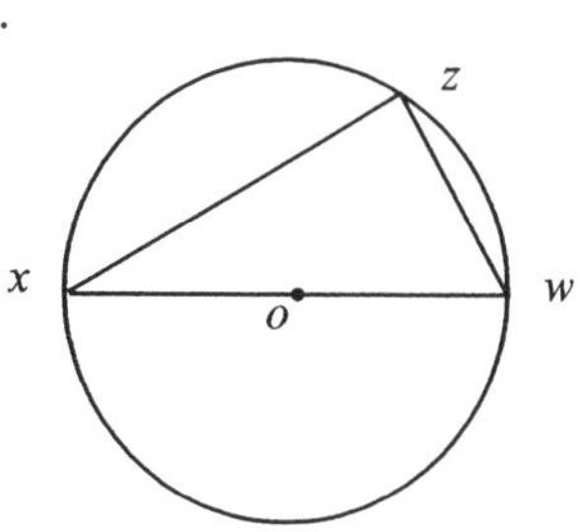

Note: Coordinate Geometry Formulae are given on Page 186.

5. **(a)** Write down the coordinates of the point t.

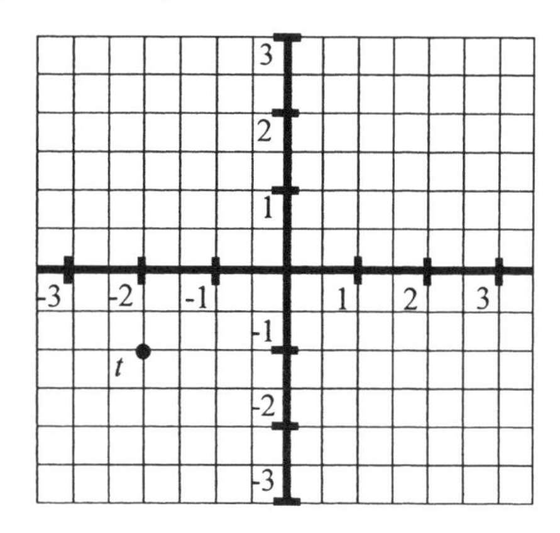

5. **(b)** p is the point $(3, 5)$ and q is the point $(1, -7)$. Find each of the following:

✍ **(i)** the midpoint of $[pq]$

✍ **(ii)** the slope of pq

✍ **(iii)** the equation of the line pq.

5. **(c)** ✍ **(i)** L is the line $7x - 2y + 14 = 0$.

L cuts the x-axis at a, $(-2, 0)$ and the y-axis at b.

By letting $x = 0$, find the coordinates of b.

(ii) Find the image of the point a, under S_y, the axial symmetry in the y-axis

Formulae

Midpoint of a line segment: $\left(\frac{x_1+x_2}{2}, \frac{y_1+y_2}{2}\right)$

Slope of a line: $m=\frac{y_2-y_1}{x_2-x_1}$

Equation of a line: $y-y_1=m(x-x_1)$

6. (a) The right-angled triangle abc has measurements as shown.

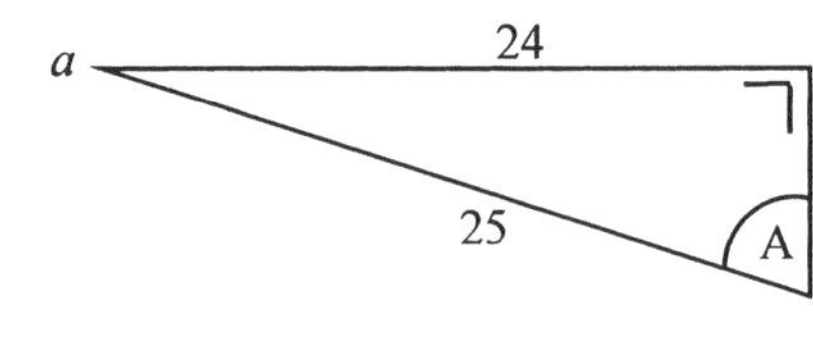

(i) Write down the length of the side opposite the angle A.

(ii) Write down the value of tan A, as a fraction.

6. (b) In the right-angled triangle pqr,

$|pq|=12$ and $|\angle qpr|=60^\circ$.

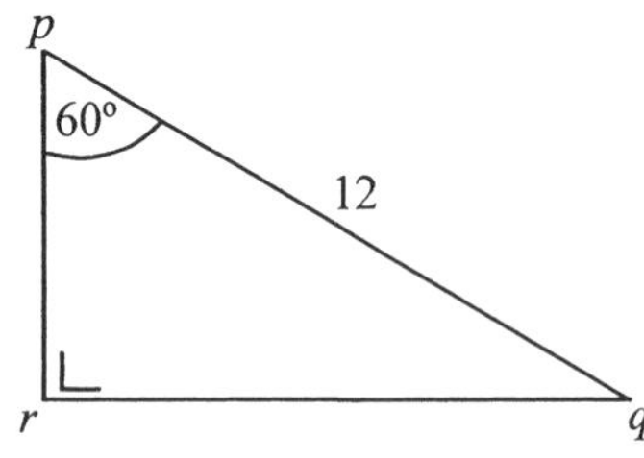

(i) Write down the value of cos 60°.

✍ (ii) Calculate $|pr|$.

6. (c) Claire is at the point c on the top of a cliff.
The point b is at the base of the cliff.
The height of the cliff is 35 m, as shown in the diagram.
She wishes to find $|ba|$, the distance from the base of the cliff to the base of the lighthouse.

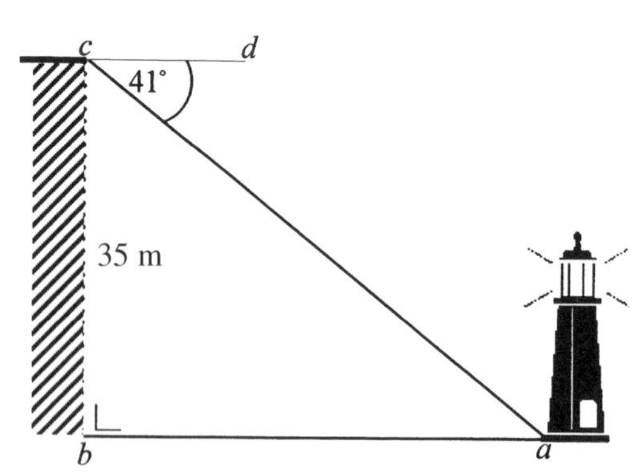

She measured $\angle dca$ and found it to be 41°.
cd is parallel to ba.

(i) Find $|\angle bac|$.

✍ (ii) Find, to the nearest metre, $|ba|$, the distance from the base of the cliff to the base of the lighthouse.

Junior Certificate Ordinary Level Maths 2006 Answers

Paper 1

1. **(a)** A, B: a, b, e in A only; c, d in $A \cap B$; f, g in B only

(b) **(i)** $\{1, 4, 6, 7, 8, 9, 10\}$ **(ii)** $\{6, 9\}$ **(iii)** $\{2, 3, 6, 8, 9, 10\}$ **(iv)** 4

(c) **(i)** Represent this information in the Venn diagram below.

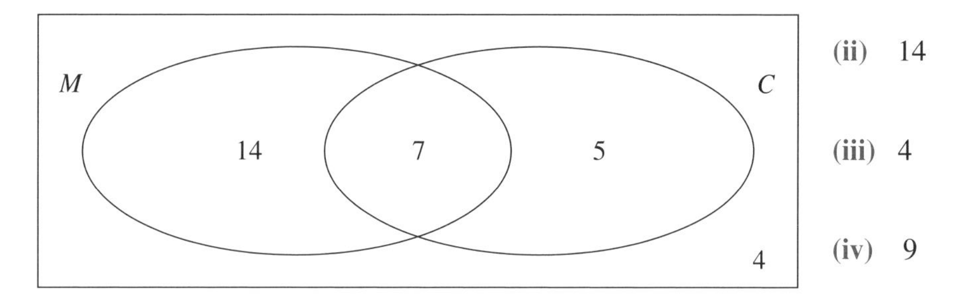

(ii) 14 **(iii)** 4 **(iv)** 9

2. **(a)** 342; 304 **(b)** **(i)** €5,500 **(ii)** 5 **(iii)** 4.9
(c) **(i)** 4,096 **(ii)** 2.62×10^3 **(iii)** 84.49

3. **(a)** €13.15 **(b)** **(i)** €907.50 **(ii)** €7,643.70
(c) **(i)** €88 **(ii)** €121.80 **(iii)** €209.80 **(iv)** €585.20

4. **(a)** **(i)** 11 **(ii)** 7 **(b)** **(i)** 7 **(ii)** $2x^2 - 7x - 15$
(c) **(i)** $2x + 3y = 84$; $4x + y = 78$ **(ii)** Jumper costs €15, shirt costs €18

5. **(i)** $14x + 20$ **(b)** **(i)** $y(x + w)$ **(ii)** $(x - y)(a + b)$ **(iii)** $(p - 6)(p + 6)$
(iv) $4a(a + 2)$ **(c)** **(i)** 7 or -2 **(ii)** $\dfrac{11x - 6}{20}$

6. **(a)** **(i)** 7 **(ii)** -11 **(c)** **(ii)** 2.75

Paper 2

1. (a) 1.5 km (b) (i) 56 m^2 (ii) 6 m^2 (iii) €46
   (c) (i) 50 mins (ii) 16:45 (iii) 40 km/h

2. (a) 972 cm^2 (b) (i) 78.5 cm^2 (ii) 131 cm^2
   (c) (i) 4,710 cm^3 (ii) 11.2 cm (iii) 8.25 cm

3. (a) 5 (b) (i) 60° (ii) 96 (iii) 32
   (c) (i)

10	20	30	40	50
2	4	6	5	3

   (iii) 31.5 marks

4. (a) $x = 56$; $y = 68$
   (b) (i) 24 cm^2 : diagonal bisects the area of a parallelogram
   (ii) 2.05 cm : diagonals of a parallelogram bisect each other
   (c) (i) 45°
   (ii) $|ac| = |cb|$ and $|dc| = |ce|$ all = radius
   $|\angle acd| = |\angle bce| = 90^o$ given
   $\therefore$ $\triangle acd \equiv \triangle bce$ SAS
   (iii) 8 cm

5. (a) $t(-2, -1)$ (b) (i) $(2, -1)$ (ii) 6 (iii) $6x - y - 13 = 0$
   (c) (i) (0, 7) (ii) (2, 0)

6. (a) (i) 24 (ii) $\frac{24}{7}$ (b) (i) $\frac{1}{2}$ or 0.5 (ii) 6 (c) (i) 41° (ii) 40 m

JUNIOR CERTIFICATE EXAMINATION, 2007

MATHEMATICS – ORDINARY LEVEL – PAPER 1 (300 marks)

THURSDAY, 7 JUNE – MORNING, 9:30 to 11:30

Time: 2 hours

Attempt **ALL** questions. Each question carries 50 marks.

The symbol ✍ indicates that supporting work must be shown to obtain full marks.

---

1. (a) (i) Using the Venn diagram below, shade in the region that represents $A \cup B$.

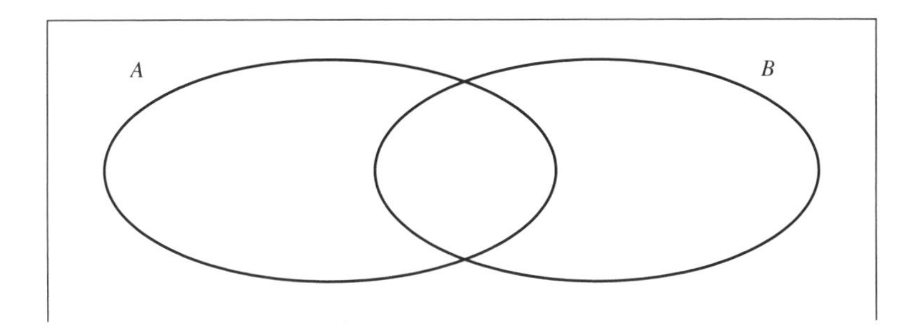

(ii) Using the Venn diagram below, shade in the region that represents $A \cap B$.

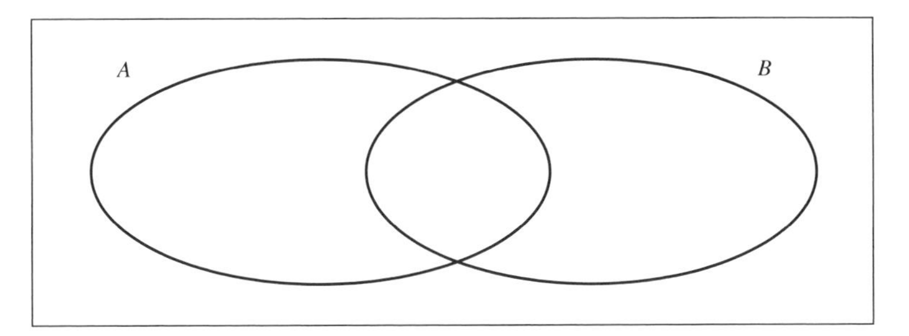

1. (b) U is the universal set.

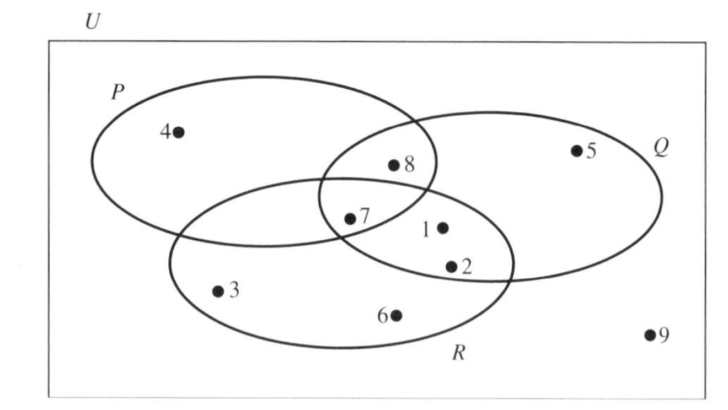

$P = \{4, 7, 8\}$

$Q = \{1, 2, 5, 7, 8\}$

$R = \{1, 2, 3, 6, 7\}$

List the elements of:

(i) $P \cup Q$

(ii) $P \setminus R$

(iii) $(P \cup R) \cap Q$

(iv) $(P \cup Q)'$

1. (c) In a class, all the students study Science (S) or Technical Graphics (T). A number of the students study both of these subjects. 22 students study Science. 12 students study Technical Graphics. 8 study both subjects.

(i) Represent this information in the Venn diagram below.

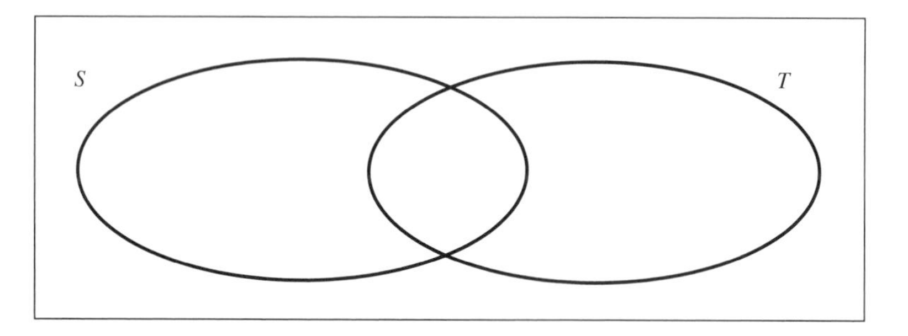

(ii) How many students study Science only?

(iii) How many students are there in the class?

(iv) How many students study only one of the two subjects?

2. (a) ✍ €6650 was shared between Ciarán and Sheila in the ratio 2:5. How much did each receive?

Ciarán =

Sheila =

2. (b) ✍ (i) Simplify $\frac{a^8 \times a^{10}}{a^5 \times a^7}$, giving your answer in the form, a^n where $n \in \mathbf{N}$.

$$\frac{a^8 \times a^{10}}{a^5 \times a^7} =$$

(ii) By rounding each of these numbers to the nearest whole number, estimate the value of $\frac{24.092}{6.1 - 2.93}$

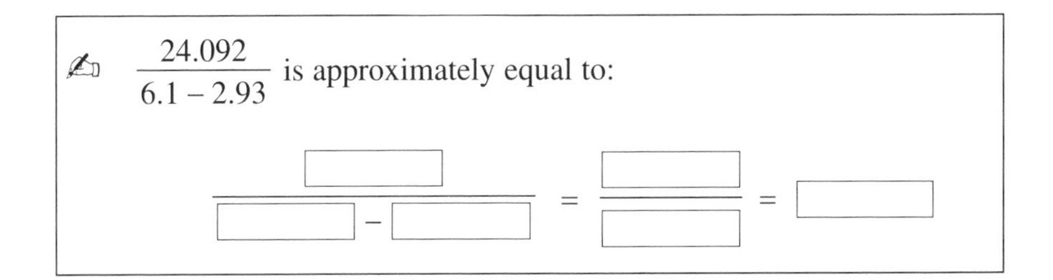

(iii) Using a calculator, or otherwise, find the exact value of $\frac{24.092}{6.1 - 2.93}$.

2. (c) (i) Using a calculator, or otherwise, find the exact value of $(2.25)^{\frac{1}{2}}$.

$$(2.25)^{\frac{1}{2}} =$$

✍ (ii) Using a calculator, or otherwise, multiply 54.5 by 60 and express your answer in the form $a \times 10^n$, where $1 \leq a < 10$ and $n \in \mathbf{N}$.

✍ (iii) Using a calculator, or otherwise, evaluate
$(6.9)^2 - \sqrt{139.8} \div 3.55$.
Give your answer correct to two decimal places.

3. (a) ✍ In one week Bríd sent 26 text messages on her mobile phone.
11 of these messages cost 8c each.
The rest of the text messages cost 12c each.
Find the total cost of Bríd's texting.

3. (b) ✍ (i) John's gross pay is €23 000. His tax credit is €3400.
He pays income tax at the rate of 20%.
Find John's take-home pay.

Gross Pay	€23 000
Tax @ 20%	
Tax Credit	€3400
Tax Due	
Take-home Pay	

✍ (ii) VAT at 21% is added to a bill of €255.
Calculate the total bill.

3. (c) ✍ (i) €15 000 is invested at 3% per annum.
What is the amount of the investment at the end of the first year?

✍ (ii) €1450 is withdrawn from this amount at the beginning of the second year. The interest rate for the second year is 3.5%.
What is the amount of the investment at the end of that year?

4. (a) If $x = 3$, find the value of:

✍ (i) $4x + 5$

✍ (ii) $2x^2 - 11$

4. (b) ✍ (i) Solve the equation $4(5x + 6) = 84$.

✍ (ii) Write in its simplest form $3x^2 - 2x + 6 - x(2x - 3)$.

4. (c) ✍ (i) Liam drove from Town ***A*** to Town ***B***, a distance of x km.
He then drove from Town ***B*** to Town ***C***, a distance of $(2x + 1)$ km.
The total distance that he drove was 56 km.
Find the value of x, correct to the nearest kilometre.

✍ (ii) Solve for x and for y:

$$3x + 5y = 13$$
$$x + 2y = 5$$

$x =$ $y =$

5. ✍ (a) Find the values of x for which $3x + 2 < 11$, $x \in \mathbf{N}$.

5. (b) (i) Factorise

(i) $16xy + 11y$

✍ (ii) $5x + 10y + ax + 2ay$

(iii) $x^2 - x - 90$

(iv) $x^2 - 121$

5. (c) ✍ (i) Express $\frac{2x-1}{5} + \frac{x-7}{2}$ as a single fraction. Give your answer in its simplest form.

✍ (ii) Hence, or otherwise, solve the equation $\frac{2x-1}{5} + \frac{x-7}{2} = 6$.

✍ (iii) Solve the equation $x^2 + 5x - 36 = 0$.

6. (a) $P = \{(1,3)\ (4,6)\ (5,8)\ (7,9)\}$
Write out the domain and range of P.

Domain =

Range =

6. (b) ✍ Draw the graph of the function
$f : x \to 2 + 3x - x^2$
in the domain $-1 \leq x \leq 4$, where $x \in \mathbf{R}$.

6. (c) (i) Given that $y = x + 1$, complete the table below.

x	0	1	2	3
y				

(ii) On the grid below, the graph of the line $y = 3 - x$ is drawn. Using your answers from **(i)**, draw the graph of $y = x + 1$ on the same grid.

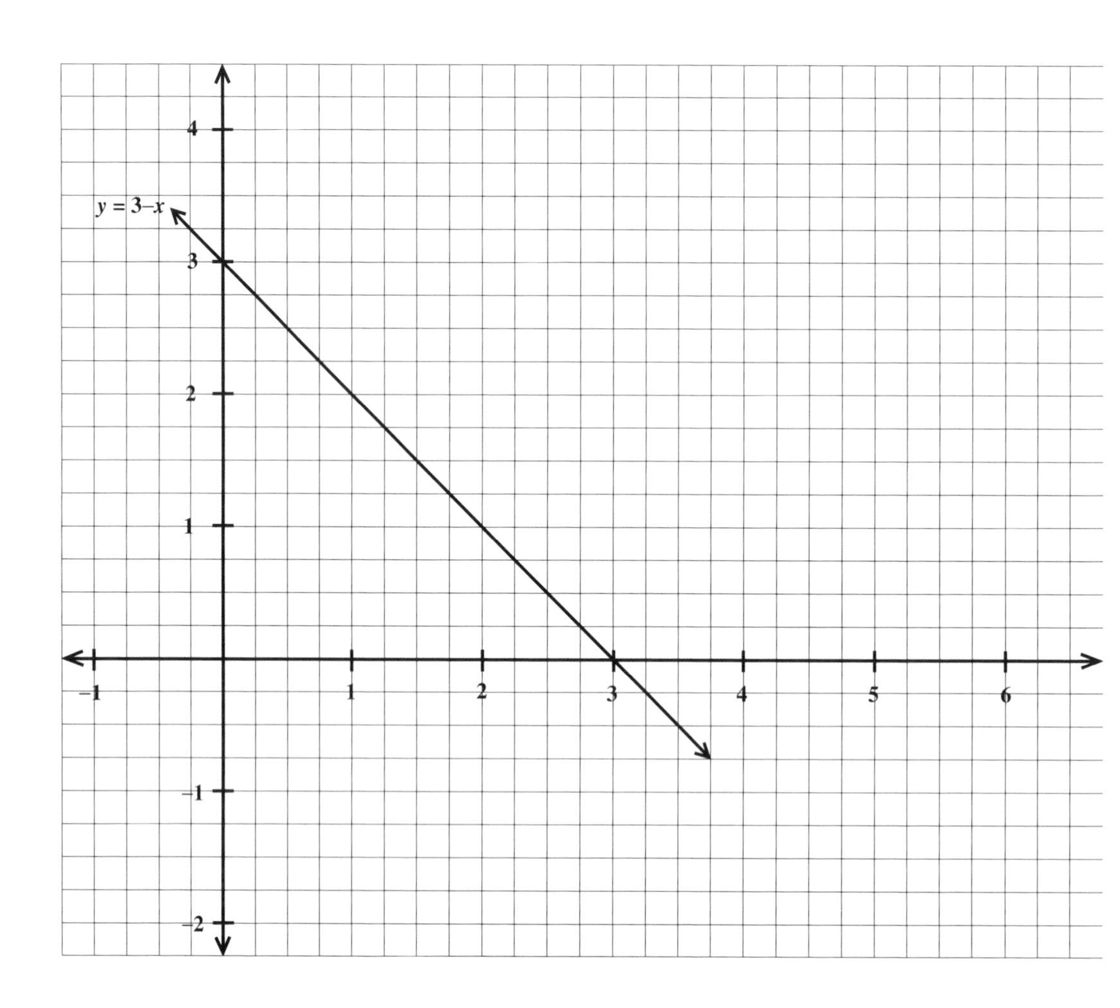

✍ **(iii)** Use the graphs drawn in **6 (c) (ii)** to write down the coordinates of the point of intersection of the two lines $y = 3 - x$ and $y = x + 1$.

JUNIOR CERTIFICATE EXAMINATION, 2007

MATHEMATICS – ORDINARY LEVEL – PAPER 2 (300 marks)

MONDAY, 11 JUNE – MORNING, 9:30 to 11:30

Time: 2 hours

Attempt **ALL** questions. Each question carries 50 marks.

The symbol ✍ indicates that supporting work <u>must</u> be shown to obtain full marks.

---

1. (a) ✍ One lap of a running track measures 440 m. James runs 50 laps of that track. What distance, in kilometres, does James run?

1. (b) Aoife books a flight from Cork to London. The plane is due to leave Cork at 18:25 and to arrive in London 1 hour and 20 minutes later.

✍ (i) At what time should the plane arrive in London?

✍ (ii) On the day of her flight the departure time was delayed by 25 minutes but the flight time was 6 minutes less than expected. At what time did the plane land in London?

✍ (iii) Aoife's fare for the flight was €48.
Excess hand baggage was charged at the rate of €3.50 per kg.
Aoife had 5.6 kg of excess hand baggage.
Find the total cost of Aoife's flight.

1. (c) A garden with a semicircular lawn and two flowerbeds has measurements as shown in the diagram.

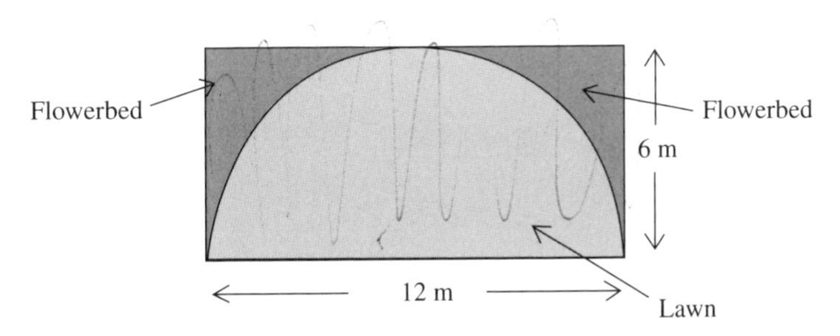

(i) Find, in m^2, the area of the garden.

(ii) Taking π as 3.14, find the area of the lawn, in m^2.

(iii) Find the area of the flowerbeds, in m^2.

(iv) Taking π as 3.14, find the total perimeter of the semicircular lawn, in m.

2. (a) A triangle has measurements as shown in the diagram.

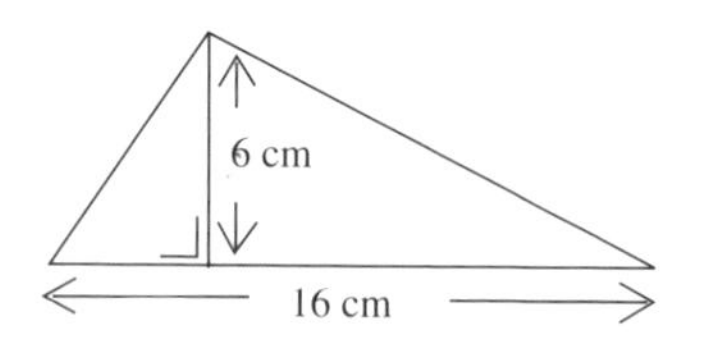

Find, in cm^2, the area of the triangle.

2. (b) A solid rectangular block of wood has length 16 cm, width 4 cm and height 6 cm.

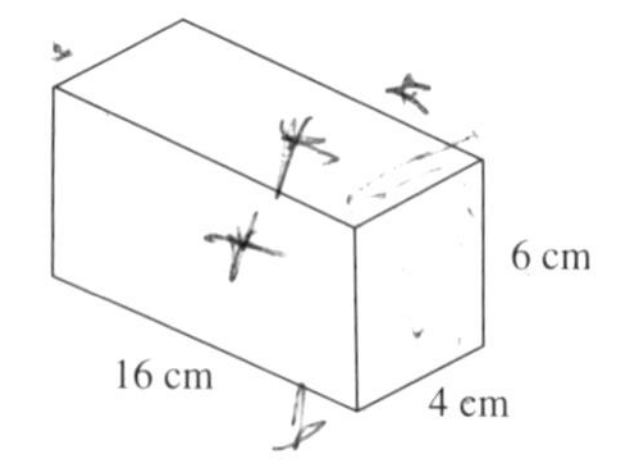

(i) Find, in cm^3, the volume of the block of wood.

(ii) Cubes with sides of length 2 cm, as shown, are made from the block of wood. Find the number of cubes that can be made from the block of wood.

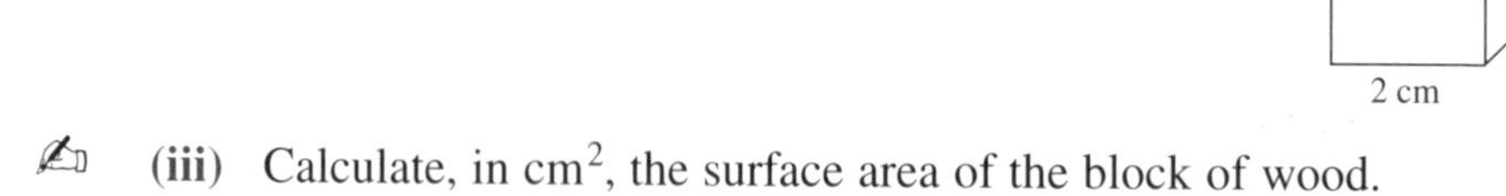

(iii) Calculate, in cm^2, the surface area of the block of wood.

2. (c) A solid trophy, as shown, has a sphere mounted on top of a cylinder. The radius of the sphere is 3 cm.

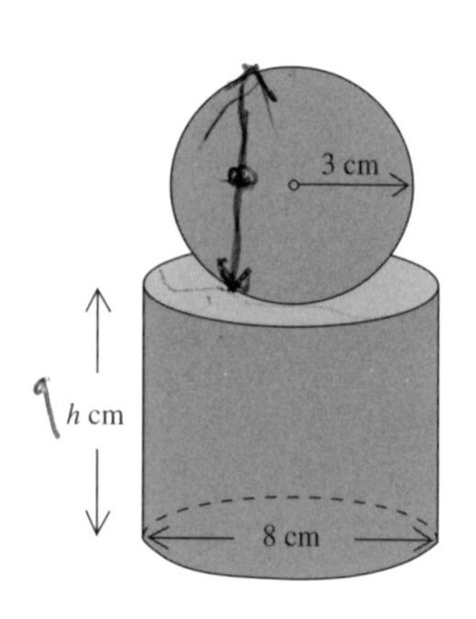

✍ (i) Find the volume of the sphere in terms of π.

✍ (ii) The cylinder in the trophy has a diameter of 8 cm and its volume is four times the volume of the sphere.
Find h, the height of cylinder in the trophy.

✍ (iii) Find the total height of the trophy.

3. **(a)** Find the mode of the numbers: 1, 4, 3, 4, 1, 4, 12, 4, 15, 4.

Mode =

3. **(b)** The bar chart shows the number of hours that Anne spent studying from Monday to Friday of a particular school week.

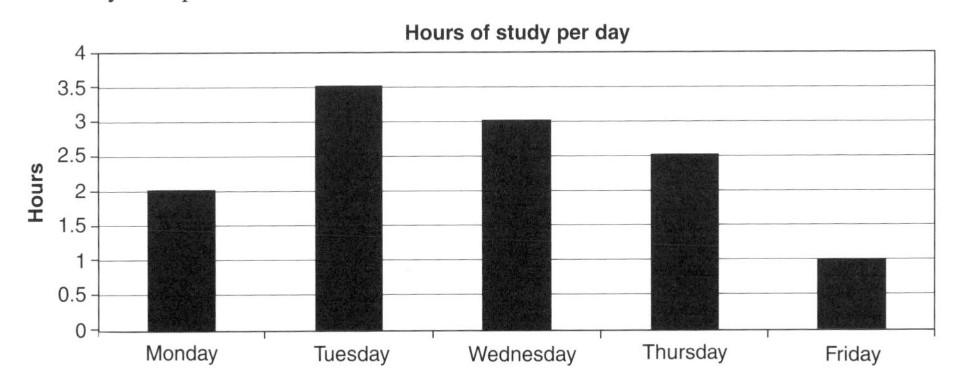

(i) How many hours study did Anne do on the Monday of that week?

(ii) On what day of that week did Anne do the least study?

✍ **(iii)** Express the hours of study done by Anne on Wednesday as a percentage of her total hours of study for that week.

3. **(c)** The table shows the price in dollars of a barrel of crude oil for the first six months of 2006.

Month	January	February	March	April	May	June
Price	50	70	60	65	70	75

(i) Draw a trend graph of the data, putting months on the horizontal axis.

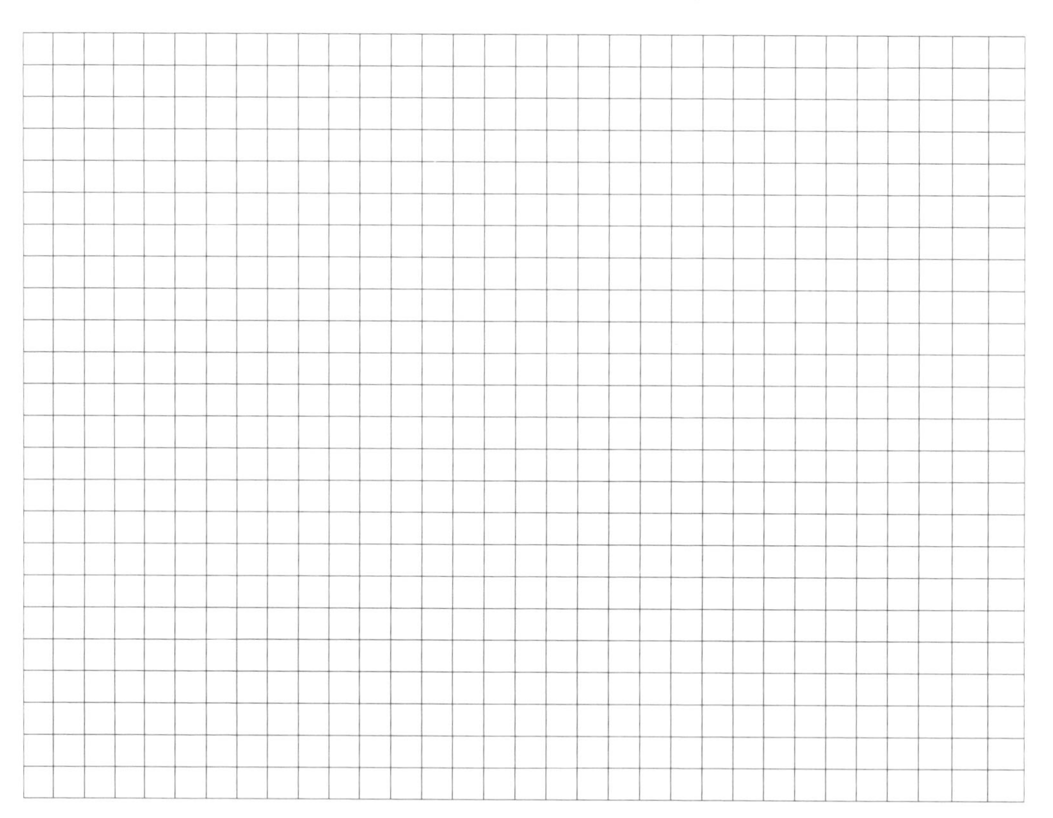

(ii) Calculate the mean price, in dollars, of a barrel of crude oil over this six-month period.

(iii) The mean price of a barrel of crude oil for the first seven months of 2006 was 67 dollars.
Find the price of a barrel of such oil in July 2006.

4. (a) Construct a triangle abc with $|ab| = 6$ cm, $|\angle bac| = 50°$ and $|\angle abc| = 70°$
Label your diagram clearly.

4. (b) $xywt$ and $xyzw$ are two parallelograms as shown in the diagram.

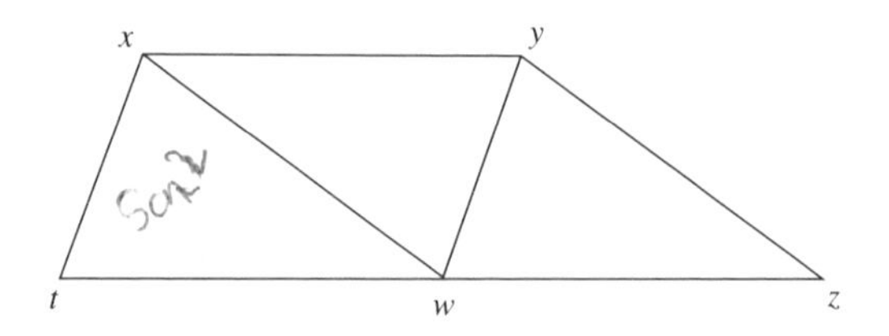

(i) Name the image of the point x under the translation $\vec{tw}$.

Image of x =

(ii) Name the image of $[wz]$ under the translation $\vec{wx}$.

Image of $[wz] =$

✍ (iii) Given that the area of $\triangle xtw = 5$ cm^2, find the area of the figure $txyz$.

(iv) Show that $\triangle xyw$ and $\triangle ywz$ are congruent.

Reasons:

4. **(c)** $[ab]$ is the diameter of a circle with centre o.
c and d are points on the circle.
$|\angle abc| = 60°$.

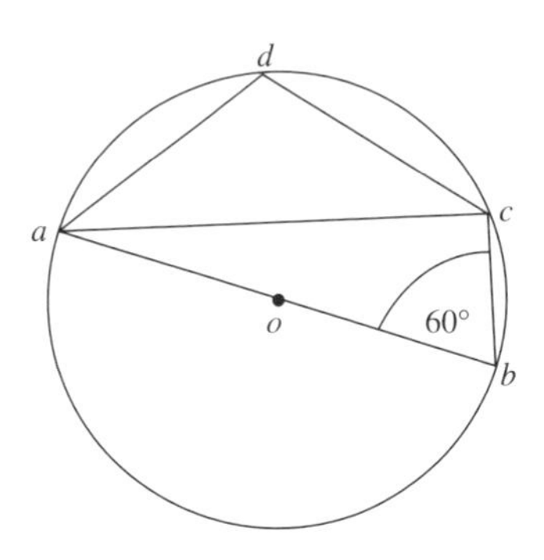

(i) Write down $|\angle acb|$ and give a reason for your answer.

$|\angle acb| =$ Reason:

(ii) Write down $|\angle bac|$, and give a reason for your answer.

$|\angle bac| =$ Reason:

(iii) Write down $|\angle adc|$ and give a reason for your answer.

$|\angle adc| =$ Reason:

✍ (iv) Given that $|oa| = 2$ cm and $|bc| = 2$ cm, find $|ac|$.
Give your answer correct to one decimal place.

5. *Note: Coordinate Geometry Formulae are given below.*

(a) a is the point (2, 1)

b is the point (– 2, – 3)

Plot the points a and b.

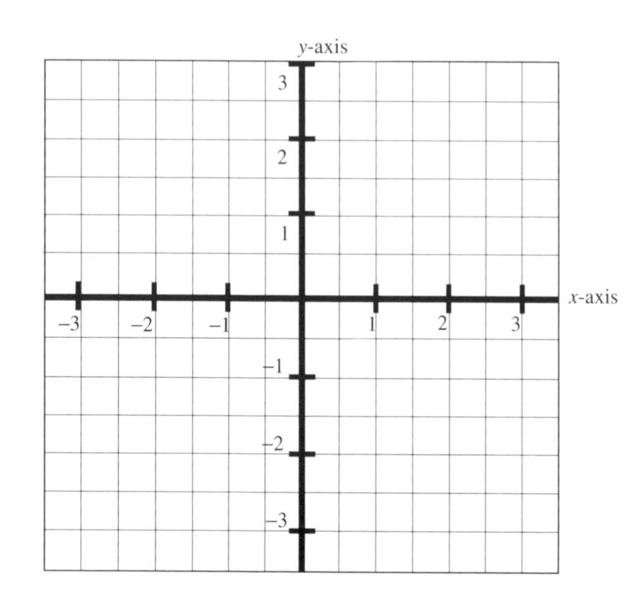

5. **(b)** p is the point (3, – 3) and q is the point (5, – 1). Find each of the following:

✍ **(i)** the midpoint of $[pq]$

✍ **(ii)** the slope of pq

✍ **(iii)** the equation of the line pq.

5. **(c)** ✍ **(i)** K is the line $2x + 3y - 6 = 0$.
K cuts the y-axis at the point r.
By letting $x = 0$, find the co-ordinates of the point r.

✍ **(ii)** Find the image of the point r under S_o,
the central symmetry in the origin, (0, 0).

Formulae

Midpoint of a line segment:	$\left(\frac{x_1 + x_2}{2}, \frac{y_1 + y_2}{2}\right)$
Slope of a line:	$m = \frac{y_2 - y_1}{x_2 - x_1}$
Equation of a line:	$y - y_1 = m(x - x_1)$

6. **(a)** The right-angled triangle *abc* has measurements as shown.

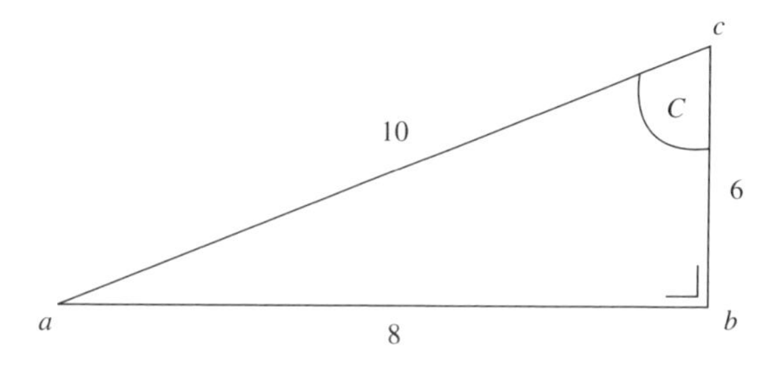

(i) Write down the length of the hypotenuse of the $\triangle abc$.

Length of the hypotenuse of the $\triangle abc =$

(ii) Write down the value of $\cos C$, as a fraction.

$\cos C =$

6. **(b)** In the right-angled triangle *pqr*, $|pq| = 8$ and $|\angle pqr| = 50°$.

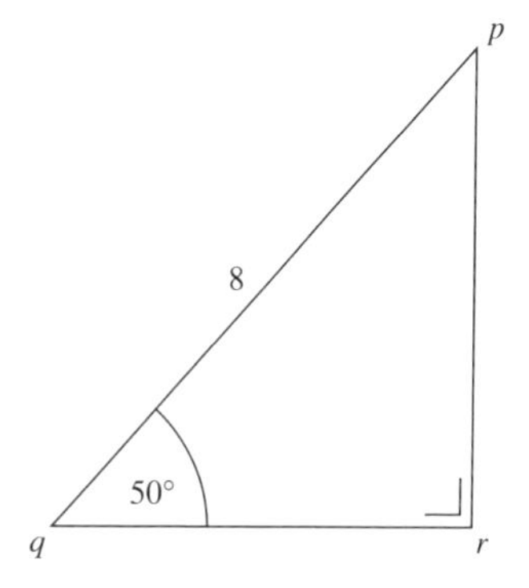

(i) Find $|\angle qpr|$.

$|\angle qpr| =$

(ii) Using your calculator, or otherwise, write down the value of $\sin |\angle qpr|$ correct to two decimal places.

$\sin |\angle qpr| =$

✍ **(iii)** Hence, or otherwise, calculate $|qr|$ correct to one decimal place.

6. **(c)** In the $\triangle abc$, $|\angle bca| = 90°$, $|ab| = 13$ m and $|ac| = 5$ m.

✍ **(i)** Find, in metres, $|bc|$.

✍ **(ii)** Find $|\angle bac|$, correct to the nearest degree.

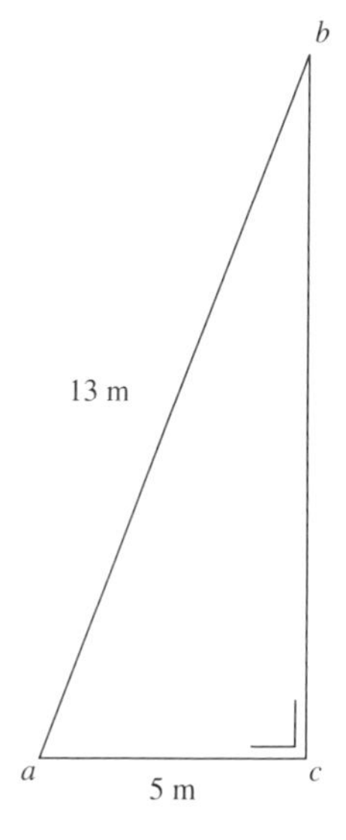

Junior Certificate Ordinary Level Maths 2007 Answers

Paper 1

1. (a) (i)

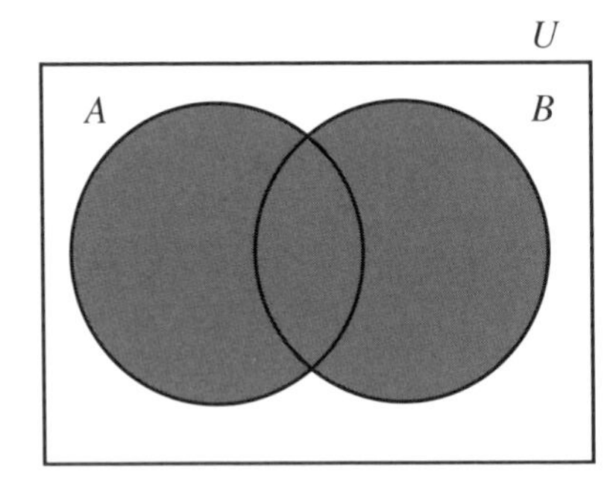

(ii)

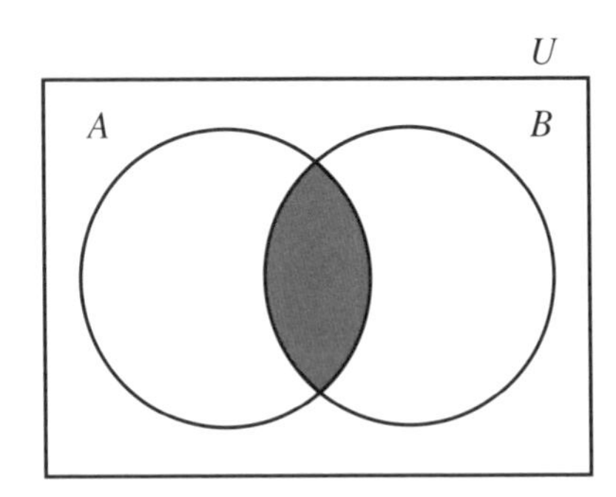

(b) (i) {1, 2, 4, 5, 7, 8} (ii) {4, 8} (iii) {1, 2, 7, 8} (iv) {3, 6, 9}

(c) (i)

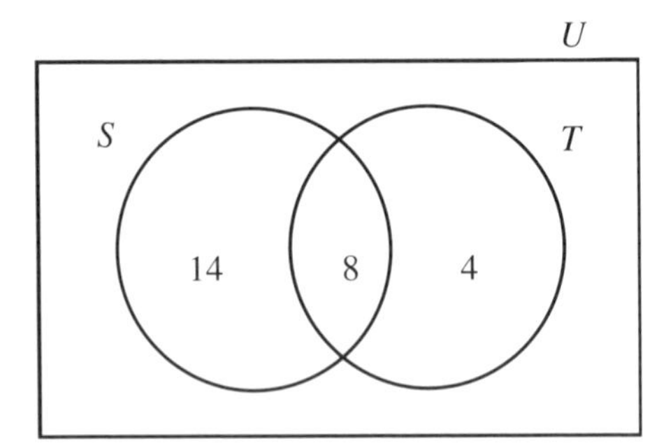

(ii) 14

(iii) 26

(iv) 18

2. (a) Ciarán €1,900; Sheila €4,750 (b) (i) a^6 (ii) 8 (iii) 7.6

(c) (i) 1.5 (ii) 3.27×10^3 (iii) 44.28

3. (a) € 2.68 or 268c (b) (i) € 21,800 (ii) € 308.55

(c) (i) €15,450 (ii) €14,490

4. (a) (i) 17 (ii) 7 (b) (i) 3 (ii) $x^2 + x + 6$

(c) (i) 18 km (ii) $x = 1, y = 2$

5. (a) 0, 1, 2 (b) (i) $y(16x + 11)$ (ii) $(x + 2y)(a + 5)$ (iii) $(x - 10)(x + 9)$

(iv) $(x - 11)(x + 11)$ (c) (i) $\frac{9x + 33}{10}$ (ii) 3 (iii) $x = -9$ or $x = 4$

6. (a) Domain = {1, 4, 5, 7}; Range {3, 6, 8, 9}

(c) (i)

x	0	1	2	3
y	1	2	3	4

(iii) (1, 2)

Paper 2

1. (a) 22 km (b) (i) 19 : 45 (ii) 20 : 04 (iii) €67.60
   (c) (i) $72\,m^2$ (ii) $56.52\,m^2$ (iii) $15.48\,m^2$ (iv) 30.84 m

2. (a) $48\,cm^2$ (b) (i) $384\,cm^3$ (ii) 48 (iii) $368\,cm^2$
   (c) (i) $36\pi\,cm^3$ (ii) 9 cm (iii) 15 cm

3. (a) 4 (b) (i) 2 hours (ii) Friday (iii) 25% (c) (ii) $65 (iii) $79

4. (b) (i) y (ii) $[xy]$ (iii) $15\,cm^2$
   (c) (i) 90°, angle in a semi-circle
   (ii) 30°, three angles in a triangle add up to 180°
   (iii) 120°, opposite angles in a cyclic quadrilateral add up to 180°
   (iv) 3.5

5. (b) (i) $(4, -2)$ (ii) 1 (iii) $x - y - 6 = 0$ (c) (i) $r(0, 2)$ (ii) $r'(0, -2)$

6. (a) (i) 10 (ii) $\frac{6}{10}$ or $\frac{3}{5}$ (b) (i) 40° (ii) 0.64 (iii) 5.1
   (c) (i) 12 m (ii) 67°

Natural Numbers — all numbers,

$ab = (a)(b)$

$<$ = less than

$>$ = greater than.

Difference of two squares

$x^2 - y^2 = 0$ ☆

$(x + y)(x - y)$

CAN'T ADD AN X + AN NUMBE